The annals of Jewish history glo
remarkable women: the matriarchs
Mamme of the Eastern European Shtetl, and the young
American Jewish women of our day. Through the centuries, the thread of continuity has been maintained and strengthened by the love and the transmission of our glorious heritage, lovingly passed on from generation to generation.

In this book, The Bas Mitzvah Treasury, National Women's League of the United Synagogue of America speaks to the Jewish girl of today who will be the Jewish mother of tomorrow. This collection illustrates the warmth of our tradition, the universality of our teachings, and the beauty of our heritage. By so doing, it helps to fulfill the objectives of National Women's League, the largest synagogue women's organization in the world. From its inception, National Women's League was dedicated "to serve the cause of Judaism by strengthening the bond of unity among Jewish women; and by learning to appreciate everything fine in Jewish life and literature, to instill the beauty of our ancient observances in the hearts of children . . . to cherish the various ceremonies of Sabbath and the Holidays . . . to teach their significance intelligently."

Almost a half century has passed since these words were written by Mathilde Schechter, the founder of our organization, and although it is a *far different* world we live in, the truths, the values expressed, are even more essential in our day. To these truths, National Women's League is dedicated: to their transmission from generation to generation, we are pledged.

May this book bring you many hours of joy and may the stories in this Treasury help guide you toward a life of fulfillment and joy.

MRS. ALBERT FRIED, President
National Women's League of the
United Synagogue of America

The

Bas Mitzvah

Treasury

The

Bas Mitzvah Treasury

EDITED BY

Azriel Eisenberg

AND

Leah Ain Globe

National Women's League
of the
United Synagogue of America

Library of Congress Catalog Card Number: 64-25064

MANUFACTURED IN U.S.A.

The editors and publisher acknowledge their deep gratitude and thanks to the authors, representatives, publishers, and holders of copyrights for their gracious cooperation in making possible the publication of this anthology. They are:

ACUM, LTD. (Tel Aviv) for "The Three Haluzot" by Avigdor Hameiri. "The Way of A Man With A Maid" by C. N. Bialik. "The Milk of a Lioness," by C. N. Bialik. "Yigal and the Inquisition," reprinted from *Look Back Mrs. Lot,* by Ephraim Kishon. Copyright © 1962 by M. Twersky, Publishers. Copyright permissions by Acum Ltd., Tel Aviv.

BEHRMAN'S BOOK HOUSE for "Beruriah and Her Sons," from *As A Driven Leaf,* by Milton Steinberg. Copyright © 1946 by Behrman House.

BERGER, SYLVIA for "Mrs. Perlberg's Partner in Heaven" from *Frontiers of Faith:* Radio Program (Jewish Theological Seminary). Copyright © by Sylvia Berger.

BLOCH PUBLISHING CO. for "The Secret" by G. Rosenthal, reprinted from *The World Over Story Book.* Copyright © 1952 by Bloch Publishing Co. "The Unknown Sanctuary," reprinted from *The Unknown Sanctuary,* by Aime Palliere. Copyright © 1928 by Bloch Publishing Co. "Milkmaid on the Jordan," reprinted from *Daughters From Afar,* by Geraldine Stern. Copyright © 1958 by Geraldine Stern.

CROWN PUBLISHERS for "A Page from the Song of Songs," and "The Inheritors," reprinted from *The Old Country,* by Sholom Aleichem. Copyright © 1946 by Crown Publishers.

FARRAR, STRAUSS & CO., INC. for "A Piece of Advice," reprinted from *The Spinoza of Market Street,* by Isaac Bashevis Singer. By permission of Farrar, Strauss & Giroux. Copyright © 1961.

HOLT, RINEHART AND WINSTON, INC. for "Of Love and Faith," reprinted from *The Jewish Caravan,* by Leo W. Schwarz. Copyright © 1935 by Leo W. Schwarz. Reprinted by permission of H. Row.

JEWISH PUBLICATION SOCIETY OF AMERICA for "Kiddush Ha-Shem," reprinted from *Kiddush Ha-Shem, An Epic of 1648,* by Sholom Asch. Copyright © 1959 by the Jewish Publication Society. "Rabban

Gamaliel, the Emperor and His Daughter," "Rabbi Joshua Ben Hananiah and the Emperor's Daughter," "The Angels Jealous of Moses," "Moses Receiving the Law," reprinted from the *Ma'aseh Book,* Vol. 1, by Moses Gaster. Copyright © 1934 by the Jewish Publication Society. "The Three Gifts," reprinted from *The Prince of the Ghetto*. Copyright © 1959 by Maurice Samuel. "Hanna Senesch," reprinted from *Blessed Is the Match,* by Marie Syrkin. Copyright © 1947 by the Jewish Publication Society. "Hemdan," reprinted from *Breakfast of the Birds,* by Yehudah Steinberg. Copyright © 1947 by the Jewish Publication Society. "The Four Dimensions," adapted from *Strangers At the Gate,* by Samuel Gordon. Copyright © 1902.

LIPPINCOTT, J. B., Co. for "The Mission" by Irena Johanes from *The Fighting Ghettos.* Copyright © 1962 by Meyer Barkai.

MACMILLAN Co. for "Letter to My Children," reprinted from *Abby Aldrich Rockefeller.* Copyright © 1950 by Mary Ellen Chase. Reprinted by permission of the Macmillan Co.

MENORAH JOURNAL for "Boaz Makes Up His Mind," reprinted from *Menorah Journal,* 1926. Copyright © by Irving Fineman.

NEW YORK POST for "My Father *Moved*" by Max Lerner. Copyright © by New York Post.

PRAGER, MOSHE, for *The Secret of the Pudding* and *A Stray Leaf from A Prayer Book.* Copyright © by Moshe Prager.

SALTZ, FLORENCE ZUNSER for "The Wedding" and "Havdalah," reprinted from *Yesterday,* by Miriam Shomer Zunser. Published by Stackpole Sons. Copyright © 1939 by Estate of Miriam Shomer Zunser.

SCHOCKEN BOOKS, INC. for "The Kerchief" by S. Y. Agnon from *The Collected Stories* of S. Y. Agnon. Copyright © 1935 by Schocken—Verlag, Berlin. "The Bath," from *Burning Lights,* by Bella Chagall. Copyright © 1946 by Schocken Books, Inc.

THE AMERICAN ZIONIST for *The Singing Name* by Alice Barr. Copyright © 1953 by The American Zionist.

THE NEW PALESTINE for *Two Steps From My Garden Rail* by C. N. Bialik. Copyright © 1926 by The New Palestine.

UNION OF AMERICAN HEBREW CONGREGATIONS for "The Upright Man" by Ilo Orleans, reprinted from *Within My Hands, My Poem Book of Prayers,* by Ilo Orleans. Copyright © 1961 by Ilo Orleans.

VIKING PRESS for "The Torah and the Menorah," reprinted from *The Buried Candelabrum,* by Stefan Zweig. Copyright © 1937 by Estate of Stefan Zweig.

WORLD PUBLISHING Co. for "The Miracle of Goerick Street," reprinted from *For 2¢ Plain,* by Harry Golden. Copyright © 1959, 1958, 1957, 1956, 1955, 1952, 1948, 1945, 1943 by Harry Golden.

TO OUR FUTURE BAS MITZVAHS

Marlene Idelle
Naomi Rachel
Rena Batya
Rebecca Mindel
Tamar Leah
Deborah Ruth
Jodi Miriam

Table of Contents

Introduction

How happy your parents are as you, a *Bas Mitzvah,* stand at the threshold of womanhood! How proud they are of your charm and development, your mental alertness and eagerness! They are also concerned about you; they wonder whether you are adequately prepared for the exciting and difficult journey through life. Is your faith in the Almighty deep enough . . . is your bond with your people secure enough . . . is your confidence in yourself strong enough . . . ? These thoughts and feelings prompted the preparation of *The Bas Mitzvah Treasury.*

The *Treasury* will introduce you to your vast cultural heritage. In it you will find enlightenment on your religion, your history and yourself—your place in the adult world you are about to enter. It does not contain facts about our sacred books, nor does it include laws, regulations or ceremonies. These, we assume, you have been taught by your parents and teachers. Here you will find intellectual stimulation, aesthetic satisfaction, identification with your people, and most of all, the realization that in becoming a *Bas Mitzvah* in the true sense of the word, you are joining the best sorority of Jewish womanhood—the ranks of those who, from the days of Mother Sarah, the wife of Abraham, the first Jew, have had the greatest, the finest influence upon the destiny of their people.

These selections were gleaned from our folklore, works of our sages and classical Hebrew writers. In these pages you will meet heroes and heroines performing their deeds of valor in diverse places and circumstances. Their greatness cannot be catalogued or measured. The bravery of Hanna Senesch is no less moving than the martyrdom of Deborah *(Kiddush Ha-shem).* The heroism of the ghetto mother *(The Secret of the Pudding)* facing her hungry children is no less worthy than that of Lena Kuchler-Silberman taking her one hundred children illegally out of Poland.

The universal love of parents for children is tenderly portrayed in *Forgiven;* conversely, a child's love for his parents is poignantly recalled in *The Kerchief*. Natural misunderstandings between the generations are reflected in *Yigal and the Inquisition.*

The Way of a Man with a Maid is an idyllic, romantic tale from the very olden days. *A Wedding on the Hill,* a modern Israeli story on the same theme, gives expression to youth's need of continuity with tradition.

All the stories in the parts *Home and the Woman* and *Love Thy Neighbor* have *Torah* and *Mitzvahs* as their central theme. What better example of the virtue of charity performed in secret than in *Mrs. Perlberg's Partner in Heaven* . . . what better example of helping others by encouraging self help than in *Judgment of the Wind* . . . what better example of the power of faith than in *The Only Kid*?

It is difficult to separate *The Good Life* from *The Jewish Way of Life,* for the Jewish way of life *is* the good life. However, some of the items, such as *The Ten Commandments, The Secret, The Upright Man,* apply to all good citizens; whereas, stories like *Torah and Menorah,* which is based on Jewish history, and *The Tears of the Generations,* which is derived from Jewish folklore, belong exclusively to the Jewish people.

You will find much thought and beauty in *The Bas Mitzvah Treasury* long after you have passed your teens, and your brothers and sisters will enjoy it as well.

For the most part, the selections for this book were made by Azriel Eisenberg, and the translations and adaptations, except those otherwise acknowledged, by Leah Ain Globe.

A.E.
L.A.G.

1

In Praise of Woman's Virtues

When God was about to create Eve, He said,
"If I create her from the head, she will be overbearing;
from the ear, she will be an eavesdropper;
from the neck, she will be impudent;
from the mouth, she will be a gossip;
from the heart, she will be envious;
from the hand, she will be a meddler;
from the foot, she will be a gadabout."

Hence, He created her from the rib, a modest part of the body.

Midrash

MOSES GASTER

Rabban Gamaliel, the Emperor and His Daughter

The Emperor said to Rabban Gamaliel: "Your God is a thief, for it is written in the Torah: 'And the Lord God caused a deep sleep to fall upon Adam, and he slept; and he took a rib of his body and made a woman thereof.'" (Gen. 2:21).

Then the daughter of the Emperor said to Rabban Gamaliel, "I will answer my father in your stead." And she said to her father: "Father dear, give me a count or a prince who will assist me and avenge me on my enemies."

Then the Emperor said: "Who has wronged you?"

She replied: "Last night robbers entered my chamber, stole my silver ornaments and put gold ones in their place."

When the Emperor heard it, he laughed and said: "I wish, my dear daughter, that such thieves would come to me every day."

Then she replied: "Father dear, the same thing happened to Adam, the first man, for God took a rib from him and gave him instead a wife who cooks and washes for him and serves him in every way."

The Emperor replied: "This is not what I meant. My question was, why did God take the rib from Adam while he was asleep? Why did he not take it from him while he was awake?"

Then the daughter said to the Emperor, "Let them bring me a piece of raw meat." And she took it and put it on hot ashes to broil it. When it was finished, she pulled it out and gave it to her father to eat without having previously washed it.

The emperor said, "I cannot eat it, the sight of it makes me sick; for I have seen it being baked in the ashes, and it is not yet fit to eat."

Then she said, "My dear father, the same thing would have happened to Adam if he had seen God taking a rib out of his body and making a woman out of it. It would have been unpleasant to him also. That is the reason why God did not make the woman out of the rib while Adam was awake."

A FOLK TALE

Alexander the Great and the Women

More than two thousand years ago, Alexander the Great reigned over Greece. After he had conquered all of the known world of that time, he decided to explore Africa and vanquish its kingdoms.

The conqueror and his mighty armies were making their way through the African desert when they saw spires way off in the distance. At first, they were sure it was a mirage, but as they continued their march they realized that they were approaching a city surrounded by a high wall. In those days, cities were built with walls around them for protection.

Alexander was overjoyed and ordered his soldiers to encamp. At last, he was to begin his conquest of Africa! What he did not know was that he had reached a city of women.

Within the city, lookouts of the queen reported that a powerful army was approaching. Word spread quickly that the Great Alexander had come to attack. She called her councillors for deliberations in the emergency, and sent a delegation to arrange for a meeting between herself and the great warrior.

Alexander was sitting in his tent with his generals, preparing the strategy of attack, when he looked out and saw a group of women on white mules riding toward them from the city gate. One rider, a few paces ahead of the others, was waving a white pennant. They were dressed in white flowing robes, and white turbans draped their heads.

"What crafty strategy is this?" Alexander exclaimed, and turning to the captain of his advance guard, ordered, "Take a few soldiers and notify them that I will accept surrender only from their men."

The messengers went forth to meet the women riders. The captain of the guard addressed them with insolence.

"The Great Alexander, mighty Emperor of Greece, commands! Tell your men to come out of hiding and surrender. The Great Conqueror will not negotiate with women!"

"We are a city without men," the truce-bearer answered. "We bring a message from our Queen. She requests an audience with the mighty warrior."

These words so surprised and perplexed the captain that he returned for further instructions.

Alexander was both amused and annoyed by the report—amused at a city that was inhabited only by women, and angry that the enemy was so weak as to rob him of the sport of conquest.

"Shall I meet with their Queen first, or shall I storm the city?" he mused half to himself and half to his generals.

"Women! Bah!" they ventured an opinion, "We can capture them with a handful of soldiers."

"What can I lose," Alexander smiled, "and it might prove interesting."

The captain returned to the waiting delegation and arranged for a meeting between Alexander and the Queen, to be held in her private castle. This was the place that she had built for rest, meditation and small parties. It was placed outside of the city wall, with a complete wall of its own that had a secret passageway leading to the heart of the city.

The Queen received the Greek Emperor in her royal chambers. On the walls hung tapestries of the finest needlework, depicting scenes of the jungle. The inlaid ivory floor was strewn with white rugs bordered in colored flowers.

The Queen sat on a throne of gold. She was small and exotic, with velvety brown almond-shaped eyes and a complexion of coppery gold. Her robe was of many shades of red, from the merest breath of pink to deep cerise, bordering on purple. She wore a tiara studded with diamonds and rubies.

Alexander smiled to himself at the weakness of his opponent, though, in deference to her beauty, he could not help but bow gallantly. Then he stiffened and said, "No doubt you wish to tell me that you are willing to accept the protection of Greece and submit to our authority."

"We strive for peace, but we protect ourselves," was the answer.

"Then, you shall all die!"

"We will defend ourselves!"

"Ha, ha, ha!" laughed the world's greatest soldier.

"The Great Alexander will not be the only one to laugh," was the Queen's quiet retort.

"What meaning is there in that?" Alexander asked in anger and surprise.

"If the Great Conqueror will raze our city, the world will mock and say, 'Alexander the Warrior showed his might by conquering women.' And if we win, the world will laugh and say 'Alexander the Great was slain by women!' "

The voice of the Queen was soft, but it floated like a tinkling bell in the wilderness, and her penetrating eyes forced the proud warrior to lower his. A hush that was almost audible hung over the room. "Then," said Alexander in a subdued voice, "let us eat the bread of peace."

"We shall prepare a banquet as befits the greatest soldier and mightiest emperor," said the Queen, and designated the following day for the royal feast.

At the appointed hour, Alexander, with several of his chosen generals, was admitted into the royal reception room. Priceless jewels were set into the domed ceiling and into the walls, creating most unusual mosaics. The Greek soldiers looked greedily at this wealth which might have been theirs. In the center of the room stood a table of bright yellow gold. No cloth covered it. Plates, goblets and knives of pale gold were set at each place.

The Queen sat at the head of the table. Her robe was the color of a desert sky. She wore a small crown of emeralds and turquoise. No sooner were the guests seated, than the Queen clapped her hands. Tall, slender maidens in pink robes and caps floated in, bearing trays. One placed bread before Alexander, another, a huge roast bird, and others set before him fruits and vegetables of every kind.

Alexander tried to cut the bread, but to his amazement and chagrin, that which looked like freshly baked bread was solid gold! On closer observation, he noted that the roast was the product of the goldsmith's craft. He touched the grapes; they were jade. The pomegranates were coral; the mushrooms were ivory—all fruits and vegetables were fashioned by artisans. Alexander rose angrily from the table. "Do you expect me to eat gold?" he shouted.

"Oh, Great and Mighty Emperor," the Queen spoke slowly in her musical and compelling voice, "is it bread that you wanted—that you have come so far? Is there none in your own country?"

Alexander sat down, blushing like a schoolboy.

Thereupon, the Queen clapped her hands and a line of maidens entered with the most tantalizingly fragrant and delicious food.

The guests ate and drank the royal meal, but their behaviour was subdued. They did not indulge in their customary loud talk and uncouth jests. But they did experience a new kind of pleasure as they listened to the Queen's drummers beat out the haunting rhythms of Africa, and as they watched her beautiful young dancers depict the struggle of life in the jungle, the loneliness of the desert, and the dangers of travel over high mountains.

When Alexander the Great was about to leave, the Queen presented him with a jeweled chest filled with emeralds, rubies and diamonds—gems larger than any he had ever seen.

As he accepted her gift, he said, "I have a gift for you, too. I will write it on the gate of your city and it will always protect you from your enemies. And he wrote:

> Alexander was a madman to have come so far
> only to be taught by women.

[ADAPTED]

YEHUDAH GRAZOVSKI

The King's Left Eye

The Khan's kingdom stretched far and wide, and at its outskirts lived a rich old man with his daughters. The youngest, named Ko-ko, was known in all the land for her beauty, wisdom and kindness.

One day, the old man prepared to go to market to sell his cattle. He bade farewell to his daughters and asked them what he should bring them from the big city.

"Buy me a pretty necklace," said the oldest.

"I want a kerchief, a red silk one," said the middle daughter.

"Nothing for me!" said Ko-ko.

"Why?" asked her father in surprise. "You love pretty things as much as your sisters do."

"There is something that I do want, but you won't be able to get it."

"What is it, Ko-ko? You know how much I love you and I won't mind the expense."

"How I crave this thing!" said Ko-ko.

"I promise it! I make a solemn oath that I will get it for you!"

"Well, then I will tell you. When you get to the fair, sell all the cattle, except the cow with the short tail. Sell her only in exchange for the Khan's left eye."

"What are you saying, child?"

"If you can't get that for me, I don't need anything."

"Ko-ko is good and kind," thought her father. "She must have an important reason for her strange request. Besides,

I have just made a vow." To his youngest daughter, he said, "Come what may, I will do as you wish."

At the fair, the old man quickly disposed of his herd, all but the short-tailed cow which he refused to sell.

"Sell us that one, too," the buyers urged.

"I want to, I am most anxious to sell it, if you will give me my price."

"How much?"

"I will sell it for the left eye of the Khan."

"Are you crazy? Do you realize what you are saying?"

"If that is too expensive, don't buy. No one is forcing you."

News quickly spread in the market place about the demented man and his weird talk, until it reached the ears of one of the Khan's officials who hastened to inform his king.

"Most illustrious Khan," said the servant prostrating himself, "an old man has come to the market place to sell cattle. He has one cow which he refuses to sell unless he is given the left eye of Your Royal Highness in payment."

The Khan ordered the old man to be brought to him. When Ko-ko's father appeared, the Khan asked the frightened man, "Greybeard, are the rumors I hear about you true? Are you out of your mind?"

The old man prostrated himself before the king and pleaded, "Pray spare my life and hearken to the words of your humble servant. I said what I did at the request of my beautiful and clever daughter, Ko-ko. I shuddered when I first heard her strange wish. But then I realized that there is wisdom behind everything she says and does, and I promised to do her bidding."

The Khan ordered Ko-ko to appear before him.

"Why have you asked for my left eye?"

"Because I knew that eventually one of your servants would hear and inform on my father and that you would command him to appear before you; and that he would tell you that the request was mine and so you would summon me. I had no other way of coming into your presence, most exalted Khan."

"Why do you want to see me?"

"To make you aware of the stories that people are telling about you."

"What, for instance?"

"They say that the left eye is of no use to the Khan. They say that you don't look with that eye."

"What does that mean?"

"When people come to you in any dispute and the rich and noble stand at your right, and the poor and those you consider lowly stand at your left, you always favor the rich and disregard the poor. Therefore people say, 'The Khan's left eye is superfluous. He has no need of it.' "

The Khan became very angry and ordered Ko-ko to stand trial. He charged the judges to decide whether her remarks were caused by arrogance or born of wisdom.

The judges deliberated for seven days and seven nights and decided to question the girl in order to better understand her. The first question that the supreme judge asked was, "If girls are sent out to gather apples, which one will bring back the most?"

"The girl who will give the tree a good shake will be able to gather the most—certainly not the one who will climb up and pick the apples one at a time."

"What is the quickest way for a man to cross a swamp?"

"He who will go around it, will continue his journey with greater speed. A straight line across the swamp will slow him down considerably."

"How can a man become famous?"

"By having compassion and helping the forsaken ones."

"What should one do who wishes to live a righteous life?"

"He must begin the day with prayer and fill it with good deeds."

"Who is the most righteous?"

"He who is most humble."

The judges exchanged glances and walked into another room to discuss the matter. They concluded that the girl was not arrogant, but very wise.

The Khan heard the verdict of the judges but would not forgive the girl's insolence. He ordered that she remain in his palace while he pondered all sorts of riddles and problems to put to her. After seven days and seven nights, he ordered Ko-ko to be brought before him.

"Tell me the value of all my possessions," was the riddle with which the Khan thought to trick her.

"I will give you the answer," said Ko-ko, "if you will order everyone in the palace to do my bidding for three days and three nights."

"So be it. But know this: If after three days, your answer is not satisfactory, you will lose your head."

"Very well," said the girl. "Now I request that no food or drink touch the Khan's lips for three days and three nights."

The Khan regretted his rash promise, but being a king, he could not go back on his word. After two days of fasting, terrible pangs of hunger gripped him. On the third day, Ko-ko brought him a tray heaped with the most delicious food and said, "May the Khan live forever! At this moment, do you admit that you would give all your possessions for the food on this plate?"

"That I do," the king agreed.

"In that case, all that you own can be summed up in this one dish! Now, eat and enjoy it!"

The famished king devoured the food. He had to admit that Ko-ko was very wise.

"If you hear anyone talking about my left eye, be sure and tell it to me," he said with a smile.

The poor of the land praised Ko-ko for her wisdom and blessed her for influencing the king in their behalf. But they feared that as soon as she would leave for her home in the province that was so far from the capital, the Khan would forget all of his good intentions.

But their fears were groundless. Ko-ko did not go home, for the Khan's son, the prince, saw her in the palace, fell in love with her and married her.

All the people rejoiced at the happy union.

[TRANSLATED FROM THE HEBREW]

YITZHAK LEIB PERETZ

Three Gifts

Once upon a time, generations and generations ago, an obscure, unimportant Jew died somewhere, and when the body had been consigned to the earth, and the first Kaddish had been said over it, the soul mounted to heaven, where it was brought to immediate trial. The court was assembled, the scales stood ready on the table, the prosecuting attorney and the counsel for defense were prepared for their roles.

The latter carried with him the bag that contained the good deeds of the dead man, the former the bag that contained his wicked deeds. The bag with the good deeds smelled as of spices, and the light of its contents shone through the cloth; the bag with the wicked deeds stank of tar, and the filth oozed through the texture.

The prosecuting attorney emptied the contents of his bag into the scale at the left; counsel for the defense emptied his into the scale at the right. The disembodied soul stood there, looking on in astonishment. It had never imagined that there was such a difference between good deeds and bad deeds; down there, on earth, it had often failed to distinguish between them and had more than once taken one for the other.

The scales rose and fell slowly, almost imperceptibly; now the right scale descended, now the left. The pointer trembled, moving conversely left and right. And always by a hair's breadth, not more. The soul had belonged to a very ordinary Jew; no great villain and no martyr; just tiny little virtues and tiny little sins; dust, almost; some of them hardly visible to the naked eye. Still, the pointer kept moving, a little bit this way, a little bit that way. And every time the scale with the virtues sank, there was a joyous response in heaven; and every time it was outweighed by the other scale, there was a sighing and sadness audible as far as the Throne.

The angels poured out the contents of the bags with great attentiveness and deliberation; one pinch of dust after another; like poor householders at the synagogue service bidding kopeck by kopeck for the honor of carrying the Scrolls of the Law.

But if a well can be drained in time, how much more a little bagful of human deeds? The angels stopped pouring.

"Is that all?" asked the court clerk, an angel like the others.

Attorney and counsel took the bags and turned them inside out. That was all! Then the court clerk approached the scales and examined the pointer: was it on the right or the left? He looked and looked, scarcely believing his eyes, for here was something that had not happened till that moment since heaven and earth had been created.

"What is it there?" asked the presiding officer. "Why is it taking so long?"

The clerk stammered: "Dead even! The pointer is at dead center!"

The good deeds and the bad deeds counterbalanced exactly.

"What, exactly?" asked the presiding officer.

The clerk looked again and answered: "To a hair."

The court retired for consultation and came back with the following sentence:

"Inasmuch as the sins of this soul do not outweigh the good deeds, the soul cannot be sentenced to hell. And inasmuch as the good deeds do not outweigh the sins, the soul cannot be admitted to paradise. Therefore it has been ruled that the said soul shall wander about in space until such time as the Lord of the universe shall in His compassion bethink Himself of it and call it to Himself."

The clerk of the court conducted the weeping soul to the exit.

"Why do you weep so?" asked the clerk. "True, you have been excluded from the bliss of paradise; on the other hand, you will know nothing of the torments of hell. You're even!"

But the soul would not be comforted. "Better the most frightful torments than nothingness! Nothingness is unbearable!"

The clerk of the court felt a twinge of pity, and said: "I have good counsel for you. Fly downward toward earth and keep close to the living. Do not look up at the sky. For what will you see from the other side of heaven but the stars? They are creatures of light, but they are cold; they know nothing of pity and they will not intercede for you; they will not remind the Lord of the universe of your existence. Only the saints in heaven will remember and take thought for an unhappy wandering soul. But listen carefully to what I say: Even the saints in heaven need little reminders; they are very fond of gifts, beautiful gifts. Alas," and the tone of the clerk became somewhat bitter, "they've picked up that habit from latter-day arrivals in heaven. So do this: Fly down to the world of the living, and watch closely. And should you come across a strange and exceptionally beautiful deed, snatch up the evidence of it and fly to the gate of heaven. That will be a gift for the saints in paradise. Hold fast to the gift and knock at the gate; tell the angel in the keeper's lodge that I told you to report to him. Hand him the gift. And I promise you that when you will have brought three acceptable gifts, the saints will intercede for you, and the gate will be opened."

The First Gift

Downward across space flew the sad little soul, downward toward the world of the living, to seek gifts for the saints in paradise. When it was low over the earth, it flew back and forth, over fields and villages and cities, pausing at every Jewish settlement. In the summer it flew among the blazing rays of the sun; in the rainy season among the glistening drops and between the slanting needles of water; in the winter among the innumerable snowflakes. And always on the alert, always watching, till it was faint from watchfulness.

Whenever it saw a Jew it descended hastily and stared him in the face, wondering if he was about to sanctify the Name of God with some deed of holiness. At night, always sustained by the same hope, it would peep in through the shutters of Jewish homes; perhaps in one of them it might perceive, growing quietly, the flowerets of God, hidden deeds of virtue. Alas! More often than not the soul started back, horrified.

The cycle of the seasons passed, and cycle followed cycle, year followed year; the soul almost yielded to despair. Cities turned into cemeteries, cemeteries became plowed fields. Forests were cleared away, rocks were worn into sands, rivers changed their beds, thousands of stars fell, millions of souls ascended; and God had not remembered the wandering soul, had not sent a single wonderful deed of goodness in its direction.

It meditated sadly: "The world is so poverty-stricken, the souls of men are such gray mediocrities, their deeds are so small! What do they know of the strange and wonderful? I shall be a wanderer and an outcast forever and ever."

But as it meditated thus, there came suddenly a flash of red light, a red flash in the darkness. The soul swooped down. The flash had come from a high window. Peering in, the soul saw a rich room, and in it, masked robbers. An old man was there, obviously the owner of the house. One of the robbers held aloft a flaring torch. A second pressed the point of a shining dagger against the owner's breast, saying, over and over again: "One move from you, Jew, and you're a dead man! One move, and this dagger goes through you!" Meanwhile the other robbers ransacked the chests and cupboards.

The Jew stood there calmly and watched; not a flutter of his eyebrows, not a motion in the long white beard which reached to his waist. It was all no concern of his. The Lord giveth, the Lord taketh away, blessed be the Name of the Lord. He had not been born with this wealth, he would not have taken it with him into the grave.

Thus he stood, watching peacefully, while the robbers opened the drawers of the last cupboard and took from it sacks of gold and silver, boxes of jewelry, precious plate. Not a word escaped him. From the tranquility of his bearing it might even seem that he was relinquishing all claim to his possessions, so that the robbers might be free of the sin of theft.

Then, suddenly, one of the robbers, reaching into the last corner of the last drawer, drew forth a little sack, hidden behind all the others, and apparently the most precious of them all. At that moment the old man forgot himself; he trembled from head to foot, his eyes flamed; he lifted his right arm and cried:

"Hands off!"

And at that moment a red stream burst from him; the dagger had done its work; his heart's blood spurted out and stained the sack in the hands of the robber.

The old man fell to the floor, and the robbers flung themselves on the little sack. This was beyond a doubt the big find.

What a bitter mistake! They had shed blood in vain. There was neither gold nor silver nor jewelry in the little sack; there was nothing in it of any value in this world. All that the sack contained was a handful of earth from the Holy Land, which the merchant was saving to put under his head in his coffin. This was the only possession he had sought to save from the robbers—the one for which he had forfeited his life.

The soul swooped down, picked up a pinch of the precious, bloodstained dust, and flew up with it to the gate of heaven.

The first gift was accepted.

The Second Gift

"Remember," called the angel after the descending soul as it closed the wicket. "Two more gifts."

"God will help me again," answered the soul, in high spirits.

The high spirits did not last. Again the seasons and the years passed and the soul found nothing. Again it was assailed by melancholy thoughts.

"Like a living stream the world broke forth at God's command and set out on its path; and the stream, pouring onward, gathers sand and silt; the waters become darker and ever more unclean; very few are the gifts to be found in it. Men become smaller and smaller; their virtues are nothing but fragments, their sins are clotted dust. Their deeds are too tiny to be perceived."

And the soul meditated further: "If God were now to take the whole of the earth and weigh the virtues against the sins, the pointer of the scales would lie in the dead middle again. The earth can neither rise nor fall; and like me, it is an outcast and a wanderer between the bright heavens and the nether darkness. The prosecuting attorney and the counsel for the defense would dispute the possession of the earth forever, as darkness and light, heat and cold, life and death, dispute its possession. The world rocks, but it neither ascends nor descends; therefore there will be forever marriage and divorce, births and burials, love and hate, forever and ever."

Again something broke at last into the soul's meditations.

A pealing of horns and trumpets!

The soul descended and beheld a German city of the olden days; sloping roofs encircling the magistrate's square, crowds in multicolored dress, numberless faces at windows, spectators clustering on towers and balconies. . . .

The court is arrayed before a table covered with a green cloth, from whose corners hang rich golden braids and tassels. The magistrates are clad in velvet robes and fur headgear crowned with white feathers held in place by silver buttons. The president sits apart at the head of the table. A lean, hungry eagle is perched above him.

At one side of the square stands a Jewish girl. Near her, ten grooms hold in rein a wild horse. The president of the court rises and, turning toward the center of the square, reads forth the sentence:

"The Jewess standing before us is guilty of an abominable crime which God, for all His infinite mercy, cannot forgive.

"On the occasion of our last sacred festival she stole out of the ghetto and polluted with her footsteps the streets of our noble city. She defiled with her shameless glances the holy images that we carried in procession to the sound of music. Her accursed ears drank in the hymns sung by our white-clad, innocent children and the sound of the sacred timbrels. And who knows whether the unclean demon, who is concealed under this exterior of a Rabbi's daughter, did not actually lay a defiling hand on one of our sanctities?

"What did this demon in lovely human form desire? For it cannot be denied that the disguise is a lovely one. She is beautiful to behold, as only a demon can be. The wanton, impudent eyes flash under cover of the silken lashes; the alabaster cheeks have not been withered by her imprisonment; her fingers are slender—the light shines through them. What did this woman desire?

"Only this: to distract a soul from its sacred preoccupation, to turn its attention away from the high purity of the moment; and therein the demon succeeded. For the sake of this demon in woman's guise, a knight left the procession, a son of one of our noblest families.

"But this insolent triumph was perceived, and the halberdiers closed in at once on the temptress. The demon in her did not even seek to defend herself. How could she? At that moment the soldiers were purified from all sin, and the devil had no power over them.

"Therefore I pronounce the following judgment on the Jewess in whom the demon lodges:

"Her long demon's plaits shall be tied to the tail of the wild horse. Then the horse shall be released and shall drag her like a corpse through the holy streets which her footsteps have defiled. Let her blood wash clean the stones which her feet have besmirched."

A wild cry of joy issues from the throats of the assembled; and when the wave of sound has passed, the condemned woman is asked if she has a last wish to express.

She answers quietly: "I have. I want a few pins."

Out of her wits with fear, is what the magistrates think, and they say something to that effect.

"No," she answers calmly. "That is my last wish and request."

They grant her request.

"And now," the president commands, "the sentence!"

Halberdiers tie the long plaits of the Rabbi's daughter to the tail of the horse, which the ten grooms can scarcely hold in check.

"A pathway!" commands the president again. The throng stirs and presses backward against the walls. A pathway is cleared. Hundreds of hands are lifted, and in them are whips, goads, rods, to urge the wild horse on. Faces flame and eyes flash; a panting rises from the mob. In the tumult and excitement none of the bystanders notices that the condemned woman has bent down and is fastening the hem of her dress to her flesh, driving the pins in deep, deep, so that her body may not be exposed when the horse drags her through the streets.

Only the invisible wandering soul has observed it.

"Release the horse!" comes the order from the president.

The grooms spring back, and with one wild bound the horse leaps forward, while at the same moment a wild cry leaps from the throats of the onlookers. The whips and goads and rods whistle in the air, the terrified horse dashes across the square into the streets and through the streets to the open country.

The wandering soul draws a bloodstained pin from the body of the condemned woman and flies heavenward with it.

"Only one more present!" says the angel at the gate, comfortingly.

The Third Gift

Again the soul descended earthward, this time in search of the last gift. And again the seasons and years rolled by. Again a deep melancholy settled on the wanderer; for the world seemed smaller than ever, and smaller than ever the deeds of men, their evil deeds no less than their good.

"Such deeds cannot alter the balance," thought the soul. "They are utterly without weight. Forever and forever the pointer will stay dead center."

But it had been decreed that the wandering soul was to be redeemed, and after many years it was awakened out of its dark mood by a sound of drums.

The time and the place were unfamiliar to the wanderer. It saw an open space before a prison wall. The heavy iron gratings on the windows threw back the sunlight; and sunlight fell, too, on the stacked arms of the soldiers, who, instead of arms, now carried knouts. The soldiers were drawn up in two long lines, with a lane between.

Who was to run the gantlet? The wandering soul beheld the little figure of a Jew, his gaunt body only half concealed by his tattered shirt. This was the culprit! For what crime was he about to be punished? Theft? Murder? Or was it—who could tell, in that world, in those far-off days?—a libel and a false accusation?

The soldiers were grinning. They seemed to be asking: "Why so many of us? He won't last half the course."

The wretched little man was thrust forward till he stood at the head of the lane. Then the blows of the knouts began to rain on him; and he walked on and on, without stumbling, without turning. The knouts whistled, the blows fell on his flesh, and he endured.

A mad anger seized the soldiers. The lashes hissed in the air like furies and wrapped themselves round the man's body like serpents. The blood started out on the flesh.

"Hu-ha! Hu-ha!" panted the soldiers.

And then it happened that one soldier aimed his blow too high, and the skull-cap fell off the condemned man.

He continued for two or three steps without noticing the loss, and then observed it. His head was bare! Like a heathen's! Like an unbeliever's! He paused, as if he were reflecting. Great God! He would not permit himself to be bareheaded! Calmly the man turned round and walked back to where his skull-cap lay in the dust. He bent down, picked it up, replaced it on his head. Then he turned again and continued the course tranquilly, blood-bespattered from head to foot, but with the skull-cap covering him, according to the commandment. So he went until he fell.

And when he had fallen, the wandering soul descended, snatched the bloody head-covering from under the feet of the soldiers, and flew with it straight to the gate of heaven.

This gift, too, was found acceptable; and the saints intervened for the wandering soul, which was admitted to Paradise.

And the saint who on earth below had been the famous Rabbi *Urim ve-Tumim,* so called from the name of his book, said:

"Really beautiful gifts! Of no practical value, to be sure, but as gifts altogether wondrous."

[TRANSLATED FROM THE YIDDISH BY MAURICE SAMUEL]

SHOLEM ASCH

Kiddush Ha-shem

In 1648 the Cossacks of the Ukraine rose in rebellion against their Polish landowners and masters. Since the Jews were the stewards and managers of the Polish estates and held leases on the forests, inns, and wells of the nobles, the savage Cossacks turned against them and massacred community after community. The Poles often betrayed their Jewish neighbors in the hope of saving their own skin. The atrocities were carried out with great ferocity on a scale which devastated Ukranian Jewry, tens of thousands of whom were slaughtered and sold as slaves; many were martyred for "kiddush hashem," the sanctification of God's name.

The horrible tragedy engulfed the city of Nemirov and the lives of a young couple, Shlomo and Deborah, who had just married. In their flight they became separated from each other and captured. Deborah's captors had a duel, she became the possession of young Yerem, who fell deeply in love with her and prepared to marry her. . . .

All day the orchard of Yerem's mother was fragrant with honey. The bees buzzed in and out of the beehives, which were built in hollow trees, and swarmed about the white, sun-bathed honey flowers with which the entire field of the orchard was covered. The branches of the trees sagged under the loads of ripe plums which kept falling to the ground. They were left there to rot in the grass and emitted the sharp odor of decaying fruit. Several sheep wandered about the orchard with long black wool and stupefied expressions, who seemed to bore themselves with nibbling the grass and, out of boredom, licked each other with their long tongues. A swarm of little ducks arrived on the scene together, like a deputation of respectable housewives on an important mission, swaying their fat little bodies on their short legs. For no reason at all, a goose suddenly flapped in, its wings spread out awkwardly, and started off with a great outcry; but suddenly coming upon the dog, Bugo, whom she woke up from his sleep, she reeled back in great fear, and in order to avoid unpleasant developments, she went off in another direction, folded her wings, and finally calmed herself.

In the orchard, among the sheep, the ducks, the geese and other domestic birds and beasts, Deborah wandered about. On her feet she wore little shackles, which Yerem had placed there in order to prevent her from escaping, and that he might always hear her footsteps. And instead of her own headdress, she already wore a Cossack veil on her head, which concealed her face. She roamed listlessly about the garden, and the bells rang mournfully in time to her slow footsteps. And in this manner, she came to the brook, which ran through the orchard and, sitting down on the bank, she gazed into the water.

But Yerem, who watched her footsteps, followed her. Slowly he came up to the brook, and sat down near her.

"Why are you still sad, pretty Jew girl? You are still unable to forget your people. You have cast a spell over me and you have poisoned my heart. Woe is me, what will I do?"

"Be silent, Yerem, you have promised me, have you not, that until the wedding you will not torment me, and will let me bewail my people?"

"Yes, that is true; true, I did promise you. But my heart becomes as withered as a parched spring only from looking at you. And you refuse to eat our bread. You insult our food and eat only what your nurse brings you—fruits and vegetables. And you are already my bride, are you not?"

"I promised my dead, Yerem, to observe their law until I shall leave them. Oh Yerem, let me observe my law. For you are good, and you love me."

"Yes, my love for you is terrible, Deborah. Because of you I shall die very young. I will commit crimes for you. I could kill my own brother for you. Say it, and I will go with you to the end of the world. We will settle on a lonely island, a little brook will run in front of our house and red poppies will blossom before our windows. And I will be your peasant and you will be my queen. Oh! Queen mine, little angel mine, you pure dove, what is this power that you have? Your eyes are like those of a dove, and they are breaking my heart and I could die here, on this spot."

The young peasant bowed before her and, burying his face in his hands, he suddenly broke into sobbing like a little child.

"Calm yourself, Yerem. You are good, and I like you. Your heart is good. Calm yourself, Yerem." And she stroked his hair with her hand as a mistress strokes her dog.

"Oh, you white little lamb of mine, Oh, you dove mine, why do you torment me so, my love? Why do you torture my heart so? Oh, make an end of my life altogether."

"Oh, you will live, Yerem, you are young and strong and you are good."

"But of what good is my life to me, if I do not know when you will be mine? You lay it off from day to day, and love gnaws at my heart as the worm at the tree, and I am withering away. Tell me, my angel, where will I build my house? Near what river and in what land?"

"Oh, Yerem, you will not have to wait long, not much longer," she said sadly.

"Tell me when?"

"You promised me faithfully that you will not torment me, for you love me."

"Good, I am silent now. If you wish it, say it; if not, tug away at my soul, tug away at my heart. Let it gnaw and gnaw until I die." And the peasant dug his face into the grass.

"Soon now the end will come, only wait a little, Yerem. It will be soon, now, it will be soon." She calmed him by laying her cool, white hand on his head, and her burning eyes sought some place in the distance.

He watched over her like the apple of his eye and followed her footsteps like a faithful slave. The Cossacks and peasants made a laughing stock of him, taunted him for sticking to his Jew girl, and a rumor began to circulate that the Jew girl had cast a spell over him: it could mean nothing else.

One day Yerem returned from the city and brought something for Deborah.

"All the Jews and Poles of Tulchin have been killed, not a single one has been left alive," he told her.

"How do you know, Yerem?" Deborah asked him.

"The peasants in the city reported it. They brought there a great many articles, which they had taken from the Jews, and here I have brought you something also, my pretty Jew girl. I bought it from a peasant for you. I gave him a sheepskin coat for it."

And Yerem took out of a shawl a pair of golden slippers and gave them to her.

"They say that the Jews buy such slippers for their brides and that the Jew girls like very much to wear them, so I bought them for you, my pretty Jew girl."

Deborah took the slippers and examined them. She recognized them. They were the slippers which Shlomo had brought her from Lublin when he came home from the Yeshivah.

"How did you come by them?" Deborah asked him.

"Bought them from a peasant. He found them on a dead Jew whom they had killed in Tulchin. The Jew held them clasped to his heart."

"Was he a young man, that Jew, or an old one?" Deborah asked him.

"I do not know, my pretty Jew girl. He did not tell me. But why have you become so pale, my little dove?"

"Afterwards, afterwards, I will tell you. The nurse, I want the nurse!"

"What ails you? Why are you so pale, little angel mine, dovelet mine? Why?" the young peasant asked, amazed.

"Afterwards, I will tell you everything. Oh, Yerem, soon, very soon, will be my wedding. Only for those slippers have I waited. Now the end will come soon. Nurse!"

"Nurse!" Yerem called.

And the old nurse barely had time to run out of the orchard, where she was feeding the chickens, when Deborah fell down on the lawn.

"What ails her?" the peasant asked the nurse.

The nurse saw the slippers in Deborah's hands and uttered a great cry:

"Lord, have mercy!" and caught Deborah in her arms. Yerem stood by in amazement.

The Golden Slippers

The same evening the little white honey flowers opened their petals and the garden was sweet with the fragrance of honey. Fireflies flashed and flickered in the air like souls astray. Far out on the steppe, little fires darted up here and there and died away. Each red poppy-head flared up. The stars huddled close together and the air shone with a supernatural light as though it were full of invisible bodies come floating out of another world.

Deborah stood in the orchard near the bonfire which Yerem had lighted. From the hut came the strumming of a "lyre" which a stray "ancient" was playing, as he sang a ballad to the assembled peasants. Drunken cries, weeping and laughter, also came from the hut where the peasants had collected all the loot which they had stolen from the Jews of Tulchin. They were dividing this loot and drinking Jewish wine. And the old man played for them on the lyre.

Deborah stood near the fire, the shackles on her ankles ringing with every move she made. She stood like a young sapling, her eyes turned toward the stars. And she spoke as if she saw somone:

"Soon I shall come to you, my husband, my chosen one. I see you in the light. Your arms are stretched out to me. Take me to yourself, my husband, my chosen one. I long for you."

She saw a blue sea flooded with light, and star-studded boats floating about. They are all sailing to the same shore. It is so light there. Impossible to look into the light. What a great light is there! The infinite, the everlasting is there! God is there, and all are floating straight into the great light. In every boat there is a Jewish family. She knows them all, all who are in the boats. And she seeks among the boats. And now she sees him. He is waiting for her in his boat. The others have all floated away. He alone is waiting. And now she calls to him:

"Shlomo, Shlomo, wait for me. I come, I come, I come." And she stretched out her arms towards the little boat in the sky.

"Whom do you see?" Whom are you speaking to? What ails you, beautiful Jew girl?"

"Do not touch me. I am fire, you'll catch fire from me. See, I am burning. I am a torch and you will burn yourself!"

Her eyes blazed and her face caught the light of the shimmering stars. Her supple young form, draped in the light-colored shawls, seemed to have been kindled in the flames of the fire. She appeared to be burning.

Yerem looked at Deborah and did not recognize her. It seemed to him that he had once seen her somewhere, but he could not remember where. Then something like a great light rose up before him.

"I know you! I know who you are! Oh, I know, sinful soul that I am! Oh! Oh!" And he sank to his knees before Deborah and began to pray as one prays before a holy ikon.

"Oh, Lord, have mercy!" And he buried his face in his hands and began to weep.

"I know. Now, I know. I have recognized you. You are a holy one, you are a saint. I saw you in church. On the holy ikon, I saw you. Oh, I know now, sinful soul that I am. Have mercy, have mercy!" the peasant stammered.

"Be not afraid, Yerem. You are good. You have a good heart. Be not afraid."

"Oh, sinful soul that I am! Have mercy." And the young peasant jumped up and ran away from her. And with a great noise he entered the hut where the peasants were assembled.

"Peasants," he cried, "God is in the orchard, woe unto us!"

The peasants put away their wine. The lyre became silent. They turned pale and asked each other:

"What is he saying?"

But Yerem was frightened and wept like a little child. He pointed to the orchard.

"There, outside!"

The peasants became infected with his dread. Stealthily and in great awe they approached the door of the hut and looked out.

"Where?"

"There, near the fire. Don't you see? Look! Look!"

"Your Jew girl is standing there, not God."

"I've recognized her. She came down from the ikon. It is God!"

"She has cast a spell over you, she has bewitched you. Don't you see it's your Jew girl, not God? Do not sin."

"Peasants, I've recognized her. I looked deep into her face and recognized her. She is a saint. She has come down from the holy ikon."

"Let her prove that she is God."

"A miracle!"

"Let her perform a miracle and we'll believe that she is God. If not, then your accursed Jew girl is a witch. Then she ought to be burned."

"She has bewitched the lad. Into the fire with her!"

"Peasants, be silent and do not sin," Yerem exclaimed; and approaching Deborah, he knelt before her from a distance and made obeisance before her as before a holy ikon.

"Tell them, show them that I am not mistaken. Let them believe in God. Oh, prove to them, holy one, prove to them that you are God."

For a long interval Deborah was silent. Then she turned her luminous face to Yerem and said:

"Call the nurse, Yerem."

But the nurse had been near her for a long time. She lay at her feet, her face hidden in Deborah's dress, and wept.

"Go, nurse, and bring me the golden slippers," said Deborah in Yiddish.

"Oh, my child, my little dove, I cannot. What are you going to do?"

"I command you, nurse. Bring me the golden slippers."

The nurse went to her room and brought the golden slippers.

"Do not weep. Be merry. Put the slippers on me as you used to do when I was a little child. Do you remember how you sent me to him once when he was a little boy with a pear and an apple?" She whispered to the nurse.

"Oh, I understand, I understand. But what are you going to do?"

"Why, I am going to him. He is waiting there for me in his little boat to sail away with me to heaven." And she embraced the nurse and kissed her.

The nurse withdrew from her, and Deborah, the golden slippers on her feet, said to the trembling Yerem:

"Yerem, take your flint-lock and fire at me."

A dread fell upon the peasants. They became infected with the panic which possessed Yerem. Deborah's words terrified them. Some began to believe that they were in the presence of something supernatural. And one of them sank to his knees and mumbled:

"Lord, have mercy!"

And Yerem trembled and shook with fear.

"No, no, I'll not do it. I am afraid."

"Be not afraid, Yerem, no harm can come to me. I am not here any more. I am already there, in heaven. I have put on the golden slippers which he sent me from heaven so that I might come to him. Go, Yerem, take your flint-lock and aim at my heart."

But the peasant continued to sob, and he stammered:

"No, no, I am afraid, have mercy!"

"I command you, Yerem. Go and bring the flint-lock, I will stand here near the fire so that you can see where to aim. Have I not told you that no harm can come to me? I command you. Do as I have said."

Illumined by the flames of the fire, she looked like a young goddess who commands. And the fear of God fell upon the peasants. They sank to their knees. One of them began to chant and the rest joined him:

"Lord, have mercy! Lord, have mercy!"

One of the peasants handed the flint-lock to the kneeling Yerem. Deborah in the golden slippers stood in the light of the fire.

"Shoot, Yerem!"

The peasants became silent. They remained kneeling on the ground.

A report was heard. A little cloud of smoke rose up, and caught the light of the fire.

"Aim well, Yerem. See, no harm can come to me."

Yerem discharged the weapon a second time. And again a little cloud of smoke rose into the air.

Deborah began to sway and to sink to her knees.

"She falls!"

"Blood!"

"The accursed Jew girl! She has cheated us!" the peasants shouted, rising to their feet and running towards Deborah with clenched fists.

"Accursed Jew girl! Cheated us!"

But Yerem now stood guard over her. He held in his arms her swaying body, from which the blood flowed into the flames of the fire.

"Why have you done it, beautiful Jew girl? I loved you so?" He stammered.

"Forgive me, Yerem, forgive me. I thank you for sending me to him. I knew you would send me to him. You are good, Yerem."

"Give her to me, she is my child!" cried the nurse, and running up she caught Deborah in her arms.

Deborah now saw the star-studded boat. Shlomo was taking her by the hand to help her embark.

"Farewell, nurse," she stammered.

"A happy journey, my child," the nurse replied in Yiddish.

And as though wanting to be alone, Deborah withdrew from Yerem, turned away from the nurse. She laid her head on the grass and the peasants who surrounded her heard from her lips the words which in those days they heard so often from the Jews:

"Hear, O Israel, the Lord our God, the Lord is One!"

And she became silent.

[TRANSLATED FROM THE YIDDISH BY RUFUS LEARSI]

AVIGDOR HAMEIRI

The Three Haluzot

I. "MURDERESS"

My friend the sculptor took me by the arm and said:

"Come on; you've got to come and see something that has been driving me crazy lately. You must come and see a woman's body."

"I've seen them. More than once. I used to drop in at Franz Stuk's studio. I've seen them."

"You've seen devils, my boy, not women's bodies. That Stuk of yours paints devils and witches. Come along and I'll show you a real angel of the Lord, a real fairy."

Well and good. We went down to the seashore.

It was sunset. A Jaffa sunset with all its futurist magic. The sea was flaming, poured-out molten gold; and the disc of the sun descended to the sea like a woman smiling as she goes down to her scented bath.

The foreshore was filled with bathers, old and young together. They were bathing, splashing and skylarking, like dragonflies round forest pools.

My friend the sculptor paced hither and thither, staring and searching, reassuring me with the hand held behind him: "Right away, right away. She's here every day, she bathes here. I'll find her at once."

I followed him.

But I found her before he did. I noticed a group of women lying on the sand with all their eyes frozen on one spot in the sea. The spot was she.

"There she is," I told my friend.

"Aha. Yes."

"Well?"

"My old teacher, Rodin," said my friend excitedly, "once said to me categorically, 'Never model a woman's body till you find one that robs you of your rest and brings you to the belief that even if you were shown no more than one breast you would be able to say exactly how old she is.'

"Well, there she is. For the last few days I can't eat or drink or sleep like an ordinary human being. You know how I always eat like a brewer's horse and sleep like a dormouse. Now I eat like a dormouse and sleep like a horse—I hardly close my eyes."

I gazed at her while he added: "That's her public, that group of curious women. They talk of her as the young beauty. They know she comes to bathe here every day at this time and they come to stare at her and feel sorry for themselves."

"Yes. She's a beauty. Who is she?"

"Who is she? I'll tell you the truth; I want to go round and ask, but I'm afraid of the answer. Why? Just look at her. Now tell me, can you estimate how long it took for that woman's body to evolve out of hairy ape-mother Eve? How many millions of years have gone to bring the body to this stage? And who and what has brought it as far as this?"

"Who? I suppose that quiet, petted, sheltered lives of gentle culture and of careful, prolonged nurture have been the lot of mother and daughter for ages and ages. Care of the entire body from her hair to her toenails."

"That's it. And that's what strikes a discord in my creative enthusiasm. A girl nurtured enough to make the working masses rise. Someone told me that she's a haluza. I believed him for a moment and then realized how far I was from acting on my teacher's instructions. How could I imagine even for a second that she was a haluza? When you look at your worn-out haluzot, tired out and withered up before their time with hard work, you'll go raving mad at that girl; her beauty flourishes at the cost of all holy and unfortunate daughters of Israel, who can't even afford to buy a cake of decent toilet soap."

"That's no affair of an artist."

"I know, but what can I do? I know it's the sort of philosophizing you can expect from a Socialist. But it's gone so far that instead of modeling the body of a beautiful woman I've decided to introduce an idea of cruelty. I'd hardly begun to model when the right name struck me for the piece—Cattelia Necans. Do you know the Cattelia Necans Orchid, the lovliest of them all? It's a wonderful flower, a destructive flower, climbing over plants and trees and pouring its tendrils over any number of other plants; it twines round them, embraces them and slays them with a kiss, sucks their sap and flourishes, its blossom laughing to the sun in all its colors and its scent making you drunk far away. And this witch here is a blossom of the same kind. She preens herself at the cost of thousands of her sisters who toil and dry up like wild roses and who shrivel up under the flaming sun. Cattelia Necans—murderess!"

I wanted to say something to him, something in the style of Samson's "Out of the strong came forth sweetness." But she had just come out of the sea alone.

The sun was sinking, a disc of pure gold, and the girl stood stretching herself. She made a step and her head entered the circle of flaming light. The rim of the sun was a diadem set round her black head.

"Just look how Chance is mocking us. A glory of gold round her head. Come along, let's go. That's enough."

As we walked along he repeated:

"Murderess . . . murderess."

II. MOTHER

I met the sculptor again and he was in quite a different mood. He had a new idea. His murderess had been dropped halfway. He was true to his social theories and did not care even for the sanctities of Art, if they did not agree with his theories. He hated that murderess and a hater cannot be a creator. Now he had a holy idea.

"I've an idea for something I've felt the need of."

"Well?"

"The Jewish Mother. It's like this. Next door to me lives a couple with two kiddies, a boy and a girl. The boy's sick lately. The wall's real Tel Aviv manufacture, thick as three sheets of writing paper, and I can hear everything that's going on. And among the rest I've found out something that never struck me. I've found out what a Jewish mother is.—It's something I can't make out. This mother hasn't slept a wink for nearly three months—not a wink. I work at night, as you know, and she's up and busy with the baby all night long. She doesn't close her eyes even for five minutes. She just doesn't sleep. How is it possible?"

"Maybe she sleeps in the daytime?"

"That's the thing! I know that in the daytime she's at work somewhere. I haven't even seen her yet. Once I got up in the morning because I hadn't been working the night before, and I heard her attending to the two children. She was suckling the little boy and singing to him, and teaching the little girl. Pure Hebrew instruction. She speaks a Hebrew we can envy her. Lately there's nobody there all day long; it's only in the morning I hear her while she's suckling the boy. I hear things that are enough to make you melt away. She suckles the baby and speaks to him in her song. I noted down some of it."

He took out his notebook and read:

"Little red flower, tiny blossom, here is a little milk, take my pure white life. Take my white blood. Drink, drink, my weeny ram, drink and become a lion. Judah is a lion's whelp. Judah-lion's-whelp must not be sick. Many are the beasts of prey, my little son. You must grow and roar, not for prey, my son, but for the word of the Lord. A lion roars, who doth not fear; the Lord doth speak, who can but prophesy? Drink, drink, my son, my milk and blood. La-la-la, la-la-la, la-la."

He closed his notebook and raised his eyes to me. His eyes were moist.

"Well, what do you think?"

"A Jewish mother. You're right."

"She's awake at night. Doesn't let her eyelids close. And by day it's Judah, the lion's whelp, and then to work somewhere or other. Sure, she's a haluza. 'Take my white blood' —Lord! We have mothers like that."

"And who's her husband?"

"I have no idea. I'll tell you the truth; I've no great desire as yet to meet her. Come along to my place!"

As we entered his room we heard the voice of a woman singing to herself.

"She's at home," whispered the sculptor.

After listening a moment:

"She's washing herself—she's about to go out. Do you know what? Let's go down to the entrance and wait for her."

We went down and stood in the entrance hall and did not have long to wait. She appeared and went into the street. We could not see her face well for it was hidden by a blue summer-veil. She passed us quickly, a tastefully-dressed young woman. I looked after her and saw that her hands were not well kept.

"Spoiled hands," I said. "They're hard and bony. A haluza."

"A pity," said my friend. "Those are holy hands."

He looked after her and was silent. Suddenly he roused himself.

"Eh, my lad! What a piece, what a creation that will be! Do you know the name I've found for it?"

"Well?"

" 'Thy mother, the lioness.' "

III. HALUZA

"You're looking for a subject and must have a social theme? Come to my place!" I said to my sculptor friend a few days later. "Come and visit me after noon. I've got something for you to chew over. After you've looked you'll do a piece with a clear, fine, simple name, 'Haluza.' "

"Something in that. You're right. That idea never struck me. 'Haluza,' the sculpture of the age."

He visited me the following afternoon.

In the middle of the sands across the street a house was being built.

"Come here," said I. "Do you see that girl over there? That one, with a red handkerchief round her head?"

"Yes, I see her. Well?"

"Just sit down by the window and watch her for a while. Sit down and watch her working."

He sat down and I left him to himself.

Half an hour later I returned. He sat like an image and stared. When he sensed that I had come in he jumped up.

"Well?" I asked.

"Do you know the conclusion I've come to?" said he as though thinking aloud. "That the first of all revolts is the revolt of the woman. You know, it's a real dirty trick; why do women get a smaller wage than men? Why, that girl over there does more alone in a single second than three men in ten minutes! Just look how she's working! She's as strong as a giant, that girl. Look! Just look how she's picking up that iron bar!"

He started forward as though he wished to run and help her.

Meanwhile the singing of a woman reached us. She was singing at her work. A sweet and pleasant voice, light, but agreeable to the ear and appealing to the heart. The men would answer back in snatches and every now and again she would laugh at their gruffness, like a stream murmuring through the soughing of the trees.

My friend was all aflame.

"What am I against such a creature?" said he in despair. "All my attempts are hopeless against such an original. 'Haluza,' of course! Still, I'll try. And she's still young and fresh, you can see. Lovely girl."

We listened again to her happy singing and gazed in astonishment at her strength and diligence, wayward as a flowing fountain.

"Let's cross over!" proposed my friend. "I want to look at her nearby."

"All right. They're finishing right away, anyhow."

We went across and were a moment or two late. They were already leaving. We followed her. She was walking with her husband.

They turned into the street in which my friend the sculptor lived. When we reached the house in which his room was, they entered.

We looked at one another like two clowns.

"That's your mother lioness," said I. "You're a great artist and no mistake. How was it you didn't know?"

We entered his room and heard her speaking through the wall:

"You attend to the children meanwhile. I won't be back for about an hour. It's two days since last I bathed."

We stared at each other as the same idea struck us. Perhaps this was the beautiful girl?

"Some hopes," said my friend. "You jump too fast. You're silly."

"Silly if you like, but come down to the hallway all the same."

We went down and in a moment she came out. It was the same "Jewish mother" we had seen coming out a few days earlier.

Looking at her face, naturally I recognized the beautiful bathing girl.

"A poet's hallucination," said my friend with mocking assurance.

We followed her in silence.

She proceeded straight to the sea.

When we arrived and found her in the sea we stared at one another as though we had gone silly.

The sun was setting. My friend caught my hand and pulled me to the right.

"Over here. Come over here. That's right."

I did not understand for a moment. But when I moved I saw her black head in the gold disc of the sun and the haluza stood on the sands, bright with a glory.

"Well, my lad, what name can you suggest for this piece?"

[TRANSLATED FROM THE HEBREW BY I. M. LASK]

GERALDINE STERN

Milkmaid on the Jordan

From the day she came to Degania and promptly sat down to milk Rushka, their only cow, Miriam Baratz has been milking cows ever since. That was forty-six years, 300 cows, seven children and twelve grandchildren ago. Degania, set like a jewel 300 feet below sea level in the lush valley of the River Jordan on the southern shore of Lake Kinnereth, is the oldest *kibbutz* in Israel. And Miriam Baratz, who left Russia for Palestine when she was sixteen, is one of Israel's first woman settlers.

The day I came to look for her I was afraid my early afternoon arrival might find the sixty-seven-year-old pioneer napping, but not Miriam. "Miriam? She's in the cowshed," the youngish-looking *maskir,* secretary of Degania, told me when I knocked on his cottage office. Whether you are sixty-seven or seven years old, in an agricultural settlement in Israel you are still Miriam or whatever your first name happens to be, whether addressed by young or old.

I started out for the cowshed accompanied by Itzhak, the genial driver who had brought me there. He had offered to double as interpreter if I needed one. We didn't know how well Miriam spoke English. We doubted if she spoke French, and Itzhak could interpret Hebrew or his native tongue, Polish. His English was good since he'd served in the British army in Palestine. We walked past rows of tall stately cypress trees that gave an aspect of venerable beauty to Degania. They had been planted years ago by the settlers, to protect their orchards and buildings from the winds off Lake Kinnereth.

Kinnereth is the same Biblical body of water that is also known as the Sea of Galilee, the name given it in the New Testament, and as Lake Tiberias, acquired later during the Roman occupation. With its backdrop of softly rolling hills across the lake, and the banana trees, citrus and olive groves of the settlement, Degania looks like a modern garden of Eden. When we reached an open area, several large cowsheds came into sight. We continued down a rutted road to the first building. And there we found Miriam Baratz, hard at work with the cows.

She gave us a warm *"Shalom,"* resting an empty milk pail against each of her high rubber boots. A blue cotton kerchief pulled tightly around her massive head hid her hair completely, partially exposing big ears. She is a heavy set woman with large features. A faded blouse, worn pants and apron were her working clothes. I told Miriam I would like to talk with her.

A broad smile lit up her face. It is a face deeply tanned and lined from years in the Middle East sun and heavily covered with freckles that continue over her arms and chest. *"Ken, ken.* Yes, yes," she said, "but please come back and visit me on *Shabbat.* I am just starting to milk the cows, so I can't talk now." She shook her head and was impatient to get on with her work. "The cows can't wait!"

I thanked her but said I couldn't get back on the Sabbath. "I am sorry, I must milk the cows. *Bevakasha,* please return on *Shabbat,"* she repeated. *"Slihah,* excuse me." She walked over to a long row of impressive-looking cows, sat down on a stool next to the first in line, tilted a pail between her knees and went to work.

It was too bad, because she looked like quite a woman. It was a pity to have come all the way and not be able to talk to her. With a reluctant *"Shalom"* and "thank you,"

Itzhak and I started to leave. Then it occurred to me that I would at least like to have her picture. "Would you mind?" "Fine, go ahead," she said as she squirted the milk accurately into the pail. I took a picture and she repeated that she was sorry that I had arrived just at that time and the milking would take too long for me to wait. The happy thought came to me, "Perhaps we can talk while you are working?" "Yes, *ken, ken.* Just so I don't keep the cows waiting." So while Miriam Baratz proceeded with her milking, I dodged the natural functions of the cows and we managed to do considerable talking. With her limited English and a little help from Itzhak and her daughter Michal, who was working two cows down, we made out fine.

She told me about her family first. "I have four daughters and three sons, all married and living in Degania, except two. They would be here, too," she explained, with the implication that they wouldn't live any place but Degania by choice, "but our son's wife has asthma and the climate in Herzlia is better for her. Our daughter, Dvora, left with her husband to build a new settlement in the Negev." The pail was filling up quickly as she spoke. A young woman, also in high rubber boots and with a kerchief on her head, took the full pail, handed Miriam an empty one and then poured the warm foamy milk through a cloth sieve into a large can. Miriam adjusted another pail between her knees and continued her dextrous handling of the udders without interruption.

She talked to the rhythm of the milking as she worked. "This is one of my daughters," she said. "Two of the girls and one son milk here. Both girls have little girls who are learning to milk, too." A pleased smile came over her face but faded when she added, "My daughter lost her husband in the war nine years ago. You saw the Syrian tank outside of Degania? One of our men working in the garden stopped it with a Molotov cocktail. Several other tanks retreated, but my son-in-law was killed in the fighting." I told her I had seen the tank. The bulrushes of the Jordan have grown up around it, but the people of Degania have left it as a monument where it was stopped in its tracks next to their gates. As we drove in, some of the younger children of the *kibbutz* were climbing up and down its sides. A happy conversion from swords into ploughshares, from tanks to tots' playground.

Miriam showed no inclination to dwell on personal hardships during the war or the destruction, since rebuilt, done to Degania by the Syrians, Iraqis and the Arab Legion. Her primary point of interest, aside from the fact that the children had been safely removed to Haifa, was how the war had affected the cows. She slipped a cloth in water, wrung it out with hands powerful from years of extracting milk, and wiped the udders. Finished with the first cow, she picked up stool and pail and moved to the next. She wiped the udders of her new subject, and while the white fluid made rhythmic sounds into the pail, she said, "During the war we had to move all the cows to Haifa in quarantine. I went with them, and all the workers for the cows went along. We stayed there two months." Not mentioning any inconvenience the wartime emergency caused her or the *kibbutz,* she recalled with a smile, "When they came back, every cow knew its own place as if nothing had happened."

Her daughter came by again to take a full pail and hand her mother an empty one. It was an efficient operation with no loss of time or motion. "My daughter there," Miriam said, "she's my oldest daughter. When she and my first son were babies I used to take them with me to the shed when I milked the cows. Sometimes I took them at night, too. And they sat or slept in the trough." She looked up and shook her head and laughed. "Nobody approved! My son was the first baby born in Degania. We weren't well organized the way it is with new *kibbutzim* today. We were groping to develop a collective life. Being the first mother and wife in our group made many problems for me. I said I would not stop working when my baby was born. Everyone was upset when I took him to the cowshed with me. They said, 'How can she take the baby there?' Sometimes the cows licked the baby. Everyone said, 'It's unhealthy. Manure!' I told them never mind, don't worry about my child. The cows are cleaner than the people. It's not dangerous for the baby. When the baby started to cry, all of Degania said, 'Miriam, the baby is crying.' I told them, 'Don't bother me. You are worried about the child. If the diaper has to be changed, change it.' "

Miriam rested her head on the cow's haunch and continued to milk as she discussed her early problems. "Some said I should devote my time to looking after the child. But I knew if I did, I would be cut off from them and from everything that was happening in the *kibbutz*. I didn't argue much, but when there were meetings, I went and took the baby along. I got up to work at three o'clock in the morning and never stopped until ten at night. Sometimes I would get up at midnight, wash the baby's clothes and then go back to bed for a while. The first child was considered common property of the *kibbutz* except when it came to taking care of him! Anybody who wanted to brought him into the dining-hall, even in the evening. I didn't object, but love of the child was one thing and the attitude towards the mother's work was another. That year it was still the practise to pay each member a monthly wage. But I was paid only two-thirds of my wages because I spent time looking after my boy. I felt it was unjust and a bad precedent for the position of women in the *kibbutz* as well as for the education and care of our children."

Miriam was a woman who had independently formed her own common sense theories without benefit of formal education or intellectual pursuits. "My education?" she said and knocked the next cow with the pail to make room for her to sit down. "I went to elementary school in Russia. I didn't learn much." She smiled and added, "I went to the University of Life in Palestine. It was a hard way to learn, but good. By the time my boy was two, I was expecting another child and another woman was expecting one also. I thought now we will make better conditions for bringing up the children. Degania had grown to about forty. It seemed like a large number then. Now we are almost 500. I suggested that one of us should work while the other looked after the children." Miriam shrugged her shoulders. "It was unsuccessful, because when it was my turn to work the other mother only wanted to take care of her own child. That brought up the whole question of the family in the *kibbutz* and we had many discussions to try to solve the problem. We were very simple then. We had yet to learn that each new child gave our life more meaning and made the group stronger. Some were afraid that the family would interfere with the development of the *kibbutz* and might affect its co-operative basis. Then came a proposal not to marry for five years." She laughed when she thought of it. "And the member who made the suggestion was the first one to marry!

"I kept on working after my daughter was born and, when I had to, I brought both babies to the cowshed with me. About that time sickness broke out among the cattle and all of us were very upset. I blamed myself. Maybe I didn't know how to handle the cattle properly. So I decided to go to Ben Shemen and study at the agricultural school there. No one approved of the idea. How could a mother of two children, one just a few months old, think of going away to study? But I packed our things and took the children with me to Ben Shemen and stayed nine months. Josef, my husband, came to see us when he could leave his building work at Degania. It was the hardest time of my whole life but I have never regretted it." She patted the cow affectionately. "We kept them from getting sick any more.

"By the time I returned to Degania, a third woman had had a child and we made one more attempt at common care. But that was to fail, too. The first World War came. All our living quarters and the farm buildings were requisitioned by the German and Turkish armies. Our temporary quarters were so bad that the children became ill and we had to take them to hospitals."

But wars didn't stop Miriam Baratz from having babies, just as babies never stopped her from going on with her work. Finally she succeeded in her fight for joint care of the children. "When my third baby was born a year later we established co-operative care of the children at last and it has continued ever since," she said. On this note of triumph, Miriam remembered the day the baby was born. "I always worked up to the last minute before my babies came. When it was announced that I had had my third, one of the members of Degania said he was sure I had had the baby in the cowshed. He had just seen me there. He rushed to the cowshed to look for me before he was convinced that I had gone to the hospital."

All of Miriam's time that wasn't taken up with children or cows, was given to the study of everything connected with her work. From a pioneer girl who just happened to take on the cows because no one else wanted the difficult hours, she has become one of Israel's leading authorities on the milking, feeding and breeding of cattle. Starting with Ben Shemen, she began to approach her work scientifically. She read about the subject wherever she could find something to read. Today her children have the advantage not only of their mother's expert instruction, but Degania has a museum of National History and Agriculture, complete with library, reading rooms and lecture halls. It is named after A. D. Gordon, noted writer and thinker, who was a member of Degania. Miriam's daughters don't have to pack up their children and run off to Ben Shemen as their mother did. They can increase their knowledge and their families at the same time without leaving Degania, or, at best, going no farther than a few miles to Bet Yerah, where an agricultural school for all the settlements of the Jordan Valley has been built recently.

Looking as though she had never left the farm in her life, Miriam readied another cow for milking and surprised me with saying, "I went to the United States twice, also Holland, England and Germany to study milking, feeding and breeding. The Jewish Agency sent me in 1925 and again in '38. I was at Cornell and the University of Wisconsin and Rutgers University in New Brunswick. I also went to California, Texas and Canada. An interpreter went to classes and meetings with me." The picture of Miriam Baratz attending classes in American universities was a delightful image. They were the extension courses of her University of Life in Palestine.

She did some lecturing, too. "I went to San Antonio for a convention of the Pioneer Women of America," she recalled chuckling. "I came by bus as we do here. I tried to dress my finest. But the delegation of women who came to meet me seemed to be surprised when they saw how I was dressed and that I took a bus instead of a train. They brought me to the hotel and asked me very carefully if maybe I needed a dress. I didn't understand what was going on. I thanked them and I said I had a dress. I was there three or four days. Before I left, I asked them, 'Tell me. What was so funny when I came? Why were you so disappointed?' They told me, 'You looked like a farmer, not a delegate. We didn't know how it would be for the meetings. But after the wonderful meetings, we forgive you.' "

Miriam told me about the time she was asked to teach young people in a new *kibbutz* how to work in a cowshed. She said, "I went to Beit Shan Valley twice a week for a year. But young people don't like to have old people teaching them. That is why I didn't continue. In the beginning they resisted but then they learned a lot. Now they have young instructors. They said that old people are pedantic." She was philosophical about the experience. "When they grow up they will see. They, too, will be pedantic.

"They have some of our cattle breed in their *kibbutz* and are doing all right with them. It's a good cross. We continue to cross them and sell cows, calves and bulls to other settlements," Miriam explained. "We cross Damascus and Holland cows. We have done it for five generations, Holland bulls with Damascus cows. We do it by artificial insemination." Miriam added regretfully, "It's more convenient for us but not natural for the cows. We also use some electric milkers," she said. "They use them in two cowsheds here. But these cows are older and don't like it. They have sensitive udders, so for them the old-fashioned way is better."

Miriam looked around at her beloved brood and said, "The other day a little boy came into the cowshed and his mother asked him if he knew all the people working here. He said one was the mother of David. Another was the mother of Ruth. When they came to me, his mother said, 'And whose mother is this?' 'Oh, Miriam. Miriam is the mother of all the cows'." She laughed heartily. "He was right. My children, my grandchildren and all the cows." Then she said, "The only times I did work away from the cows in Degania was when I broke my arm." Miriam recalled a series of arm breakings. "Once I had an accident in a taxi in Tel Aviv. Once I fell in the cattle house at night. And once I fell in our house in the dark." But not even broken arms could idle her. "I worked in the kitchen each time until it healed," she said. "Then I went back to the cows again. I used to work eighteen hours a day, now, only nine or ten." Only by seeing her in action could I believe the hours of work that Miriam stated. And now, at sixty-seven, she was down to a mere average or better than average work day.

"That sounds like much work to you?" she asked me. "Better than not enough," she observed. "I'll go to the next cow and then I'll tell you how it was when I first came to Palestine." Miriam settled down with the animal waiting for her, and while she directed a steady stream of milk into the pail, she recalled coming to Palestine during the period of the Second *Aliyah.* The first Zionists came about thirty years earlier from Eastern Europe. "That was in 1906," she said. "I came from Boguslav, a small town in the Ukraine. We were six children. My father was Joseph Laib, the leaser of a ferry on the River Russ. We never wanted for anything, but we always talked about going to Palestine. A country with pogroms was not healthy. At Passover in 1901 our mother died and our home changed completely. My two older brothers and a sister left for Palestine. I wanted to go with them, but Father said I was too young.

"In the summer of 1906 Father went to Palestine and bought 110 dunams of land at Kfar Saba for planting almonds. When he came back in August, I begged him so much he finally agreed to let me go with my grandmother and grandfather and a cousin who were leaving. I was sixteen then. He used to say, 'What will you do there?' And I told him I shall work. He would laugh and say, 'Who needs you there?' I was hurt, but I didn't argue with him. I just said to myself wait till he sees what happens and then he will change his mind." It was clear that Miriam was smart about not making issues of things. She said little and went right on accomplishing her objective.

"We were on our way three weeks by boat," Miriam continued. "We were met by my two brothers and sister at Jaffa and we all went on to Petah Tikvah. They had been working there in the orange groves. But there was so little work to be had that we decided to move on to Kfar Saba where we would till Father's land and make a home for the rest of the family. Grandfather set up a kind of restaurant which I cooked for, and I ran the home, too. But in summer there was no work in Kfar Saba and it was lonely, so we decided to go back to Petah Tikvah where we had good companions. Then I began to work in the orange groves and live on my own." Miriam smiled as she thought back. "I had lots of young fellows after me. Our life was rich in friendship but poor in work. I took any work that came along, but sometimes I could only get two days a week. The farmers didn't want girl workers and hired mostly Arabs. Those days we never had enough to eat, often only bread and olives.

"Finally I found work with the farmer Kroll in Petah Tikvah," she said. "I worked eight months for him raising seedlings for the groves. I watered more than 100 garden plots with tins of water, dragging two tins together, and I raised a first-class nursery. I was so happy, I never wanted the day to end. Kroll always used to come and stop me because I never dropped the hoe."

Miriam spoke of both success and failure as one of the first girl pioneers. "At Purim they began to plant a tree nursery for the Herzl forest near Lydda. But only young men were wanted there. My comrades, who were members of the Roumanian Commune, left in the morning after we had danced all night at a wedding. I said good-bye to them in tears because I wanted to be one of the first Jewish workers to plant a nursery on Jewish National Fund land.

"I kept working in the orange groves until I was nineteen and then one day I received a telegram that my comrades wanted me to join them in Daleika. They had moved there to develop the Kinnereth land. They sent me ten francs to make the trip and I took my bundle and went to the Galilee. The trip took two days then instead of two hours as it does now. I went by wagon coach to Haifa, then several hours by train from Haifa to Samakh. And from Samakh I crossed to the western shore of the lake by sailing boat." Miriam paused in her work momentarily, rested her hands in her lap and looked up, smiling as she recalled fondly, "That is when I met my Josef, when the wagon coach stopped at Athlit. My brother was working there cutting stones for the buildings of the colony. And when I went to find him in his tent, Josef was with him." She was to see Josef Baratz soon again.

"I went on to the Galilee. Those were days of work. I ran the tumbledown house for twenty-five of us, getting up at three A.M. and working till eight or nine in the evening without a break, cooking in the open over stones with blinding smoke. Days of much work but also rich with life and joy; many happy moments, but also problems. I was not ready to link myself with one man and I thought I should leave and not hurt my comrades.

"So I went to Mizpeh for a while and then to Hadera," Miriam continued, "where there was a call for Jewish workers to uproot the *humtza* weed. To get there I walked enough for the rest of my life! I walked from Petah Tikvah to Jaffa, about ten miles, where twenty-two workers were selected, I the only girl. The next morning we met on the Petah Tikvah-Kfar Saba road and walked all day, most of it through deep sands, about twenty-five miles to Hadera. When the farmers heard that a girl worker had come to Hadera to pluck *humtza* they laughed. They said a girl couldn't possibly know how to do that work. I felt insulted," Miriam shrugged, "but I was getting used to that and I wouldn't give up. I tried some of the farmers, but they wouldn't take me on. Then I suggested to one of them, as a trial, I would work for him free and he agreed. After my first day's work, he gave me a regular wage." Miriam had a pleased expression on her face as she reported her success as a victory for all the women workers in Israel who have come after her.

"Before long," Miriam went on, "the comrades whom I had left wrote me that they had decided to leave Kinnereth and asked me to find a place in Hadera where we could work and live together. The only place I could find was a *khan,* an Arab hostelry for men and animals. And that is where we lived. We all worked for farmers. Each brought his monthly wage to me and I bought what we needed, shoes for one, trousers or a hat for another. If anything was left over, it went on trips and postage for letters."

Whether her companions came to Hadera to pick *humtza* or to further personal interests with Miriam, she did not make clear. But if it was the latter, they were fighting a losing battle. Josef Baratz had already made several trips to see the girl he had met in her brother's tent at Athlit. The chance meeting blossomed into a romance that has lasted for close to fifty years. I heard of only one rumored threat to the Baratz union. It involved the late Jo Davidson, the American sculptor, who stayed in Degania for a time in recent years. Everyone who goes to Degania falls in love with Miriam. According to the friend who told me the story, the sophisticated sculptor got on with Miriam like a house afire. He told his wife if he had met Miriam forty years ago, she wouldn't have had a chance. Mrs. Davidson is reported to have replied, "You know, I really believe I wouldn't." Miriam is one of the two women Jo Davidson chose to do heads of in Israel. The other is Golda Meir.

"By that time," Miriam continued, "I was very much attached to Josef. On the eve of *Rosh Hashanah,* when I was working in the orange groves at Hefziba near Hadera, we told the others of our engagement. They were happy with the news, and although on that *Rosh Hashanah* there was little to eat, we decided to celebrate. With the few *bishliks,* Turkish coins, we had, we bought bread and rice, some lentils and oil and prepared a feast. Then," Miriam added with enthusiasm, "we danced all that night."

As she got up with pail in one hand and stool in the other, Miriam dropped the pail under another cow, the stool alongside, big as this.' She sighed, recalling youth, love, dancing and orange picking and walking miles through deep sand to get to work. "The only exercise I get now is in my hands and the rest of me none." Miriam dropped the pail under another cow the stool alongside, seated her still agile enough body and put her hands into perpetual motion once more.

"While we were at Hadera," she resumed, "the Palestine Office decided to experiment with developing the land on the other side of the Jordan, the Um Juni land. One of our members, Israel Bloch, went there for a year to try it out and then recommended that our commune start a permanent settlement. It was a great responsibility, but we decided to do it. We were eager to create something fine and be our own masters. Another girl, Sara Malkin, joined us. Sara and I with ten men came to Um Juni in the fall of 1911, right after the Day of Atonement, and we called it Degania after *dagan,* the corn that we planted."

Luckily for the men, Sara was there to look after them, because Miriam's father called her back to Russia shortly after the group moved to Degania. "My father asked me to come back for a visit," Miriam said. "I agreed, with the understanding that I would return after a short stay. But as soon as I got there he said he wouldn't let me leave again." Miriam's quiet determination proved to be stronger than her father's demands and the laws of the land combined. "Even though I was twenty-one, I could not get a passport without my father's permission," she explained. "So I left without money or papers and went to Odessa. For three months nobody knew what happened to me. I had only enough money for a lodging place for two nights. But I was recognized by someone there who had been in Israel and he helped me to find a place to stay, and also helped me get back. He made arrangements for me to pass as the twelve-year-old daughter of a friend of his who was going." Miriam laughed as she recalled meeting her "adopted" father on the boat for the first time. "I'll never forget the expression on his face when he saw me. There I was a big and well-built twenty-one-year-old! But there was nothing he could do about it. I was registered on his passport as his daughter and he had to bring me with him.

"My comrades gave me a fine welcome and Josef and I were happy to be together again. He had gone to Degania with us. The men had worked hard while I was away to make a start on the first buildings. It was a difficult task. Everything was still very primitive. There wasn't even a pump," Miriam said. "Now we are so civilized. Electricity, running water, the whole *meshek* (farm) irrigated! At that time we drew water out of the well in barrels. We only had one cow. Her name was Rushka and we got her from the mountains of Golan." Miriam shook her head. "I remember the day we came here. The first thing I did was milk Rushka." Then she added, "You see, I never keep a cow waiting."

With that Miriam moved to another cow and continued talking. "Soon after my return, Josef and I decided we would get married. The entire commune took part in the discussion of the wedding plans and it was decided to hold the wedding when the harvest was in. Towards the end of summer, 1912, we were married in a joyous harvest celebration. People came from all over the country, even though the journey from Tel Aviv and Jaffa took them two days."

Miriam said enthusiastically, "And of course, we danced all night!"

Miriam's daughter came by again, strained another pail of milk into the can, and went on. Her mother's eyes followed her as she left. "Yes, Josef and I have had a good life and a good family."

MARIE SYRKIN

Hanna Senesch

Hanna Senesch has become a national heroine of Palestine and hers was the name which I heard most frequently upon my arrival. I heard men say, "At last the Jews have a Joan of Arc." In their youth, their sense of dedication to their people's cause, and their death there is a certain resemblance. But there is little purpose in pressing the analogy too far. Joan of Arc led the armies of France to victory. Hanna Senesch accomplished little in terms of the number of individuals rescued. And one cannot be an unsuccessful Joan of Arc. The great miracle of the Maid of Orleans lay in what she did, not only in how she did it. It is beside the point to speculate on whether in a more brutal and sophisticated age even a second Joan could have done more than try and fail.

Hanna Senesch was no Joan of Arc. She did not conquer the enemy, nor did she save the Jews of Europe. I stress the obvious not because I believe that the legend of the young and charming Hungarian girl, who so valiantly sacrificed her life, should be kept within rational limits. The romantic enthusiasm aroused by this girl's history is natural enough. I mention what Hanna did not do and could not do, to underscore the point that even if Hanna had been the equal of Joan in vision and power, she would have been essentially helpless, for she was the heroine of a people without armies to be led and without a land to which to lead them. Hanna, with all her valor and rich intelligence, hurtling herself down in a British uniform to a hostile land, was a part of the general Jewish tragedy. She had the hero's equipment, temperament and purpose, but she was bound to fail when viewed against the background of the Jewish drama. However, the attempt to breach the fortress of the foe was more than a glorious gesture. It indicated a new approach to the Nazi terror—a readiness to take independent action which, had it been repeated on a larger scale, might have effected a substantial improvement in the situation.

How much this readiness was treasured has already been indicated. That the chief measure of worship has been accorded to one of the least successful of the parachutists reveals the deep wound in the Jewish spirit. It is not sentimentality which has made Hanna's aureole the brightest. In a period dominated by the vision of the endless march to the extermination center, every figure who rose out of the nightmare to the level of action was cherished in proportion to the will that he displayed. The sensitive poetic girl became the symbol of awakening.

Every Jew in Palestine can recite the four simple lines of the poem Hanna wrote shortly before she was executed.

> Blessed is the match that is consumed in kindling flame.
> Blessed is the flame that burns in the secret fastness of the heart.
> Blessed is the heart with strength to stop its beating for honor's sake.
> Blessed is the match that is consumed in kindling flame.

The Hebrew original has a beauty which is lost in a literal translation, but the concept is clear. The poem celebrates the self-immolation of the hero. There is no assurance that the ultimate issue will be life. There is only insistence on the sacrifice. That such a sentiment can be described as the national slogan of Palestine Jewry indicates the bitter lesson learned from the Nazi decade. The attempt to cling to life will surely result in death. The only hope lies in the readiness to die. *Ashrei ha-gafrur* —"Blessed is the match"— I heard these lines many times in Palestine. The application was always immediate. The youth I encountered was prepared to be consumed, as Hanna had been, in the hope that their people might live. This ardor is to be found in no other Jewish community; and when one senses this prevailing mood, Hanna and her fellows become more comprehensible.

I have no intention of writing Hanna's biography. One cannot, however, disassociate her career as a parachutist from her past. Her evolution helps one to understand the paradoxical Jewish hero who emerged in the Hitler era —this being, hyper-intellectual, ultra-sensitive, who became under the pressure of events a parachutist, a partisan leader, or a ghetto fighter. The heroes of other peoples have, for the most part, backgrounds which explain their subsequent careers, but the Jewish heroes did not come from the playing-fields of Eton. Most of them had not been athletes delighting in swiftness of limb and strength of muscle.

The Shield of David was forged in the ivory tower, in the synagogue, in the meeting-halls of sects arguing fiercely how Utopia should be shaped. The visionaries and artists became the chief doers. The Jewish hero became such, not because of temperamental or physical aptitude, but because of faith. Perhaps the paradox is not as strange as it first seems. Where the odds were so great, only the exaltation of the believer could provide the necessary impulse. This type is to be seen at its purest in Hanna Senesch.

Under ordinary circumstances she would probably have devoted herself to one of the arts, but the Nazi triumph ended all chance of anything approaching a normal existence. The span of her life—July 7, 1921 to November 7, 1944— coincided with the development of the Nazi party, its seizure of power, and World War II. And whereas another girl similarly situated might have sought to escape from the cataclysm, it was inevitable that she should be drawn into its center.

She was born in Budapest into a wealthy, distinguished, assimilated Hungarian-Jewish family. Perhaps, without Hitler, Hanna would have become a Hungarian minor poet instead of a major Jewish heroine. She was too self-conscious, and too conscientious, to have been without awareness of herself as a Jewess even in the best of circumstances; but in another period there is no telling what form this awareness might have taken. Once, however, the Jewish issue had been posed on any part of the European continent, Hanna, though living in the material comfort and apparent safety of a well-to-do Hungarian home, could not fail to react. Her solution was Palestine.

She was caught early by the Zionist fever.

Before she is eighteen, she is already proclaiming in her diary: "I want to read the Bible in Hebrew," and on the same day she quotes a letter from her brother in which he writes, "It is good to die for one's country." The seventeen-year-old girl remarks: "This last is very actual in Palestine, for the British have just concocted a White Paper with dreadful contents." This is 1939 and her reference is to the Chamberlain White Paper.

On her eighteenth birthday she writes: "To-day is my birthday . . . I am eighteen. It is hard to believe that I am so old already." But this typical adolescent melancholy is accompanied by another note: Life is beautiful because "my idea fulfills all my life." Friends warn her of disappointment, but she is sure! "I know I will not be disappointed. I want to do everything to bring this dream nearer to reality, or the reality nearer to the dream."

A few days after the birthday which made her feel old, she writes exuberantly: "I've got it. I've got it—the certificate to go to Palestine. I read the good news again and again." There is only one drawback to this joy. Her widowed mother dreads the young daughter's departure. Hanna, who is passionately attached to her mother and brother—these are to remain her chief loves—is aware of the suffering she is inflicting on her family, but she is as one possessed. She describes her mother "as a great heroine. This is a great sacrifice for her," but her own course is set.

A few months later she is already in the agricultural school of Nahalal in Palestine, training herself for a life on the soil. It is a very different world from that of Budapest and begins a crucial period of adjustment. More than one enthusiast who came to Palestine full of a poetic fervor for "pioneering" found his resolution unequal to the actual business of draining swamps and "making the desert bloom."

Even Hanna had her moments of faltering, which can be sensed in the diary. She has received a letter from a friend in Hungary describing a gay party. Hanna, remembering the frills and furbelows of the past, writes: "My eyes surveyed my hands, sore from work . . . . I wondered if it was not simply romanticism which had driven me from a comfortable home to a life of physical work . . . . but, no, I am right."

She is too complex, too full of eagerness for intellectual and artistic experiences, not to be aware of what she has relinquished by her choice. In Nahalal, in addition to the practical branches of farming, the students learn something of the science of agriculture. After a botany class, she writes: "To-day we learned about certain cells which penetrate the soil first, which prepare the way but are themselves destroyed in the process. The teacher called them 'the pioneers of the plant.' " And Hanna, thinking of the girls with whom she is training in Nahalal and of their future, adds: "These cells are cleopadra. And we, shall we all be such cells? Is this our fate? These questions interest me more than a lecture on botany."

The sense that she is dedicated, or, rather, that she must dedicate herself, pursues her everywhere—in a botany class, in her room, on a hike. She visits Kfar Gileadi, in northern Galilee, where Trumpeldor and those who fell with him in defense of the settlement lie buried. The wild beauty of the Galilean hills, the purple mountains of Moab towards Transjordan, can move even the most apathetic. The memories associated with this place, both ancient and recent, stir the young girl deeply. She observes in her diary: "In the freshness of the dawn, I understand why Moses received God's command in the morning. In the mountains, the question arises of itself: 'Whom shall I send?' "

She answers the immense question that she senses everywhere. " 'Whom shall I send?' Send *me* to serve the good and beautiful." And though she adds, as any young girl might, "Will I be able?", the fundamental assurance that *she* must be sent, although she is as yet uncertain as to what form this sending must take, is hers already.

Her diary reflects the history of the period as well as the *Sturm and Drang* of her spirit. The day when Jewish refugees are sent from Palestine to Mauritius is specially black. But on the same page she writes: "I feel that I can't live without writing . . . I have much to write . . . I would like to write about my mother. The theme involves not only my mother, but all Jewish mothers . . . however, not all have her modesty and her heroism."

The longing to be a writer in no way weakens her determination to become a member of an agricultural collective where the day's labor leaves little room for the cultivation of the spirit. She faces the problem squarely. A play composed by her indicates the nature of the conflict. The heroine, a gifted violinist, must choose between developing herself as an artist, or living in a collective settlement. She decides that service to her people through the collective is more significant than the development of an individual, no matter how endowed. The plot of the play is transparent. It is Hanna's problem and choice. "I have chosen to work on the soil. I want to be a part of the working class in Palestine. This is not theoretical, because it permeates all my actions."

This is not theoretical! These words explain Hanna's peculiar strength, for she is never lost in a daydream. At the same time that she is consumed by the vision of a heroic future, she becomes an expert and competent worker in the various branches of farming. She even tries to devise all kinds of little innovations to improve poultry-raising. "I am thinking of a device to mark the color of each egg . . . but I suppose the poultry will be organized without me."

She does not spare herself in her diary. In a mood of skepticism, she exclaims: "Sometimes I think I am deceiving myself—playing a game—and that the only thing I really care about is whether my blue blouse and shorts are becoming." She has a normal girl's liking of a pretty dress, a normal girl's interest in boys, but the boys she meets do not content her. She is looking for an "impossible he." And whether the blue blouse is becoming is essentially a minor concern among the passions which possess her.

She has intensity, but not simplicity of purpose. Joan of Arc left no diary, but from what we know of the young shepherdess all her emotional capacity could probably have been concentrated within the range of the religious exaltation and conviction which ruled her. The call of the archangel was unmistakable. Hanna Senesch belongs to another category. She is the complex child of a more complex time. Conflicting impulses agitate her: the need for artistic expression, the quest for personal happiness, the desire to play a part in the political life around her (she admits that), the stern creed which bids that all this must be subordinated to "poultry-raising," and, above all, the mysterious assurance that she has been chosen for some great purpose. "Sometimes I feel I have a mission; what it is, is not clear to me. Sometimes I think this is all nonsense. Why all these efforts of the individual?"

In the midst of her work in the settlement of Caesarea, which she enters after completing the course at the training school in Nahalal, she is active and gay. She mentions the unexpected satisfaction one can have even from working in the laundry of the settlement. She is as good a comrade in the actual life of the communal settlement as she had been in the school. Her comrades testify to that, and the witnesses are significant. They would be quick to spot a shirker and mercilessly critical of one who proved unequal to the exigencies of hard, unglamorous work. Hanna is never paralyzed into inactivity by the dream, nor does she substitute a grandiose fantasy for scrubbing clothes or cleaning the chicken coop. The processes are simultaneous.

The climax is approaching. On January 8, 1944, she writes: "This week has been an agitating one. Suddenly an idea occured to me: I must go to Hungary, be there at the present time, help to organize youth-*aliyah,* and bring out my mother. I realize the absurdity of this notion, and yet somehow I think it possible, and I keep figuring how it could be done."

But the "absurdity" becomes real. Within two weeks she is approached by the organizers of the parachutist group. She cannot write the details in her diary, but the answer is clear:

How strangely things develop! On January 8, I wrote of the idea which suddenly stirred me . . . a few days ago a comrade came and told me of the mission being planned . . . just what I had dreamt of . . . . I feel a fatality in this, just as at the time before I went to Palestine. Then too I was not my own master. I was caught by an idea that did not let me rest. I knew that I would enter Palestine, no matter what difficulties were in my way. Now I again feel this tension towards an important and necessary task—as well as the inevitability of the task. Possibly nothing will come of all this. I may receive a brief notice telling me the plan has been abandoned, or that I will not be accepted. But I think that I have the maximal capacities for this task—and I shall fight with all my strength for it.

At night, I find it hard to fall asleep because of what I picture. How will I act in this situation—how in another? How will I inform my mother of my arrival? How will I organize the youth? All is unclear. We will see what the future brings.

She is accepted for training as a parachutist. Any day she may be called to Cairo. The fantasy has come true. She will go to Hungary, descending from the skies in a parachutist's dress. One of the last entries in the diary reads:

> May 27, Caesarea, I am wholly taken up with one thing —my departure. It has become actual and close at hand. I may be called in the next few days.
>
> I place myself in various situations and sometimes I think: "To leave this land, and freedom?" I would like to fill my lungs with fresh air with which I will be able to breathe in the choking atmosphere of the *Galut* and to dispense it to those who have been so long denied the taste of freedom. But these are merely thoughts around the indisputable fact and the necessity for my departure. I am aware of the difficulty and the danger, but I have the feeling that I will be able to fulfill my task. I see everything that happened before as a behest and preparation for this mission.

The final entry of the diary is made on June 14, 1944:

This week I go to Egypt. I am mobilized; I am a soldier. I want to believe that what I do and will do is right. The rest time will tell.

One cannot help comparing these sober, restrained words with the exuberant "I have it, I have it, the certificate to Palestine" written in Budapest, in 1939, just five years earlier. The vague ecstasy of the eighteen-year-old girl is approaching fulfillment; the young woman of twenty-three makes this last restrained entry, gives her diary and her poems to her *kibbutz* (collective), and leaves for Egypt. The five years in Palestine are over.

IN A HUNGARIAN PRISON

The goal had been reached; the Palestinians were in the heart of Europe. Unfortunately, among the guides provided by the partisans were members of the Hungarian counter-espionage force. The Palestinians were permitted to reach the Hungarian capital because the police were anxious to discover their true purpose and to learn the nature of their contacts. Joel and Perez soon realized that they were being shadowed and attempted to find safe hiding-places. For several days they thought that they had shaken off the trail of the Hungarian sleuths, and they attempted to utilize the time to establish contacts with the underground movements, particularly the Jewish underground. Once this had been done, the first link in the chain of communication would have been forged. Even if arrest should follow, the local underground would know of the presence of the parachutists and further links could be created. But despite all precautions, the feared arrest followed soon after Joel's arrival in Budapest. He was taken into custody.

In the prison Joel learned from the guards that a young Palestinian girl had been captured two weeks earlier. As a final blow he was shown the uniform and weapons he had left in Yugoslavia, presumably in a trustworthy hiding-place. The Palestinians had been betrayed at every point. Joel was questioned about the whereabouts of his friend, Perez. Following the usual underground technique, they had lived in separate quarters and been careful not to know each other's address for fear of weakening under the third degree. He soon discovered, however, that Perez had also been arrested. The whole group was in prison.

Convinced that the cause was lost, and anxious to forestall torture by the Gestapo, Joel attempted to commit suicide by cutting his wrists with an American aviator's aluminum identity disk left behind in his cell. A guard found him after he lost consciousness. The Hungarian prison officials did not allow him to be taken to a hospital; he was revived and kept for questioning.

The grilling began. It was essential that Joel's antecedents and the nature of his military mission remain undisclosed. He kept assuring his interrogators that he was a Palestinian who had enlisted in the British army, and who therefore was entitled to the rights of any captured British airman, since he had been arrested in uniform. The Hungarians, on the other hand, were convinced that he was not a simple prisoner of war, but a dangerous character with a special espionage and sabotage mission whose sponsors and scope it was imperative for them to discover.

Joel insisted that he had no military mission. He admitted only that he was a Palestinian—not a Hungarian or a Rumanian—whose purpose was to help save the Jews of Hungary of whom hundreds of thousands still remained alive.

The interrogations revealed the fears and confusions of the Hungarians. On the one hand, they behaved like victorious captors determined to break their prisoner down by any means. On the other hand, they were anxious to discover what their own chances might be in the case of a German defeat. This was already the end of June, 1944, and even the most enthusiastic of Germany's cohorts were growing nervous. The Hungarians were particularly eager to know if the long-hoped-for Anglo-American attack on Russia was likely to take place. The desire to get information on these troublesome questions made Joel's cross-examination a combination of third degree and discussion. There would be periods of torture alternating with hours of political debate which Joel would use to score his own points, and, though he did not succeed in convincing his examiners, some of his arguments made a visible impression.

Joel assured the Hungarians that an understading between Nazi quislings and the Allies was out of the question—particularly because of the Hungarian adoption of the Hitler anti-Jewish program. Paradoxically enough, both the Nazis and their henchmen in Nazi-occupied countries seriously believed that the democratic powers would make an issue of the Jewish massacres, and that the Jews were, consequently, a hostage in Axis hands. The Goebbels propaganda in regard to the extent of Jewish influence had convinced not only the ignorant masses, but even the supposedly hard-headed leaders. Naturally, this was a belief which Joel attempted to exploit to the utmost. He urged the Hungarian police to enable him to meet the Secretary of State, so that he could lay his plains for the rescue of Hungarian Jewry before him; such cooperation would later aid the Hungarians in their hour of defeat. Though Joel's arguments were listened to, not only for the purpose of discovering his aims, but on their apparent merits, the Hungarians decided to hand him over to the Gestapo. They were still not sufficiently sure that the Nazi cause was doomed.

The German officers treated both Hanna and himself in a "gentlemanly" fashion. They never failed to address him in accordance with his rank, *Herr Lieutenant,* and never called him *Jude,* as they did the other Jewish prisoners. Towards Hanna they were especially respectful. This Joel explains on the basis of an unwilling admiration elicited by the Palestinians' courage and refusal to cringe. But the "gentlemanly" behavior of the Nazi officers in no way interfered with the brutality of their orders. The "gentlemanly" Germans dispatched prisoners to death as unblinkingly as the ruffianly S. S. men.

Life in a Hungarian prison was apparently less rigidly controlled than in a purely Nazi establishment. The sense that the war was running to an unsuccessful close affected the guards and made them willing to curry favor with the prisoners, particularly the British and the Americans. The cells faced the courtyard, and it was possible to shout to friends from the windows. By means of strings they could throw messages across the yard. Some guards could be bribed to open the cells at night. This made meetings between the prisoners possible.

Finally, after two months, through bribery, Joel and Hanna had an opportunity of meeting. They had a long talk in the course of which Hanna was able to tell Joel of the series of events which had led to her capture. She had been caught as soon as she had crossed the border, because the smugglers who had been engaged to assist her lost their nerve. Two of her three escorts had gone into a village on the Hungarian side of the frontier to look for smugglers who would help her board a train to Budapest. They were caught. One committed suicide. This frightened the local peasants who knew that Hanna and a partisan were hiding in the vicinity. To protect themselves from charges of complicity, they disclosed her whereabouts.

The Hungarian police found her radio code and her

radio apparatus. By means of the third degree, they tried to force her to reveal its purpose. When physical torture failed, they hit upon something even more persuasive. They located her mother who was still in Hungary.

Those who have read Hanna's diary and poems know how passionate was her attachment to her mother and how bitter were her self-reproaches in regard to what she conceived to be her "unfilial" conduct. It had not been easy to leave her widowed mother alone. The five years in Palestine had been lived under the cloud of this separation and of the sense of guilt from which the daughter suffered, particularly because the mother had been unfailingly tender and understanding.

At last, the long-awaited meeting took place, in a Hungarian prison, under the eyes of police who threatened Hanna that the mother would be killed unless she revealed the nature of her mission.

Hanna did not tell. Somewhere the sensitive girl found the will to face her mother and her torturers and permit the adored and adoring mother to be led away without knowing what her fate would be.

The most intimate picture of Hanna's last days is that provided by her mother. The story of Mrs. Senesch is in its way as dramatic as that of her daughter, and as organic a part of the tragedy of the Jews of Europe. The tall, slender, gracious woman—originally remote from Zionism and with few specific Jewish interests—came to Palestine in the fall of 1945, a year after her daughter's execution. I saw her for the first time at a memorial service for another parachutist, Enzo Sereni, who had been executed in Dachau. In the quiet, grave face of the woman I watched from a distance one could sense the stoicism which had flamed into a more spectacular heroism in the daughter. But this was a year after the girl's death. Since that summer day in 1944, when she first saw her daughter again after five years of separation, there had been time not only for Hanna's execution but for the apotheosis of the girl into a national heroine. A year before, in the prison, the comfort of the legend had been absent.

Sitting in a small hotel room in Tel Aviv, Mrs. Senesch told me of her reunion with Hanna in a Budapest prison. The cultivated Hungarian lady symbolized a phase of modern Jewish experience as vividly as Hanna herself. She had been thrust fiercely into the very vortex of the Jewish tragedy; her daughter had leapt into it of her own volition. The path which led Mrs. Senesch to a new life, in the collective farm of which her daughter had been an eager comrade, has its place in any account of contemporary Jewish history.

When Mrs. Senesch was summoned by the Hungarian police she went secure in the conviction that, whatever happened, her children were safe in Palestine. (Her son had reached Palestine the day before Hanna set out on her mission.) To her suprise she was interrogated about Hanna. Why had the girl left Hungary? How had she studied? The mother could proudly refer the official to the girl's brilliant school record. When the mother added that despite the pain of the separation, she was glad that her daughter was not in Hungary, the questioner smiled mockingly. Finally he asked again, "Where is your daughter now?" And when she answered again, "In Haifa," he seemed convinced that the mother was truly ignorant of her daughter's activities. He announced: "She is in the next room. We will bring her in. Persuade her to speak, otherwise this will be your last meeting."

Hanna was brought in. She ran up to her mother, embraced her and began to weep, crying: "Mother, forgive me."

She was not in uniform. Her clothes were disordered; her hair dishevelled. She had a bruise under one eye, and one of her teeth was broken. Even as the mother spoke to me, a year after the girl's death, I could see that she was still troubled by the bruise and the broken tooth.

Mother and daughter were left alone for a few minutes. Stunned and bewildered, the mother kept asking: "Why are you not in Palestine? How do you come to be here?", to which Hanna did not answer; and she also kept asking: "Are you hurt?" to which Hanna said: "No."

The mother was sent home with strict instructions not to talk of her experience. Within a few days, however, she was arrested, this time by the Gestapo. The Germans, more pedantic that the Hungarians, began an exhaustive interrogation, which lasted for several days, in the attempt to discover whether the mother knew anything of her daughter's acts. At this time, Mrs. Senesch still had no idea as to how Hanna had reached Hungary from Palestine. The Germans were finally satisfied that the mother had no share in the mission, but she was not released. She was kept in prison for several months. This, however, had its compensation. Within a few days Hanna was brought to the same prison.

Many of the prison attendants were apparently impressed by Hanna's valor and charm and by the pathos of the mother's presence in the same prison. At any rate, several of them cooperated in making an occasional glimpse of Hanna possible. Once, the mother was called when Hanna was in the toilet, and they had a few minutes together. Hanna looked better. Her hair and clothing were neat. The bruise was gone. But the mother had to find out about the broken tooth. "I got it coming down in the parachute," Hanna explained and added laughing: "Mother, if I only lose a tooth in this, it will be well."

During their brief, stolen meetings—sometimes while at exercise in the courtyard, sometimes through the connivance of a sympathetic attendant—the mother would ask: "What did you undertake?" But on this point Hanna was silent.

Finally, the mother asked: "Was it something of Jewish interest?" And Hanna said: "You are on the right track." And when the mother wanted to know: "Is it worth risking your life for an idealistic impulse?" Hanna answered simply: "For me it is worth-while."

Hanna told her mother that she viewed her stay in the prison as not wholly unprofitable, because she had converted many of her fellow-prisoners to Zionism. She had an unerring sense for the grand gesture. Her fellow-prisoners, being Hungarian Jews, all wore the Star of David. As a British subject she was free from the requirement. So, to demonstrate her solidarity with Israel, she traced a Star of David in the dust of her windowpane and maintained it there for all to see.

In September, after nearly four months, the mother was freed. The parachutists also hoped for release. By the beginning of October, every one knew that Hungary's collapse was certain. In the desire to forestall vengeance, the prison guards would come in and introduce themselves with the communist greeting and offer the prisoners cigarettes.

When Hungary capitulated in October, the mood of the political prisoners was jubilant. Each one had a daydream to fulfill. The Palestinians had their program. They would meet Hanna. Then they would go to a hotel where they could get a big dinner, a hot bath—all the things which had been impossible in the months of imprisonment. It would have been easy to make a jailbreak. Discipline was at its lowest, and there was no real attempt to enforce it. But the guards begged the political prisoners to wait a few hours more for their formal liberation. Otherwise the common criminals who were in the jail would take part in the escape. Since the prisoners had no knowledge of actual conditions in the country, and believed that if

Hungary laid down her arms there could be no fear of a fascist counter-attack, they agreed to wait.

But the fascist coup came at once. That night, shots were heard in the city. In the morning the guards did not come near the charges they had so recently wooed. No breakfast was served. The brief interlude of hope was over.

Within a few days, new interrogations began. The men were summoned to a court-marital. Hanna was sent to a civil court. This increased the belief that Hanna would be the one to survive. Joel and Perez were certain that they would be shot, but confident that the story of their venture would at least be told by Hanna.

Hanna was the first to be tried. The accounts of the trial are pieced together from the report of eyewitnesses and of Joel's information received through the usual prison channels. Hanna was brave, and she made the kind of addresses to her judges that might have been expected. Perhaps they were impressed by the girl's valor and touched by her youth and charm; but the prosecutor nevertheless demanded the death penalty. The judges did not pass sentence at once. Hanna was remanded to her prison. On November 6, 1944, an officer came to her cell and told her that she had been condemned to death. Did she wish to plead for mercy? Hanna answered that she had been condemned by a lower court, and demanded the right to appeal to a higher court. Again she was asked whether she wanted mercy. And she answered: "I ask for no mercy from hangmen."

The execution took place on a cold, foggy autumn day. Joel remembers it because he heard the shots of the execution. Hanna was brought into the courtyard. Witnesses tell that she refused to have her eyes bound, but stood straight and unmoving as the order to fire was given.

In the meantime, the mother had no knowledge of her daughter's fate. Mrs. Senesch kept trying to arrange for a visit to the prison but was prevented by a series of obstacles. One day there was an air-raid. Another time the officer who could grant permission for visits was out of town. Besides, Jews had the right to leave their homes only between the hours of 10 and 12 in the morning. As the prison was some distance from the mother's home, it was impossible for her to complete the trip in the allotted period. Finally, on the fatal November 6, completely ignorant of what was to take place that day, she covered the yellow star on her coat lapel with her handbag and ventured out an hour before the permitted time.

When she gave her name to the guard at the prison, he seemed startled and embarrassed. "Hurry," he said and directed her upstairs to the officer in charge. The officer bade her sit down; he glanced toward the window which gave on the courtyard; a shot was heard. Then he turned to the mother. He recounted all the acts of which the daughter had been guilty. He concluded his indictment with the sentence: "Those acts merit the extreme penalty which has just been executed."

That was the end of the story. There was nothing more to tell beyond the shot in the courtyard whose significance she had not known at the time. The girl, vibrant, gay, affectionate, who had been so vividly evoked by the mother's words that there were moments when we both forgot that she was dead, vanished with the shot. In her stead came the national heroine who had chosen to dash herself against Hitler Europe.

Several years before, Hanna had written:

To die, to die in youth,
No, no, I did not want it;
I loved the warmth of sun, the lovely light.
I loved song, shining eyes, and not destruction.
I did not want the dark of war, the night.
No, no, I did not want it.

The poem went on to declare that since fate willed that she live in the midst of bloodshed and ruin, she was grateful that she could live—and die if need be—on the earth of her homeland.

She did not die upon the earth she loved. Her body lies in the Jewish cemetery of Budapest, in the "lot of the martyrs." But her wish was fulfilled in even richer measure than she dared imagine. There is a special memorial room for her in Caesarea, the settlement in which she worked. And her young, smiling figure, in military uniform, may be seen in every village and town of Palestine.

Hanna Senesch's poems and diary have become part of the national literature of Palestine and quotations from her writings have become daily slogans: "Whom shall I send? Send *me* . . ." In her life, as in her words, she had been the ideal *shaliach,* one of the "messengers" who appeared in various guises in every ghetto of Europe. And be it remembered, when one strives to measure the achievements of those who answered the call, that, etymologically, even an angel is only a messenger.

IRENA JOHANES

The Mission

The night had been a night of strenuous work, of great fear; and it was coming to an end. The noise of the machine, that was knocking a little after operating so long, stopped. Maresia, sitting on the edge of the bed, was holding in her hands the first copy of the leaflet. She started to read it to Justa. She tried to memorize its contents, but this was difficult for her.

The leaflet called to the Jews to awaken, resist, give battle. In short sentences it explained that the deported Jews were being taken to their death.

The mind of Maresia was too tired to understand. Her eyes were closing from lack of sleep. It was as though Marek, who was walking back and forth in the room, was at a great distance; and Justa, who had worked feverishly at the typewriter, and the leaflets and paper spread all over, was in the next room. How strong was her desire to bring herself back to consciousness and to keep awake!

Marek assembled on the table two revolvers, a little ammunition, a bundle of Aryan documents and a package of bullets—fruits of a whole night's labor, a night which had been punctuated by moments of fear when there was a rustle behind the windows or the sound of footsteps outside.

The day before, Maresia had gotten everything that was necessary for the trip. Now, the only thing she needed was to pack everything nicely, and change her clothes so that she would be dressed as a farm girl.

She put the revolvers in the bottom of the basket. On top of them she put a handful of straw, and on top of that, eggs. The documents she placed in a second basket, and covered them with apples and flowers. Beneath the simple old farm girl dress she wore a beautiful suit. Justa was always laughing at her coquettishness, but Maresia didn't pay any attention to her. She put a powder compact into her pocket, covered her head with a colorful kerchief, and she was ready to go on her way.

At the last moment Marek remembered that he wanted brought over to Cracow samples of some facsimile signatures. These were on small pieces of paper, and she hid them among her curls; this was not the first time they had been used to hide small things of great significance.

The parting from Justa and Marek was brief. Maresia had received her orders the day before. After making sure that no one was following her, she walked out, not looking back even once.

It was a November morning, cold and dark. Puddles at the side of the road were covered with ice. The road went through a field, and was far from exciting. Maresia overcame her disappointment and hurried, the sooner to reach her destination.

From time to time she had to stop. The heavy baskets hurt her arms, and cut her fingers. But this was no time to rest, and she tried to take her mind off the pain and get to the bus station. Being acquainted with the driver helped her to get a good place to sit. She put her baskets beneath the bench, where no one would notice them.

Past Moganlani, in a place where the ground was more level and spreads away to the horizon, her eyes were still fixed on the road; but she noticed far away the morning light flickering as it glanced off military hats. Before she could figure out why the Germans were in this area, a great fear took hold of her, and her hands, painful as they were from the baskets, froze on her knees.

What could she do? How should she act if they questioned her? What kind of a bluff should she put up? A variety of plans came to her mind, but she pushed all of them aside. Not one of them was convincing, and she didn't even have her own documents with her. She had purposely left them behind, for documents from the German office weren't suitable for a village girl. The impending danger didn't scare her now. If she didn't admit that the packages belonged to her, she thought, the most that could happen to her would be that they would send her to Germany as a slave laborer. In those fearful days, that was indeed not the worst that could happen. But she did know how important and how valuable her baskets were. To obtain ammunition was very difficult and took a great deal of effort, and a very high price had to be paid for it. The two revolvers that she was carrying with her were for the fellows in the forest. For them it was a question of life and death. And she decided to guard the treasure until the very last minute. When the bus stopped by order of the police, she tried to control herself and to look and act quite indifferent as she stepped off.

"What do you have there?" yelled the sarcastic voice of an officer, in Polish.

"Fruit and eggs," Maresia answered, trying to say the words with the same accent a village girl from the mountains would use.

"You want to bring it to town, you want to speculate. But, I'll fix you, you will go right to work. The documents!"

Now the trouble had started. Thoughts flashed like lightning through her head, and for an answer the German stretched his hand toward one of the baskets. Fear overcame her—she always said fear was her closest associate— it made a choking noise in her ears, and she closed her eyes for a second. But she pulled herself together quickly; she saw that the German had removed the flowers and was spreading out the apples.

She walked over to him and in a small voice asked him to leave her the basket. The German was shocked at her nerve and turned to look at her. Burning with anger, he kicked the basket with all his strength. The basket turned over and the apples started to roll into the sewer. Unconsciously, she stiffened and gathered her strength to try to escape. A long time ago she had decided that in a situation like this she would make a run for it—and let the end come right then. She took her eyes from the basket and looked the German in the face. He was turning to the second basket.

It seemed that he didn't see anything strange. There was something right in front of his eyes and he didn't see it. The edge of the gray leaflet was sticking out from under several pieces of fruit.

"I must get his attention, so he will not look in the second basket," she thought. Again she tried to calm her voice and turned to speak to the German, but his anger only got worse. He picked up an apple that rolled toward his feet to throw it at her.

His senseless hatred restored Maresia's equilibrium, and she got control of herself. The German reached toward the basket and with great excitement he pushed his hand inside. Maresia didn't know whether he would turn everything out of the basket, as he had the other one, or whether he would take it with him. But anyway it didn't matter. She jumped toward him and took the basket from his hand. She surprised herself by her own sudden outburst. Extending her hand, she begged in a trembling voice that he take the eggs but let her keep the basket.

Everyone knew that the Germans were always trying to get provisions and food. His eyes sparkled. For a moment he considered what he should do. Then he ordered a soldier to bring him his traveling bag. It was a giant case, probably kept around in anticipation of an opportunity like this. One more successful move, however small, and everything would come out all right. The soldier, as ordered, put the eggs in the bag and returned it to the car. The German wouldn't bother himself any longer about the people, not after Maresia and his now full travel bag. He turned toward his car and ordered the driver to go ahead. The car moved from its place carrying several prisoners.

Cracow was still six kilometers away according to the road sign. But it didn't make sense to go to Cracow empty-handed. The few apples she had recovered weren't enough to fill even one basket; so she decided to wait till she was alone and then hide the documents and the ammunition.

She went to the nearest hut to buy some corn flour. With it she filled the baskets so that they were heavy again; and she started off afoot toward Cracow. After walking a long time she could see the city in the distance. The road curved to join the main road.

At the crossroads she looked around. There were several dozen soldiers and policemen busy loading a truck with men and women. She didn't have time to get out of sight before they saw her, and one policeman pointed at her. He walked toward her and called to her to come toward him. Without asking for her documents, making any investigation or finding out anything about her, they put her on the truck just as they had the rest; and when the two trucks were filled they started off for Cracow. She learned from those in the truck with her, her friends in suffering, that the whole area was being scoured, and they were kidnapping hundreds to send to forced labor in Germany.

Having had a great deal of experience in this sort of situation, she tucked the baskets in a corner of the truck. If worse came to worse, she would deny that they belonged to her. She was no longer nervous or excited. She had become merely indifferent.

Time stretched endlessly. It seemed an eternity since she had left Michslenitz, though it was not even near noon.

Without warning, she suddenly felt very tired. A tiredness like this she had never felt, even when she was walking on foot. It seemed to her that all her fighting and struggling had been ridiculous and unnecessary. She couldn't understand the desire to live that seemed to be rising within her. She paid no attention to her neighbors in the truck. And oddly, large burning tears rolled down her cheeks, tears of relief.

The journey took only a few minutes. The truck rushed through the suburbs and stopped before the building of the Obitzund (Labor Department). The men were ordered to get down and were surrounded by armed soldiers. Maresia left the baskets in the truck. She was quickly swallowed up by the crowd of people who had been gathered together there previously.

When the last prisoners had jumped down from the truck and no one had taken the baskets, the soldier in charge became nervous. He wanted to close up the truck. He called for the owner to come and get the baskets, and he threatened; but no one came to get them. Having no alternative, he took them off the truck and set them on the sidewalk.

The corn flour didn't attract anyone's attention. The soldiers had already started to count and number the people; there were about one hundred.

Maresia's mind now really started to work. First of all, she decided, she would get out of there before they got around to making the final selection. Deliberately and politely, Maresia walked over to the guards at the gate of the building who were watching those who had been caught and asked them to let her go into the building. They answered her angrily and pushed her away, just to one side of the crowd. But it is hard to abandon an idea when one is trying to obtain one's freedom. So she didn't let her bitterness or pride get in the way; she turned to another policeman who was watching from a little farther away and explained to him that she had a kidney ailment, and she would like to ask him to let her go into the building for a little while. After she had begged him, he agreed to it.

It was very difficult for her to control her joy when she walked up the stairs. She hurried as she passed through the long halls, looking for the ladies' room. She found it. She waited for a while till an officer who was passing by had left. Then she walked inside and locked the door. Here, her coquettishness stood her in good stead: With one swift motion she pulled off her village dress and the kerchief from her head; she fixed her hair, and with the aid of the powder compact she powdered her nose and made herself into a city girl. The dress and the kerchief she folded up into a small bundle which she hid behind the sink.

She hadn't had time to think, and when she walked out into the corridor she didn't know what strategy she would use. So she walked slowly, reading the German signs on the doors of each and every room. Her glance fell on a notice that a manager of the Department of Occupation was seeing people by special appointment. In the rest of the rooms were less important departments. Slowly she returned to the door of the Department of Occupation. Here was the doorknob. Should she open it? Her hand trembled, her heart pounded. To go in or not? What should she do? It was hard to decide. At the same time she heard a young man's voice from the other side of the door. Somebody had laughed. It was strange laughter, it didn't fit the place at all. No doubt it seems peculiar, but the girl, hearing the laugh, regained her poise; it made her forget the seriousness of her situation.

She didn't know why, but she decided to open the door. Before her was a tall man, slim, dressed as a civilian. He was in deep conversation with a secretary, and when Maresia was asked how she got there and for what purpose, she smiled freely and explained in a quiet voice the purpose of her coming. She tried to put up a joyful, calm front. But it seemed that this German paid no attention to the smiles of women. With a sour face he answered that he was very busy.

Maresia didn't move away and she didn't give up. She remembered that she had lived through terrible hours and she was still alive, and that the worst that she could now expect was to be sent to Germany. She felt good luck was with her; she was not in such a bad position and she could afford to allow herself a little risk.

The German continued his conversation with his secretary about the problems of his office. Maresia used the minutes to calm herself. She tried to take her mind off the baskets she had left in the street, and she tried not to think about the fact that someone might want the corn flour and try to steal her treasures.

The hard voice of the German brought her back from her revery. He turned to her and gave her a small card. It was a permit to pass. The girl couldn't believe her own eyes. She read it and read it again. It was a freedom card and security for a while. But something was missing from the card. If one more word were only added to it!

She gathered all her courage. She was fluent in German, so she asked him to add just the phrase, "with belongings." In answer to his question, she said she had a small suitcase with her, containing her personal belongings. The face of the German became very angry and she took fright. What had she done? It would have been possible to try some other way. He forgot that just a minute before he had acted like a human being. In a rough voice he ordered her to bring her belongings and have them checked. The permit pass he took out of her hands. Maresia turned toward the door, then stopped. She said apologetically that her belongings were downstairs in the hands of a policeman, who had already checked them; and that actually the belongings were nothing—a towel, some underwear and a pair of shoes; but if he insisted upon it, she would bring them to him; but she didn't think it was necessary.

She saw the German write something on the card. Was it an order to the policeman about this miserable suitcase? Without looking at her, he brought the card to her and walked out, using some vulgar words.

But Maresia didn't hear him. She didn't know how she reached the door. After she calmed down she was able to read what he had written on the card: under his signature, he had written in large letters, "p.s.: With belongings."

So the precious ammunition was again saved.

[TRANSLATED BY MEYER BARKAI]

LENA KUCHLER-SILBERMAN

Flight

Lena Kuchler-Silberman, a Polish Jewess, was the only member of her family to survive the Nazi holocaust. After the war, she returned to Crakow, the city of her birth, and gathered Jewish orphans from the streets, from the convents, and became a mother to them. She succeeded in obtaining a house in the mountains and had it equipped as a children's home. There she hoped to restore the health of her unfortunate little ones and to give them a happier childhood.

No sooner had Lena and her children settled in their new home, when anti-Semitic riots began to rage over Poland. Even the children's home was attacked. Lena decided that the only way to save the children was to take them out of Poland and bring them to Palestine (as Israel was then called).

It was the year 1942. Leaving Poland was illegal and was fraught with danger. Lena obtained false passports and money with which to bribe the officials. The following is a description of their departure and crossing of the Polish and Czech borders. It is taken from her autobiography.

We began to get ready even before four o'clock. Everyone dressed quickly, the older children not having to be told to help the younger ones. I walked from room to room, my head clear, my nerves completely under control. Knapsacks had been distributed the night before, and now they were being stuffed and tied. We sat silently, staring at the still-dark shadows outside the building.

The children climbed into the huge truck that was waiting outside, their knapsacks secured to their backs. We were supposed to have had two trucks, but only one had arrived. I said nothing to anyone; our timetable was far more important than our comfort. When the truck was fully loaded, we found ourselves crowed together like proverbial sardines. It was uncomfortable, but there was nothing to be done.

When we were ready to leave, I ran back to the house. I tried to be casual as I said "good-by" to the children who were remaining behind, waiting to be picked up by parents and relatives. I had told them earlier that those who were not going to stay with us could not join in this particular outing. Some of them looked at me disappointedly now; others called out, "Have a good time!"

At the door, Dr. Fisher waited for me. She was tearful. I held her arms and whispered: "Don't worry, we'll be all right. You won't call before tomorrow night?" She shook her head and embraced me. "May God protect you all!" she called out. I stood in the doorway, looking about for a moment. Then I waved to her and walked away smiling.

My happiness was real. I walked to the truck, never looking back. The children helped me in, and we lowered the tarpaulin.

"Mr. Menlich, tell the driver to proceed," I called out. The word was passed, and in a few moments we could feel the first vibrations of the engine. It was still dark outside as we drove off, heading west. On all sides, I could almost touch the children's smiles.

We had been driving for nearly six hours. The sun was directly overhead, shining in through several slots we had made in the tarpaulin. Mamusha was massaging the feet of the smaller children. Sandwiches and tea had already been distributed. With the exception of one little girl who had become nauseated, our travelers were bearing up well.

We drove in almost complete silence, although the desire to sing was very strong. The driver, a husky, ill-mannered man in his late thirties, had warned us not to call attention to ourselves. I noticed that as the day progressed, and traffic along the highway became heavier, he veered off to the smaller, dirt roads, where there was less chance of encountering trouble.

Once we stopped at the foot of a steep hill. Gershon, who was in the cab with the driver, ran back to us and called in through the partially-open cover:

"Lena, he says he can't make this hill with the children inside. It's too steep. They'll have to get out and walk up to the top."

I didn't like it. It was the middle of the afternoon, and there was a considerable amount of traffic moving on the highway. I told the children to put on their knapsacks and march in single file, keeping away from the road. Mr. Menlich went to the head of the long procession; I took up the rear. The younger children were escorted by the teachers. It took us nearly an hour to walk up the steep mountain road; wordlessly, in a single file, we trudged to the summit. From time to time a boy would step out of line, turn his back on the procession, pass water, and then hurry to take his allotted place again.

Every few minutes I looked back at the truck behind us. It was ascending very slowly, the engine straining and groaning.

Saul and Victor walked beside me; they too looked back every few minutes.

The three of us were armed. For that one hour on foot, we were completely exposed to danger.

Toward nine o'clock we reached our destination, the tiny border town of Zebrzydowice. With Gershon, I hurried to the small shack where I had been told the frontier guards were waiting; even in the dark, I could see that the barriers separating us from Czechoslovakia were down. Not very far away was a train, waiting and ready.

I entered the narrow building, a bundle of passports in one hand, several thousand zlotys and a bottle of whiskey in the other. Two uniformed Polish guards were seated at a crude table. They hardly looked at us, accepting the money and the liquid refreshment in silence. They waved the passports away. One of them rose and cranked up the wooden rail that separated us from the train. He motioned us to proceed.

I hurried back to the truck, stumbling in the dark. The children had already alighted and were lined up in columns of two. The lack of illumination frightened me. I became panicky at the thought that one of the children might wander off into the dark. I gave the order to move, seeing to it that each child held the hand of his partner. I counted the children as they passed by, grateful that all were accounted for. We were short four passports, and I watched as Edna walked by, carrying little Ilek in her knapsack. Strapped to Victor's back was Frank, and Menlich was carrying Jasia. On my own back I could feel the embrace of Aliza's thin arms, my coat thrown over both of us.

Stumbling a little in the dark, we approached the waiting train. Behind us the barrier had already been lowered. Shouting at us in Polish, the conductors were saying, "All right, Jews, let's go! All aboard! Move on!" They helped the smaller children negotiate the high steps.

In a few minutes we were all seated in the darkened train. I realized that ours was the only passenger car; ahead of us was the engine and a number of freight cars. Slowly, we felt the train begin to move. Children and adults sat silent, fearful of the dark and of what still lay ahead. I was thankful that nobody was crying.

We had only moved a short distance when the train came to a sharp stop. The lights in the car were suddenly switched on, blinding us momentarily. A stern voice called out recognizable words in what I assumed was Czech: "Passports! Let's have all passports!"

I rose from my seat with difficulty, since Aliza was still perched on my shoulders. I handed our bundle of passports to a uniformed Czech officer, who looked us over with disdain.

"Remain here!" he ordered. "These have to be checked." He left the car and I felt my heart contracting. I looked at Gershon—his face was ashen.

We sat in the cold railway car for close to an hour. The younger children fell asleep; the older ones looked as concerned as the adults. Finally, the stern-faced officer returned, accompanied by another Czech official. The latter spoke to me in Polish:

"These passports are not in order. You'll have to return to Poland."

I did not know what to say and stood there like one petrified. Gershon, however, rose from his seat and began to talk to the Czechs. He whispered to them in German, gesticulating and pleading. I was still too numb to listen carefully, but snatches of what he said came through " . . . the Poles chased these children out . . . survivors of concentration camps . . . orphans . . . to go back is suicide . . . "

The Czechs shrugged their shoulders and left the train.

"Take the money you have," I whispered to Gershon. "Give it to the engineer and the conductors. Hurry! This train must not move back."

He proceeded to distribute the funds that had been given him for just such a contingency by the Rescue Committee.

The train did not move, but we were not allowed to disembark either. It was already midnight, and almost all of the children had fallen asleep, exhausted from the day's travel. Shortly after midnight, one of the officials returned.

"You may go into the station—only for tonight," he announced.

Huddled together on the floor, we spent the night in the Czech frontier post, waiting for the sun to come up and bring with it an end to this unexpected delay. Mrs. Menlich passed out sandwiches, urging the children to eat and keep up their strength. I slept fitfully for a few hours.

In the morning, the official in charge told us he was awaiting instructions from Prague.

"We are not remaining in Czechoslovakia," I said. "We are in transit, that is all. You can see that we have visas for France."

"It's up to Prague," he replied.

For three days and three nights we remained in the station building. The children were sneezing and coughing, many of the small ones were wet. All of us were dirty and grimy. On the second day some Czech women carrying hot soup entered the building. Without asking permission, they distributed the warm food. I could only offer them a weak smile of thanks. With each succeeding hour my hopes grew fainter. I did not know what I would do if they compelled us to return to Poland.

Gershon had telephoned Mrs. Shapira, who was in Prague. "She is doing everything possible," he assured me. He did not sound very confident, however.

On the morning of the fourth day, I roused myself. Selecting ten of the children to accompany me, I decided to make one last appeal to the Czech official—who had remained deaf to all our previous pleas. I knew that he and his wife breakfasted together, and I timed our visit to a moment when they would be in the middle of their morning meal.

Without knocking, I opened the door to his office-dining room and stood in front of him, the children surrounding me.

"Sir, I beg of you to end this torture. These children will be murdered if you order us back to Poland. In God's name, have pity on them! They have known enough suffering." I had begun to cry, uncontrollably. The children with me, except Saul, were sobbing, too. Saul shouted at the frontier official: "If you want me to die, shoot me here! Just like the Germans did, go ahead! We're not going back to Poland, to die like all the other Jews!"

The official's wife had become pale. She turned to her husband, pressing his arm: "Let them go, for God's sake. Let them go!"

I ran back to the frontier post and ordered the children to get ready. "All right—once again, children, line up with your partners. Hold hands. We're leaving for Prague." In a matter of minutes we were standing in the morning's sun, our dirty faces smiling. I counted the pairs that passed by me. One of the frontier officials was watching Edna, on whose back was strapped one of our "Bobola" children. He called out to her:

"Hey, Miss! I think your tea bottle is leaking."

I followed his eyes to the yellow liquid dripping down her back. Edna called over her shoulder: "Thanks! I'll fix it later. I probably forgot to cork it tightly."

When we were all on board the train, which had now begun to pick up speed toward its first stop in Prague, little Ilek smiled sheepishly as Edna handed him a dry pair of underpants.

[TRANSLATED BY DAVID C. GROSS]

AZRIEL EISENBERG

Foster Mother of the Poor

Little Rachel stumbled through an open door and found herself in a classroom of women from immigrant families of the lower East Side. She started to speak but tears streamed down her cheeks, choking her words. One woman, different from the others, hurried to the sobbing child and knelt down by her side. The lady's name was Lillian Wald.

Lillian Wald was indeed different from other women. Born to wealth, raised in luxury, educated in private schools, beautiful and stately, Lillian had become dissatisfied with the life of ease that awaited a girl of good family in the 1890's. In her early twenties she decided to take up nursing and then medicine.

At the medical school, Lillian was asked to teach nursing to young immigrant women for a Jewish Sabbath school. The rich, charitable Solomon Loeb wanted to interest women in the nursing profession. Lillian accepted at once. Her class met on Henry Street, a street that was some day to become famous throughout the world. Lillian was showing her pupils how to make beds, when the ragged, tear-stained little girl broke in.

Lillian Wald took the child's dirty hand in her scrubbed nurse's one and asked in a whisper, "Tell me, dear, what's the matter?"

Rachel tried to speak, but sobs wracked her body. Finally, Lillian was able to understand her. Rachel's mother was sick, very sick.

Lillian paused to consider. Her duty lay with her class, but she was a trained nurse, and Rachel's mother needed help.

"I'm going with this child," she told them. "Class is over for today."

Holding little Rachel's hand, she set out to treat the sick woman. It was a short walk, but it changed Lillian's entire career, brought new life to the East Side, and transformed the world's ideas on how to deal with slum neighborhoods everywhere.

Lillian knew the sights and sounds of the Lower East Side's crowded streets. On her way to and from her class, she had seen the bargaining at the pushcarts, the children dodging the wagons as they played their games in the streets, the ragged clothing, the dirt underfoot, the rotting garbage, the dark hallways, the pale men and women, the very smell of poverty. But she had never entered a tenement building before. Now when Rachel led her into a foul-smelling hall, Lillian gasped. As she groped up the dingy stairs behind Rachel, she remembered her own home—light, airy, roomy. How could people live in a place like this? She had seen better kept stables and kennels.

But worse lay ahead. Rachel opened a door and held it wide for Lillian Wald to enter. It was a two-room flat with no heat of any kind, almost no light, no bathroom, and a hallway toilet shared by many families. Around the walls of the flat were rough planks—beds for boarders. In a shadowy corner, surrounded by hungry, half-naked, whimpering children lay Rachel's mother—cold, pale, more dead than alive. And when Lillian moved over to examine her, she saw that this woman was one of her own pupils!

Lillian made her patient comfortable, eased her pain, advised her. How little did she really know these people among whom she had been working! Now that she became aware of their plight, she was determined to help them. But how?

The very next day, Lillian called on Mr. and Mrs. Loeb, the charitable couple who sponsored her class.

"We wouldn't let animals live in a place like that!" she said. "And these people are human beings—brave, good people. They came to this country to give their children a new life. They risked all their money to pay for a new chance and all we offer them is filth, poverty, slums, disease."

Her eyes blazed with pity and anger. "That woman kissed my hands when I left her yesterday, she was so grateful for the little I did for her. Grateful—after what we've all done to her! You'd think she'd want to hit anyone who has three meals a day. Mrs. Loeb, we've no right to destroy a human being, to put him in a position where he feels so grateful for so little."

Mrs. Loeb was impressed. This young woman wasn't like her charitable friends, who gave thousands of dollars to charity, but never said anything about human dignity. And as for going into the slums, and visiting the poor in their homes . . .

"Would you like me to help this family?" she asked.

"Perhaps," Lillian answered, but on second thought, nodded her head firmly. "I want to live in that section of the city—with a friend, another nurse. We could be useful there. It wouldn't cost much. We could live simply. Will you support such a project?"

"You want to live there?" Mrs. Loeb echoed faintly.

"Yes! These people would get to know us as neighbors. Then they'd feel free to call on us for help, like on someone they really know, someone who shared their life. They need so much! But they're proud, and afraid. They don't know much about clinics. They think clinics are for other people. But if we lived with them, we'd be able to bring the clinic right into their homes. And we'd learn more about the real East Side ourselves, so that we could tell other people what needs to be done there!"

Shortly afterward, Lillian and a friend, Mary Brewster, moved into a tiny flat on the East Side. Mrs. Loeb and her son-in-law, Jacob Schiff, paid their costs. One of their monthly reports listed expenses of $99.86. This included $30.00 to enable a tubercular girl to enter a sanitarium. Other items included the following:

Eggs for Mrs. Boardman	$ .25
Two prescriptions for Mrs. Stein	.40
Milk bill to Lee-Lo-Sing for Mrs. B.	.30
Carfare	.20
Beech baby at day nursery	.90
Mrs. Schiller's medicine	.20
Repair of Mr. Lipschitz' spectacles	.18
Mr. Klein, to buy coal to sell	1.00

Nursing, medicines, food, clothing, jobs, hospital, ice, coal, camps and outings for children, admission to rest homes—these and a thousand other items occupied Lillian Wald and Mary Brewster every day. The work they had undertaken had no limits. The people needed everything and they tried to provide everything. They got their friends to help. They taught East Side women how to shop, how to prepare, how to improve their homes, how to be good wives and mothers.

Lillian became widely known throughout the East Side. People knew she would listen, advise, help. Here are some incidents from her life story:

One day she saw a group of boys around a little fellow. She overheard them speak.

> "Look, fellas," the little boy gloated, "I can pull my skin off." His feverish eyes shone brilliantly.

"Hey, look," yelled his friend, "Joey's skin is loose. Can I pull some off, Joey? Huh? Let me?"

And "Me, too," shouted the other boys, crowding around Joey and taking turns in peeling the skin from the proud boy's arms.

A nurse came across the group and realized with a shock that the boy had scarlet fever. What to do with him? She pulled him away from the group and immediately took him to Lillian . . . .

Another time Lillian met a boy in the street. He was crying bitterly.

"What is it, little boy? What's the matter?" she asked.

"First the cop snitched my dice, so I began to play with my cat." (A "cat" was a piece of wood sharpened at both ends and used in a popular game.) "But the cop took that, too. So I had a piece of chalk and was drawing on the sidewalk, but they kept chasing me away. So I got my ball, but the cop came along again and took it away. There's no place to play around here."

Once she was called to visit a patient at home. She found a pretty girl lying propped up in bed. She was ill with tuberculosis, so common it was known as the "Tailor's Disease." But the girl couldn't afford to waste time, even in bed with tuberculosis. Her pale fingers rolled tobacco shreds in rice paper, manufacturing cigarettes. The tobacco dust clogged her throat, and she coughed. Between wracking coughs, she moistened the paper with her tongue. She was dying, but she was earning a living . . . .

Cases like these convinced Lillian that the people needed institutions to help them. She got Mrs. Loeb, Mr. Schiff, and a group of friends to buy a house on Henry Street, in the heart of the slum area. Lillian made this "Henry

Street Settlement" the center of many social service activities. It became famous the world over. From it grew the Outdoor Recreation League, the Public School Nursing Service, Public Health Nursing, Public School Recreation Centers, Federal Children's Bureau, Neighborhood Players Association, Henry Street Music School and the Visiting Nurses Association, whose headquarters it still is to this day. We owe these and many other organizations to Lillian Wald's love of the people. She was revered throughout the East Side as the foster-mother of the poor.

Lillian Wald travelled all over the world, spreading her ideas, encouraging others in settlement work. But always she returned to the Henry Street Settlement, to her "family." When she died, in 1940, a housing project was named in her memory. The Lillian Wald Houses are a fitting monument to this noble woman, but the best tribute to her memory is the love with which her people still speak of her on the East Side, and countless others who can never forget her. Single-handed, she changed the lives of millions. Her love, her devotion, her eagerness to help them, made her life a thrilling experience in *tzedakah*.

2

Parents and Children

Man should revere his father and mother as he reveres God, for the three are partners in him.

Midrash

YITZHAK LAMDAN

The Magic Word

The huge statue was completed. The sphinx in all its beauty and splendor rose above the sands of the desert and looked off into the far distance with its cold, stony eyes.

The sculptor who had just put the final touches to the sphinx was overwhelmed by what he had made. He was convinced that this work of art would withstand all time and that his fame would endure forever. He stood for a long time looking at the powerful statue, its beautiful woman's face, its huge breasts, its lioness' hands. The artist bowed his head and whispered, "Sphinx, Sphinx! I have done well indeed. I have made you outstandingly beautiful. You will be immortal. But why am I unable to breathe the spirit of life into you? Could I but bewitch you and awaken life and movement into you, how fortunate would I be!"

Thus the sculptor knelt in the shadow of the sphinx until he was exhausted and fell into a deep slumber. In his sleep, he heard a voice from afar. "Your prayer has been heard. Your wish will be granted. There is a word in the language of men, a simple word, that can accomplish what you, with your great art, cannot do. With the power of that word. life can be breathed into stone and human kindness can be aroused in cold and silent rock."

The sculptor awoke—it was a dream! For a long time, he was absorbed in thought. What could that magic word be, the word with the power to breathe life into stone? Suddenly he shuddered, lifted his head to the sphinx and shouted, "Immortality!" But the sphinx did not move.

Silently the massive stone crouched and continued looking off into the great distance with its frozen eyes.

Years rolled by. Generations were born and passed on. The artist's name was forgotten but the huge statue remained standing and the strange dream remained in the hearts of men. Through the ages, parents told the story to their children. But the magic word was never revealed.

One day a mighty king, a conquering hero, stood before the sphinx. He had subdued many peoples, ruled over many lands and his name was known and feared throughout the world. The warrior was just returning from battle with the conqueror's wreath on his brow. Behind his soldiers came the many captives with an immeasurable amount of booty.

When the king approached the sphinx, he remembered the story of the sculptor and his dream and the magic word that was never found, and he commanded his army to encamp there. With bold steps and haughty manner, the king climbed upon the sphinx till he reached its head. He stretched out his right hand to the numerous captives and soldiers, and they bowed down before him as one man. Then, in an arrogant and thunderous voice, he shouted, "Power." But the sphinx was as motionless as it had ever been and its eyes looked out, as always, into the distance.

More centuries passed and with them generations and generations of people. One day, a handsome youth came from afar. He wore a crown of flowers on his head, and in his hand he held a harp. Sweet poetry poured from his lips, and haunting melodies fell from his fingers when he plucked the strings of his instrument. The youth had been wandering from one country to another, up hill and down vale and wherever he went, he sang songs of love. He was overjoyed to see the sphinx. Its face was that of a beautiful woman. "How strange!" the poet thought, "no one has discovered the magic word—the word to put life into cold stone." Hurriedly, he climbed upon the sphinx, lovingly he bent his head towards the face of the statue and, in a voice trembling with passion, whispered the sweet word, "Love." But the sphinx remained as motionless as ever.

Many more years passed. A group of refugees, wandering across the desert, seeking a haven from their enemies, pitched their tents near the sphinx. Suddenly, they noticed that the horizon was covered with black clouds and the sun's light was extinguished. Fierce winds began to blow and lift the sand in every direction. Wilder and louder blew the winds, raising ever thicker clouds of dust.

The members of the caravan knew the fearful signs of the dreaded desert storm, the simoom that had the power to bury man and beast in its wake. In haste and fear, the refugees pulled out their tent poles, gathered up their belongings, mounted their camels and were off.

In the shadow of the mighty sphinx, a little girl, one of the refugee children, lay fast asleep. In their panic, the members of the caravan had left her behind. The wail of the desert grew in intensity. The sun was completely hidden behind the black clouds. The howl of the simoom was coming nearer and closer.

The child awoke, looked about her, and saw that she was alone in a frightening desert storm. Trembling with fear, she climbed up on the huge statue seeking protection in the bosom of the sphinx woman, and from her lips, burst forth the heartrending cry, "M-o-t-h-e-r!"

Behold! The wonder of it! The giant body of the sphinx began to move! A warm breath, the breath of life, heaved from its stony breast, the face of the sphinx woman softened with pity and love for the unfortunate little girl, and protected her from the perils of the desert.

[TRANSLATED FROM THE HEBREW]

SAMUEL GORDON (Adapted)

Four Dimensions

Tarphon was overjoyed! He had just become a father of a son! Mirzah had given him permission to pick up the two-hour-old mite. He looked at this huddled-up, swaddled morsel of humanity and a great feeling of thanksgiving welled up in his heart.

"Thank God for this gift of life," he said. "He's wonderful, Mirzah. And you're wonderful, too!"

"Give him back to me! You'll swallow him with your eyes!"

"Don't be selfish, Mirzah. I've waited ten years to be a father—ten long years."

"Tarphon!" and the tears in the big, wan eyes said the rest.

"Please, Mirzah, I didn't mean anything—just that I am so happy." Returning the baby to her, he continued, "He will be a great scholar. His fame will spread over the whole world. I am going out to tell everybody—my brother, my neighbors—but first let me take another look at him. I won't hurt him!"

No wonder Tarphon was so excited. He was blessed with many worldly goods—acres upon acres of rich farmland, many hired hands, a luxurious home, a beautiful wife and now—the climax to crown all of God's gifts: a son, an heir.

Several hours later, he returned exhausted, and slumped down at Mirzah's bedside.

"I am not tired from walking, but from carrying all the good wishes. Mirzah, I was thinking that I should make a handsome contribution to the synagogue, something important, that shall be remembered for generations."

"When I shall be strong enough," said Mirzah, "I plan to embroider a cloth for the reader's table in the synagogue. My sisters will surely help. We talked about it before the baby came."

"That'll get worn out and it's not an important enough gift."

"We might also donate a golden wine cup," she suggested.

"That might be stolen. Wait, I just thought of something! Benesh, the best scribe of Gostroneon, has just finished a scroll of the law, which he claims is better than any he has ever written. I don't know what his price is, though I am sure it is expensive. But the harvest has been good and we've had a year to be thankful for. I'll buy the scroll."

The next morning, Tarphon went to the home of Benesh. He found the old scribe sitting in his workroom, examining an old parchment that needed repair.

"I heard you have a scroll," Tarphon opened.

"Do you mean the one I have just completed? I have worked at it for years."

"May I see it?"

"It is already as good as sold. A congregation from another city has offered me 1150 dinars for it."

"I'll pay you 1200 if I like it."

"There is only one man in this community who could do that—Tarphon."

"I am Tarphon, and yesterday my wife gave birth to a boy. I would like to present the scroll to the synagogue to commemorate the occasion."

"The gift is worthy of the man and the occasion," said Benesh. "Come, I'll show it to you."

"Benesh unlocked the door to his cabinet where many valuable scrolls were kept and from the back he took out his most precious Torah. It was of medium size, not bulky so as to weary the arm of the holder. Benesh's eyes glowed as he unrolled it.

"Many years have I worked on it. Every tittle and jot is in place. The spacings and margins are measured to a hair. Now, look at the handles. They are ebony from India and the cover is made from Indian silk, the finest of the land."

Benesh pointed to the breastplate of solid silver with the Temple of Solomon worked out in bold relief. When the scroll was rolled up, it was topped by two silver headpieces. Inside, the bells gave off a sound like cymbals. The pointer was in the form of a palm branch that tapered off into a delicately sculptured hand.

"All these were fashioned by my son," Benesh said beaming with pride. "I assure you, no finer scroll exists, unless it is in the Garden of Eden from which the Patriarchs read the Sabbath portion. It'll be yours at 1250 dinars."

Tarphon gazed open-mouthed at the splendors before him. He didn't have the heart to haggle over the fifty dinars that Benesh had added. The man deserved the price.

Tarphon could barely wait to tell Mirzah.

"What a scroll!" he said as he dashed into the room. "Something no eye has ever seen. It was like drinking from the very glory of God!"

"Hush! Not so loud! The baby is sleeping. And don't talk so big. If anyone feasts his eyes on the glory of God's works, it is I, as I look upon my son."

"My son—our son!" Tarphon whispered. "Wasn't he born on the stroke of eight? Well, Benesh told me that that was the very instant in which he put the last touch to the scroll. He had worked on it till morning. What do you think of that? They were born at the very same moment. Isn't that strange?"

"Not really. God is provident enough to give many blessings at one time. Let's not say it's strange, but rather a happy omen."

Tarphon stooped over the child, kissed it and whispered, "Dear as the Torah is to the Almighty, so dear shall you be to Him."

Tarphon was very busy for the next five days. The story of the feast that he prepared in honor of his son's *brit milah* is still legend in the land. It is said that two wedding feasts could have been served from what remained. Among the important guests was Rabbi Eliezer, the renowned Cabalist, who, the story goes, had once caught an angel by the foot and would not let him go until he had been promised a permanent place in the future world. Now, Rabbi Eliezer was blind and palsy-stricken. Only a man of Tarphon's standing in the community would dare invite him. Tarphon had come to him and told him of the wondrous coincidence of the birth of the child at the very moment when the scroll was finished. Rabbi Eliezer consented to grace the *brit milah* with his presence.

During the feast, Tarphon brought the child, who had been named Ephraim, to Rabbi Eliezer for his blessing. The Rabbi placed his shrunken hand on little Ephraim's head, lifted his sightless eyes to heaven and spoke. The old man was toothless; his speech was jumbled and incoherent. But those who sat nearby were sure that these were the words they heard.

"As you were both born at the same moment, so may the soul of the Torah be thy soul. There is nothing more pure than the soul of the word of God. The Eternal breathed into it, the limitless vast void, and it became the four things of His dimensions. You shall live by the blessings of your twin soul. Whatever happens to it, shall happen to you. If the twin soul passes all the trials, then shall it live its appointed days, and so shall you."

All the guests who heard wondered what the blessing meant, but no one could explain it—not even Rabbi Eliezer; he died on the way home from the *brit*.

The dedication of the scroll took place on the following day. A holiday spirit was in the town. Tarphon carried the scroll from his home to the synagogue, accompanied by the officers of the congregation. The synagogue was packed. The women in the galleries threw down little bags of candy, raisins, nuts and tiny cakes for the children to catch.

Tarphon's generosity knew no bounds. When the scroll was opened, there were some letters in the beginning of Genesis that were left only in outline. He chose the characters that made up the name of his son "Ephraim Ben Tarphon" to be filled in. For each letter he paid five dinars. He did the same with the last sentences of Deuteronomy that also had been left blank. The money went into the community chest for the needy.

On the day of the first month of the child's birth, the boy's "redemption" took place. Since he was a first-born, Tarphon had to pay the *Kohanim,* the descendants of Aaron, the High Priest. He gave every *Kohan* in town five dinars and prepared another big feast.

Tarphon sometimes thought of the strange blessing that Rabbi Eliezer had uttered over Ephraim. He always dismissed it as unimportant, yet, he couldn't forget it. It seemed to imply that an extraordinary destiny hung over his son —whether good or evil, he did not know.

Ephraim proved to be a constant source of joy to his parents. At the age of two, he knew the alphabet backwards and forwards. At three, he was already versed in "The Sayings of the Fathers."

One afternoon Mirzah left her child napping and went out. She had no fear for his safety for the servants were in the house. Anyway, who would want to harm him? But there was a monster in the room where he slept, a monster of glazed bricks that reached to the ceiling. Its innards were filled with burning embers, the flue was choked up and the poisonous fumes were forced into the room. The child awoke, coughing and screaming with all the strength that remained in his tormented chest. Fortunately, Mirzah came back just then, ran in and snatched him from the room, two heartbeats before it would have been too late. Ephraim was sick and dizzy all that week, so that he was unable to go to the synagogue. The child was disappointed, for he was very proud to worship with his father. He was usually given the honor of putting the silken girdle around the scroll after it was rolled up. Although it was a little hard for him to handle and one of the wardens was always nearby to help him, he felt very grown-up and important.

That very Sabbath, a strange thing happened in the synagogue. Naphtali, the reader, was reciting the weekly portion of the Torah, when he suddenly stopped, took off his glasses, rubbed his eyes, put his spectacles on and looked hard at the scroll once more. There was a mistake, without a doubt. Though he rubbed spots out of his eyes, he could not rub away the error. The word for "breath" that should have been in the passage, was missing from its place and the sentences ran on without making any sense. How could such a thing have escaped notice? At every reading prior to this one, three men had read that very passage—Naphtali the reader, the person who was called up to pronounce the blessing, and Tarphon who stood by, pointing.

The next day Benesh was notified. He hurried over, all aflutter. "I don't know how this happened," he defended himself. 'I went over each line carefully, after I had written it. The scroll was letter-perfect; this is very baffling."

Then, with a shrug and a sigh, he corrected the error. All who watched him admired the skill with which he wrote the letters of the missing word, for when he finished, it looked as if it hadn't been retouched, but had been written perfectly from the beginning.

The mistake in the scroll had upset Tarphon, but his unhappiness vanished very quickly when he found on coming home that his son had completely recovered.

As time went on, Ephraim continued to grow and to excel in his Hebrew studies. At the age of seven, he was studying *Rashi* and *Targum Onkelos* and the Rabbinic commentaries. His teachers praised him for his keen mind and his parents were very proud.

Though Ephraim was very good at his studies, he also loved to play with other children. Once, when they were playing "hare and hounds," he was chosen the "hare." He looked around for a place to hide and noticed a large tank in the courtyard. The tank was three feet high and Ephraim thought that it contained dry fodder. He jumped in, thinking that he would climb from there into the next courtyard and be safe from his pursuers.

Splash! The tank was full of water with a mere sprinkling of dry chaff on top. He was going down for the third time when a stableman rushed over with a pitchfork, caught the boy's doublet and pulled him out. Ephraim was very sick after that.

On Saturday, Tarphon went to the synagogue to offer up thanksgiving because his child had been rescued. The portion of the week was the crossing of the Red Sea. When Naphtali came to the passage where the water parted, Tarphon suddenly took hold of the Reader's wrist and asked him to stop. The word *mayim,* which means water, was written in such a way, that the final *mem* had the same shape as the first *mem.*

The congregation came up one after the other to examine this monstrous error. People began talking about Benesh; his work belied his reputation. A cobbler's apprentice could have done better. Benesh was summoned. He shook his head and tapped his forehead.

"This is not my work," said he. "I am not so ignorant as to have done such a thing. There is a mystery in this scroll. An evil spirit or Satan must be causing the mischief. Some agreed with the scribe. Others were skeptical. Benesh made the correction and left. When Tarphon came home, Ephraim was sitting up in bed, eating a hearty meal.

Ephraim continued to grow and develop. He made great progress in his studies. When he was ten, he began to keep the fast days. He never missed a synagogue service, whether it was morning or evening. If his father couldn't go because of business, he went by himself.

Once, before the *Shavuot* holiday, when Ephraim was eleven years old, he went with his friends to gather bulrushes. It was the custom for people to strew them on the floor since they gave off a very sweet scent. In his eagerness to pick very good ones, Ephraim strayed from his comrades and did not notice how marshy the ground was becoming. Suddenly it slipped away altogether and he was up to his waist in the slimy ooze. He grasped at the branches of a willow tree that hung overhead and clung to them. A washerwoman who had come out to hang clothes spied him from the distance, ran over and pulled him out. Ephraim begged her not to tell his parents and she promised. He came home and managed to wash and change before his parents saw him.

The washerwoman did not keep the story of Ephraim's mishap a secret. As soon as Tarphon heard what happened to his son, a vague, undefined thought passed through his mind, a feeling as if he must link the child's accident with something else. The more he tried to remember the thought, the more it eluded him. It left him with a great uneasiness, and then it returned to torment him at the next reading of the Torah. There was another mistake in the scroll. The passage spoke of mortar and the word *aphar,* which means loam or earth, was slightly shifted from its line, so that it stood at a slant below the level of the other words. Tarphon had seen this passage eleven times in eleven years and never before had he noticed this peculiarity. He knew that it would be useless to send for Benesh, so, on the following day, he came to the synagogue and without a word to anyone, corrected it himself. But he couldn't get the incident out of his mind.

Ephraim's Bar Mitzvah was approaching and Tarphon decided to celebrate the occasion with befitting splendor. The boy read the whole portion of the week before the congregation and he also read the corresponding chapter from the Prophets. He delivered a fine oration, every word of which was written by himself. The town was full of his praises. Ephraim was preparing to go to a famous *Yeshivah* a month later to continue his Hebrew studies, for he planned to become a rabbi. On the eve of his departure, he became ill and took to his bed. He was feverish and his fever continued mounting. His parents sat at his side, watched every breath he drew and noted every movement of his body. Mirzah fell asleep from exhaustion. Tarphon buried his head in his hand. There was no time for weeping. He was busy tracing the flimsy thread of memory that he was sure was lurking in the recesses of his mind. All at once, he remembered a phrase—"The four things that are His dimensions." Where had he heard it? And then, another phrase—"If the twin-soul pass all the trials thereof, then shall it live its appointed days." He remembered. These were the words that Rabbi Eliezer had uttered when Ephraim was brought into the Covenant of Abraham. The meaning of the words became clear. In the week that Ephraim nearly choked from inhaling the smoke, the word *"ruach"*, meaning air—the clean pure air that one must breathe, was missing from its place in the Scriptures. When Ephraim nearly drowned in the cattle tank, the word for water was found incorrectly written—the first letter looking like the last, even as the child had thought that the bottom of the tank was like the top.

With mounting fright, Tarphon thought of the time that Ephraim had gone to gather bulrushes and then, in the scroll, the word meaning earth, was not in line with the others. Ephraim had run the gauntlet of air, water, and earth, and in each case the scroll had had some error. Now it became clear to him that the four dimensions of God were the four elements. The twin-soul was the spirit that animated both his child and the scroll; they had both come to life at the same moment. What further proof did he need? He looked at his son who had become delirious in his fever and thought—the child is burning up. Burning! That was it! Tarphon jumped up, like a madman. There was some word signifying fire, flame, or burning that needed to be corrected. If that were done, the danger would pass. The elements would be conquered and his son would live to a ripe old age. Tarphon ran through the door. He would search the scroll from beginning to end! When he came outdoors he noticed that in spite of the fact that the sun had set hours earlier, there was a reddish glow in the West. As he gazed upward, the light became larger and brighter. Then he saw people running towards it shouting, "Fire! Fire!" The synagogue was in flames! Tarphon ran and pushed his way through the crowd like a maniac, shouting, "The scroll, the scroll. Save the scroll or else he dies!" People tried to hold him back but he seemed to possess the strength of Samson. He dashed into the burning synagogue like a demon and in a few minutes came out, hugging the scroll to his breast. Only the silken mantle was singed. The scroll itself was untouched. Tarphon did not wait with the crowd that stood by in horror as the synagogue went up in flames. He ran with the scroll, his heart pounding, and burst into the house. His son's fever had subsided. The child smiled wanly at his father and said "hello" to him in a whisper. Mirzah was sitting at his side, weeping for joy. Tarphon looked at his son and then at the scroll. He heaved a great sigh of relief and thanksgiving. His son was safe now. He would live a full life and grow up to be a man of honor and learning in Israel.

[ADAPTED]

SAMUEL JOSEPH AGNON

The Kerchief

Whenever Father came home from the fair, he brought us many gifts. He was so wise that he always knew exactly what each of us wanted. Most of the presents didn't last long, as is true of all material things. We would play with a toy and on the following day it would be on the ash heap. Even my beautiful siddur, the one to which I would turn for advice on anything and everything, eventually tore, and only a few pages remained. But there was one gift that Father gave Mother that lasted for years. After it was lost, it remained in my heart and I haven't forgotten it to this very day.

At that particular time when Father came home, it was Friday afternoon and we were off from school. Those few hours before the Sabbath were more precious than all the days of the week. On all other days, the child was glued to his books; he didn't dare lift his head for a minute. But on Friday afternoon, he was free from his studies and could do anything that his heart desired. Friday at noon the world was paradise.

Mother called me for lunch, but I was reluctant to interrupt my play. When we finally did sit down to eat, my little sister cupped her right hand to her right ear and lowered her head to the table.

"What are you doing?" Mother asked.

"I am listening."

"What do you expect to hear?" and as Mother spoke, the napkin she was holding started to dance and say, "Father's coming, Father's coming!"

Soon we heard wagon wheels. They came faintly at first, then louder and nearer and louder still. We threw down our spoons and dashed out to welcome Father. Mother (may her soul rest in peace) dropped her napkin to the table, stood to her full height, placed her hands on her heart and waited for him to come into the house.

How big Father looked at that moment! I always knew that he was bigger than anybody else's father, but on that day, he was taller than tall. He hugged and kissed me, asked me what I had learned, and before I could answer, picked up my brother and sister and was kissing them.

In recalling how I felt at that time, I also remember the expression on Father's face (may his soul rest in peace) when he was surrounded by his little children. It was so beautiful, it cannot be compared to anything in the whole world.

The driver came in with two trunks; one was tremendous and the other was small. Father looked at us out of the corner of one eye and with the other, he looked at the smaller trunk and lo!—the trunk seemed to have eyes that were smiling at us.

Father took a bunch of keys from his pocket and said, "We'll open it and take out the *tallit* and *tefillin*." I knew he was teasing. Who needs *tefillin* on Friday afternoon? As for a *tallit,* Dad had a special one for the Sabbath.

We got busy untying the rope and at the same time watching Father's every motion. He found the right key at last, examined it and smiled a smile of love. The key smiled right back at him; that is, the rays of light shone on the key and it looked as if it were really smiling. Finally, he put the key in the lock, opened the trunk, put his hand in and laughed. What was the meaning of his laugh? Did he forget our presents? Did someone in the hotel steal them while he was asleep? I had barely finished saying a secret prayer that nothing like that might have happened, when Father took out some lovely things, one by one. Everything we had ever wished for was there.

It may sound foolish to praise things that are no more, but I must describe the gift that Father brought for Mother. It was a silken kerchief, heavily embroidered in flowers and buds. The background on one side was grey with white flowers and on the other side the colors were reversed. Mother spread the kerchief out before her, smoothed it with her fingers and looked at Father. Their eyes met; they were both silent. Then Mother stood up, folded the kerchief, put it away in the closet and said, "Wash and eat!"

I ran outdoors to show my gifts to my friends and played until it was time to go to the synagogue with Father.

I remember how pleasant that evening was, when we walked home after prayers. The sky was dotted with stars and the houses were lit with Sabbath candles. The people, in their Sabbath best, walked home leisurely so as not to hurry the Sabbath angels who accompanied them (as Sabbath angels always do) from the synagogue.

Our house was aglow with Sabbath candlelight. The smell of freshly-baked white bread filled the air. The table was set, covered with a big white cloth, and the *challa* on it was covered with a little white doily.

Father entered, saying, "Blessed and peaceful Sabbath." Mother responded by repeating "Peaceful and blessed." Father looked at the table and started to sing *Shalom Aleichem* while Mother sat with an open prayer book in her hand. The large copper chandelier with its ten candles (like the ten commandments) poured down its light. Opposite them shone the Sabbath candles, one for each member of the family. Although we were so much smaller than our parents, our candles were the same size as theirs. I noticed that my mother's face looked different from usual—that her forehead was shorter. The kerchief did that—it was placed low on her head where her hair and forehead met. Her eyes were unusually large and were focused on Father as he walked back and forth chanting, "A woman of valor, who can find?" The ends of her kerchief hung down and touched her apron and trembled slightly because the Sabbath angels were flapping their wings and making a little breeze. There was no wind; the windows were closed. Who but angels could have done that? I looked at Mother and realized that she was very important to have Sabbath angels fluttering about her. Then I felt someone patting my cheek and I didn't know if it was angels' wings fanning me or the corners of Mother's kerchief caressing me. Fortunate is the child whose mother pats his head on Sabbath eve! Fortunate indeed is he over whose home the Sabbath angels hover.

When I awoke, the sun was already shining. The spirit of Sabbath morning filled the world. Father and Mother were about to leave—he to the synagogue and she to the house of study where my grandparents prayed. Father was dressed in a long black coat and sable hat and Mother wore a black dress and a feather hat. In the house of study, the prayer was not prolonged with much singing, so that Mother was able to return early. When Father and I came home, she was already seated, wearing her new kerchief. The table was set with wine, brandy, cakes and cookies of all kinds and shapes.

Father entered with the greeting "Sabbath peace" on his lips, and put the *tallit* on the bed. He then sat down at the head of the table, chanted, "The Lord is my Shepherd," made *Kiddush* over the wine and sang "A Song of David." I had the same feeling of exhilaration that I have when this psalm is being sung in the synagogue on New Year's Eve. If Mother hadn't taught me it was bad manners to stand on chairs and shout, I would have done just that. I would have shouted praise to God and His wonderful world!

The corners of Mother's kerchief accompanied her hands as she cut the cake for the children. Fruit and crumbs dropped and stained her apron, but her kerchief remained unblemished—clean as the day when Father took it out of his trunk. A woman does not wear a silken kerchief every day. While she is cooking, what does she have to dress up for? On festivals, the days of rejoicing that God gave to the people because He wanted them to have happy days, Mother would wear her feather hat to the house of study, and at home she would wear the kerchief. On the Day of Atonement I would look at her—her eyes shining from praying and fasting—and she was like a prayer book of patience bound between silken covers.

Mother kept the kerchief neatly folded in the closet. Though she was most meticulous, I never saw her wash it. Had it not been because of me, she would have had it all the days of her life and it would have remained after her. But the judgment came down from above that I should lose the kerchief. It happened on the day of my *Bar Mitzvah*. Mother tied it around my neck and I came back without it. That which meant so much to me, I myself forfeited—I did it with my own hands. . . .

[TRANSLATED FROM THE HEBREW]

ZALMAN EPSTEIN

Blessing the Candles in the Snow

Father had business reverses at the time when we were five small children. He wandered around for a year, trying to establish himself, and it became Mother's responsibility to support the family. It was very hard for her to earn enough for our needs, but she never weakened. She would never think of asking help of anyone—she considered that the lowest degradation. The merchants from the nearby town of Buberesk (we lived in a tiny village) gave her merchandise on credit which enabled her to open a store. Her diligence and thrift earned enough to keep us from want.

One incident of my childhood remains in my memory. Mother journeyed to Buberesk to buy goods. She had hired a village peasant as her driver. The trip was scheduled to last a week, and she was to return on Friday. There were delays, it was winter, and the loaded wagon moved slowly. The sun was beginning to set; it was candlelighting time and they were many miles from home.

It had never occurred to Mother not to light the Sabbath candles. Were she to wait till she got home, it would have been much too late and not permissible. She decided to light the candles on the road, in the snow, just where she was. Since the lighting and blessing of the candles herald in the Sabbath, and after that, one is neither allowed to carry anything nor to travel, Mother emptied her pockets, placed their contents in the wagon, took out four candles from her bundles of merchandise in the wagon, and placed them in a row on a frozen mound. She then lit them, lifted her hands and said the candlelighting prayer just as she would have done had she been home.

It is easy to imagine the surprise of the peasant wagoner at this unusual sight, and all of Mother's explanations in Russian could not make him understand the reasons for her strange behaviour. The candles were left shining on the snow, and lit up the white expanse. The air was clear and dry, and completely without wind. Soon night fell and the stars sent down their heavenly light. The moon coyly sent her silvery beams to meet the twinkling candles in the snow. The rays of light from above and from below were united, for the eternal God from His hidden store of holiness had created them all.

The Jewish woman, who had placed her altar to God, left the burning candles and followed the wagon on foot.

We children had given up hope of having Mother home for the Sabbath. We presumed that there had been a delay on the road and that she had stopped at an inn. Suddenly, we heard horses' hoofs and wagon-sleds. Mother had arrived! Joyous shouts and endless questions greeted her.

The Sabbath had long been ushered in with the lighting of the candles by my oldest sister, and the table was set. We were amazed at Mother's late arrival, but she quickly assured us that she had not, Heaven forbid, desecrated the Sabbath. She lit candles, but she did so in the open field and she then continued her journey on foot all the way home. She told the story as if it were an everyday occurrence.

I bowed my head in reverence before that modest and trusting soul—my mother, the embodiment of sympathy and love. Sabbath candles are indeed beautiful wherever they shine, but the candles that she lit on the highway in honor of the Sabbath Queen were infinitely more beautiful. When they shone upon the pure white snow under the heavenly dome, when she lifted her hands and prayed to the living God that the eyes of her children shall be lit by Torah, did not the good angels accompany her and answer "Amen?" And did they not take her prayer, pure as crystal, and fly with it to the Heavenly throne of the Almighty?

[TRANSLATED FROM THE HEBREW]

JUDAH STEINBERG

Forgiven

Abraham-Jose Karminski is one of the richest men in town. He has so many people in his employ that he can sleep till three in the afternoon. But there are two days a year when he rises with the sun. No matter how early he gets up on those days, he complains of being late. They are the day before Passover and the one that ushers in the Day of Atonement. He is in such a great hurry on the day before the Day of Atonement that he literally rouses the dawn!

There is so much to do that day, not counting the *kaparah* ritual and the special prayers of penitence that are really said after midnight. It is a day that is part holy and yet, somewhat of a workday too, for there are mundane matters to be attended to, such as the settling of debts that have fallen due, appeasing those whom you have offended and accepting apologies from those who have provoked quarrels with you. Then, there is the eating and drinking—it is considered a *mitzvah* to indulge yourself on that day because of the long fast that follows. You have only till midday to do all this, for the afternoon is devoted to an accounting of the soul—a reckoning that must cover the entire year that passed. Is this a trifling matter? How many days are there in each year and how many footprints of sin does man make as he lives through each day? Indeed, the very time in which you are preparing yourself for the great and awesome Day of Atonement is veritably reckoned as the holy day itself.

It was the day before the Day of Atonement when the following incident took place. The first thing that Abraham-Jose did that morning was to rush to the bathhouse, scrub himself in the tub and dip himself in the *mikvah*. Then he ran trembling to the synagogue and after a hasty prayer, returned home. On the way, he reviewed the tasks that were still undone. He counted them off on his fingers, but there was one specific chore for which he had no finger.

"No!" He was emphatic. "I won't do it. It's no concern of mine!"

He entered the house in a holiday mood. "Good day!" he called out to his wife. "Let's have some refreshments."

"Good day," Sarah-Leah answered with a sigh that belied her jollity and she placed some sweets on the table.

"May the Holy Name bring a sweet year to all of Israel. May He give strength to the fast on the holy day—the pregnant women . . ." and she stopped short.

Abraham-Jose was aware of the fact that the wife of his only son was pregnant. "No one came?" he asked casually, as he nibbled at some pastry.

"No one," his wife answered in an offhand manner, as if she didn't know what he referred to and whom he meant.

"It is possible," Abraham-Jose mused, "that he won't come? Not even today? No respect for a parent? And what of fear of Heaven and of the Day of Judgment? Even if he does come and does apologize, I won't forgive him. He insulted his mother and me. He talked back to us most shamefully. No! Though he would leave humiliated and embarrassed, I cannot forgive him. Maybe this hurt will cleanse his soul and the Holy One, blessed be He, will forgive him.

"A generation of barbarians, these youngsters! But they are really good at heart—merely stubborn. He'll probably send a relative as peacemaker. But it won't help. It will be of no use. I won't forgive him. Let the youngster feel how deeply he has provoked us.

"And for such a reason—he came to his wife's defense! Who is she? A baby that hasn't finished teething. What manners! No respect for one's elders.

"What was all the rumpus about? What did Sarah-Leah want of her? And all for her own good, too. Is it not unseemly for a daughter of Israel to appear out of doors with her locks exposed? And how can a woman permit herself not to step into the synagogue on the Sabbath when the new month is blessed? Is it possible that she doesn't know the laws that a Jewish woman should know? And, to top it all, she takes no interest in housework. She should do something to keep from being bored, even if she has no desire to help her mother-in-law.

"How angry that young fool of a husband became! 'Ignoramus!' he shouted! Imagine! A son calling a father ignoramus! You couldn't really tell at whom he was directing his insults. He was so furious that he didn't look at me. The truth is, that in his fury he didn't know what he was saying. But yet, it was the height of impudence."

Abraham-Jose busied himself listlessly, interrupting his work constantly to look out of the window, or to turn toward the entrance hall with a feeling that someone was there. Time and again, he would call out to his wife, "Who's there?"

"No one!" The answer was always the same.

"I thought I heard someone," he would justify his question.

He kept pulling his watch out of his vest pocket and looking at it. "It's getting late. Time doesn't stand still."

Suddenly, he remembered that he had to meet with a debtor who had promised to pay, though he was not certain if it was to be before or after the Day of Atonement.

"I'll go and see him. If he will pay, well and good. If not, nothing's lost. But I'll have to pass the house of those young brats. How irresponsible is this new generation! They just scooped up their belongings and moved into an apartment with a stranger, as if my house wasn't big enough. Well, what does it matter? I'll walk on the other side of the street."

But Abraham-Jose found himself walking on the side of the street where his children lived. He did not do it intentionally, certainly not. He just happened to forget. The door was open and his grandchildren were playing in front of the house. When he saw them, he stopped, turned to the north and thought he detected a cool wind blowing.

"The children are naked and barefoot," he called out angrily. "They could catch their death of cold. That's a mother and father for you! What can you expect? They are still babies themselves. I must go inside and reprimand them. It's a matter of life and death."

He picked up his little grandchildren, pressed them to his bosom and entered the house with bold steps and obvious anger.

"How mean can you be—not to take pity on your own children!" he shouted. "The north wind is blowing and the children are practically naked."

His son, on seeing him, got to his feet and lowered his eyes in embarrassment.

"How penitent!" thought Abraham-Jose and his heart was filled with compassion for his son.

"Better not to sin than to sin and repent," he chided gently.

"But father . . ." the son started to answer.

"Enough, enough! Let's not go back to how it all began."

"But . . ."

"I said I forgive you."

"I forgive you," the daughter-in-law repeated the words in a tone of disparagement. "And what about the insult to me?"

"Sarah-Leah will forgive you, I am sure. You needn't worry about that. Where's the maid? Run and fetch Sarah-Leah. Tell her I'm here!"

The maid dashed out of the house to call Sarah-Leah while Abraham-Jose continued chiding the parents for not knowing how to care for their young.

"You think one catches cold only in winter? Spring and autumn colds are much more treacherous. You are committing a crime against your own children."

He was still talking when his wife appeared and fell on her daughter-in-law's neck. The father embraced his son and the house was filled with the twittering of kisses.

Towards evening, when Sarah-Leah blessed her candles, tears filled her eyes to overflowing as she prayed, "Master of the universe, give strength to my daughter-in-law to fast on this holy day. . . . Let no harm come to the unborn child."

[TRANSLATED FROM THE HEBREW]

HARRY L. GOLDEN

The Miracle of Goerick Street

Considering the poverty of the family, it wasn't such a big miracle, which is precisely what made it so fascinating, so utterly defiant of reasonable explanation.

It happened about 1910 and it involved a family of five living in a tenement flat on Goerick Street on the Lower East Side. The father was Reb Sholom, the cantor of a small congregation of immigrants from the big city of Odessa on the Black Sea. The cantor himself had come to America about five years before his wife, Clara, and their three children—Jacob, who was now ten; Philip, nine; and Esther, six.

The cantor's earnings were dependent upon the pledges of the members of the small congregation, who were mostly pedlars and garment workers. To these wages he was able to add a few small fees every Sunday at the Washington Cemetery in Brooklyn, where people sought him out to chant the prayers at the gravesides of departed loved ones.

Despite poverty, it was a happy family, and this was because the cantor was a man of dignity, kindness and piety. Years later, his children would look back on it all and say that their father was what we would call a "morale-builder." He kept his family together with honor, good humor and wisdom. He often told his children that he would never interfere with their hopes for their future, but they would be much happier as Americans, in whatever station they chose, if they continued to follow the rules and rituals of the Jewish faith. Let it be said, too, that the family's devotion was shared by neighbors and members of his congregation. The poor cantor achieved the respect reserved for a learned rabbi.

It was about this time that the miracle first occurred.

It was a Wednesday night and the two boys had asked their mother if they could afford to have their shoes repaired, and she said that she would see about it on the following Monday. But the shoes were not repaired on the following Monday; they were repaired that very night. And no one knew how. They all remembered the same details. The cantor and the boys had recited the evening prayers; they had supper; the older boy did some homework; the little girl helped her mother with the dishes; they sat around the table and talked for a while; then everyone went to bed. Everything was the same as on every other weekday night. The boys had put their stockings into their shoes, placed them under the bed, the lights were turned out, the door was bolted. In the morning, the boys pulled their shoes from under the bed and they had been thoroughly repaired—with new soles and heels and a high polish. They did not know what to make of it, and when they asked the cantor for a possible explanation, he shook his head, "Well, let's get on with our morning prayers."

But the matter did not end there. Not at all. Three months later, the shoes were repaired again, under similar circumstances, and this time little Esther's shoes also were rebuilt. BUT WHY THE SHOES? If it was really a miracle, why repair just shoes for a family that needed so many other important things? They asked themselves this question over and over again. They wondered about this each time a pair of shoes was repaired during the night, and it happened every few months over a period of six or seven years—and no one could explain it.

Of course, the children did not let it rest at that. When a pair of shoes needed repair, they watched and they watched.

They took turns and watched all night, time after time. Nothing. It was only on a night when they finally gave in to sleep that the miracle happened. They never saw or heard anything during all those years that their shoes were periodically repaired.

The story was told to me by a lawyer in one of our large Eastern cities. He is Jacob, the eldest son of the cantor, Reb Sholom (the cantor died in the late 1920's). I was an overnight guest of this lawyer, who enjoys great prestige. The oldest families in his city make him the administrator of their estates, and while he did not say so, he was actually relating everything that he had achieved to what his father had meant to him, and what his father had taught him. His brother, Philip, is a manufacturer, and the sister, Esther, just as the cantor had hoped, had married a "learned man."

The miracle of Goerick Street?

Reb Sholom had made his decision as he walked off the gangplank into America. He was not a cantor in Russia. He was a shoemaker; and he did not come from the big seaport, Odessa (which is like saying you're from Chicago or Philadelphia); he came from the small village of Glotsk. He yearned for status, not for himself, but for what it would do for his children. They would not be the children of the poor shoemaker.

He was wise enough to know, too, that in America the social classes did not have the meaning that they had in the old country, but he also knew that these distinctions were too deeply rooted not to survive for at least one generation.

No, Reb Sholom thought, even if he were to remain poor, he would make a new life—one in which he would attain status without money, so as to bring to his home conversation and fellowship and the kind of environment that helps a son to become a lawyer, and helps a daughter marry a learned man.

He then tackled the most difficult part of his goal with determination and optimism. Study! He read far into the night, every night. He practically memorized the Scriptures; he studied the Talmud and the Commentaries; he read the books of the learned men of the past; and he went to the *shul* every day and listened; he remembered everything he heard at the weekly discussion the rabbi conducted with his elders. And all of this took him about four years, while his wife earned enough to keep the family by taking in the sewing of a garment contractor.

About this time, the old cantor of the *shul* died and Reb Sholom applied for the position. He had had no cantorial training at all; in fact, he did not even have much of a voice; but there was something about the manner in which he chanted the prayers. His deep affection for every word he was uttering convinced even those highly critical Orthodox Jews that all this man had to do was *recite* the prayers to hold them in the spell of his own piety.

And now his son, my lawyer-host, was filling his pipe, and I took advantage of the moment to ask the obvious question.

He shook his head in answer. "No, not even my mother could tell us where he kept his shoemaker tools. I am convinced she never knew.

"But, since none of us ever heard the tap of a hammer, we suspect that on these occasions he got out of bed in the middle of the night and repaired our shoes in the cellar of that tenement house on Goerick Street."

MAX LERNER

My Father "Moved"

My father died on Saturday, as gently and peacefully as he had lived, and he was buried yesterday. At 87 he had lived beyond the Biblical assignment, yet even an old man leaves a gaping hole when he breaks through the skein of life and hurtles into no-being.

As I stood at his grave, listening to the service that has come down through the centuries, my mind wound back through the corridors of his life. He came of a line of scholars, men of the Book, simple folk who warmed themselves by the lamps of the past and gloried in the exploits and tragedies of their people.

In Russia he had studied at a "yeshiva," and traveled from village to village as an itinerant scholar. But Czarist society was stifling. My father and his young wife wanted a chance to earn something, and wanted their children to breathe a freer air and become someone. At 33, in 1903, he came to New York as part of the great migration of the century, and my mother followed in 1907 with her four children. He went through the familiar immigrant odyssey: He was a small peddler, worked in a garment loft, became a Hebrew teacher, turned to farming and failed at it, tried a milk delivery route, became a small grocer. Finally he went back to what he loved—his work as a Hebrew teacher, keeping at it until a few years before his death.

His was one of the millions of American stories that have woven the history of this country. Life was not easy for my father. He had disappointments, frustrations, tragedies. He was never a big success at anything, nor did he make a great noise in the world. But he loved and was loved, and he had joy in his children. Had he stayed behind in Europe he and they would long ago have been ashes at Auschwitz or ciphers in a Soviet ant-society.

* * *

When I saw him toward the end of his illness, while he could still talk, he asked me to bring him his notebooks. They were a confusion of ledgers, journals, loose sheets, on which over the years he had written his reflections on a variety of themes, covering his life within and the world outside, dealing with the early prophets and the latter-day secular figures, with Hitler and Stalin and Nasser, Roosevelt and Truman, Weizmann and Ben-Gurion.

I am, alas, an ignorant man. With all my years of schooling I am unable to read the languages in which my father wrote, as my sons are already able to read mine. I shall save the bundle of pages on which he spent the burden of his hours, driven as he was by a strange necessity to find a garment for what he felt and dreamt.

Some day I may repair my ignorance and discover what thoughts they were that coursed through the mind of this patient, reflective man.

* * *

His killer—the killer of so many—was cancer. Mercifully, once it struck it did its work fast. In his last few days he was unconscious.

I think I was the last person whom he saw and recognized. When he whispered my name, I felt a stab of the fitness of it. Surely it is a good thing for a father, in his final moments of consciousness, to know that his son is near him. The father-son relation is the basic link of continuity in life, carrying the male principle and the tradition of responsibility from one generation to the next.

The need for a father is as crucial as the need for a son, and the search of each for the other—through all the days of one's life—exempts no one. Happy the man who finds both.

* * *

My father was a gentle and permissive man. When I think of him I think of the lines of the great E. E. Cummings poem:

"My father moved through dooms of love
Through sames of am through haves of give,
Singing each morning out of each night
My father moved through depths of height . . .
Because my father lived his soul
Love is the whole and more than all."

Death seems all the more pitiless when it comes to these gentle people. When I last saw my father, just before he died, he seemed so shrunken and wasted that I fear I broke down shamelessly and wept. It was for more than my father that I wept. It was for death which shows up the final helplessness of life, and for the crazy tragic absurdity of the whole human condition.

And then, along with the other mourners, I heard and spoke the thunderous syllables of the great "Kaddish"—"Yisgadal V'yiskadash Sh'me Rabbo," and I looked at the little huddle of my father's friends of many years who stood around, and the absurdity became a little less absurd. Even the most rational of us must admit that there is a healing power in the ritual words when you face what reason cannot fathom.

* * *

I keep thinking of my father's last words to me. I had been sitting by his side while he slept. Then my father moved a bit, and his eyes half opened. I bent close to him, and barely made out his whispered words. "They are calling from Zion," he said.

It is a good belief with which to die.

EPHRAIM KISHON

Yigal and the Inquisition

Two men sat down next to me on the Rothschild Blvd. bench and mutely immersed themselves in their papers. One of them was an old gentleman, his glasses had slid down to the tip of his nose, he read some Yiddish periodical, mumbling. The other was hardly ten, one of those sabra youngsters. In his hands he held a blood-curdling thriller.

The boy suddenly turned to the old gentleman.

"Grandpa" he said. "What is 'Inquisition'?"

Grandpa ponderously folded his paper and pushed his glasses back into the saddle.

"Hundreds of years ago"—he began with unconcealed relish—"in the dark Middle Ages, our forefathers' fate was bitter indeed, Yigal. They were herded into high-walled ghettos, and every Gentile, even the lowliest, could kick them, spit on them or humiliate them to his heart's content. Yes, yes. The tax collectors of the Church robbed them of their hard-won pennies, provided they had anything left after paying the emperor's taxes. They burned our sages alive, sold our sons into slavery, our women . . ."

"All right"—Yigal interrupted him. "That will do. I asked you, grandpa, what 'Inquisition' was?"

"Don't be cheeky, Yigal! I'll tell you presently . . . The Inquisition was nothing but a diabolic way to intimidate those doubting the dogma . . . The victims naturally were almost exclusively Jews. . . ."

"Why 'naturally'? Why?"

"Quiet! Will you listen quietly?"—the old gentleman raged. "In the torture chambers of the Inquisition, the red-hooded monks quartered their victims, pulled out our martyrs' nails with red-hot pincers, hanged them head down over slow fires and broke them on the rack . . ."

"All right"—Yigal again interrupted. "Skip the rest until the revolt . . ."

"What revolt?"

"What a question! The Jews' revolt against the monks."

"Don't interrupt me, Yigal. Our forefathers were God-fearing, meek Jews, who did not revolt against the Lord's will . . . ."

"What? The Lord wanted . . . that . . . the Inquisition . . ."

"Shame on you, Yigal! How dare you speak like that? If you must know it, our forefathers were great heroes who were not broken even by the most horrible tortures! Their faith never wavered, they gave proof of an unprecedented inner strength. . . ."

"Good! So they clobbered those monks after all, didn't they?"

"Yigal!" The old gentleman flared up. "What did I tell you? Our forefathers, blessed be their memory, suffered the most horrible tortures at the hands of their executioners but even with their last breath they praised the Lord for protecting them against their foes. 'And though I, walk in the Valley of Death' "—the old gentleman psalmodised, "no harm will come to me, because Thou, O Lord art with me . . . ."

"This I don't understand"—Yigal reacted to the psalm. "How could they sing about no harm coming to them with the monks just burning them. Now if the singing had been done by the monks . . ."

"Your only excuse, you brat, is that you don't realize what you are saying. Our forefathers' faith in the Lord deeply moved even the executioners who were seized by such terror that they had to kill more and more innocent victims."

"Grandpa"—Yigal implored. "Please! Tell me about the revolt."

"Will you keep quiet, yes or no . . .?"

"Just a small revolt!"

"Quiet, shegetz.[1] Don't desecrate our forefathers' memory. Had they, instead of resisting, succumbed to the horrors of the Inquisition, you wouldn't be a Jew today. . . ."

"That's not true"—Yigal flatly rejected this theory—"I would be a Jewish boy even then, because I was born here in Israel. . . ."

"You are a heathen, that's what you are. You don't appreciate our forefathers' heroism!"

"Humbug!" Yigal shouted, deeply hurt. "You want me to believe that it is the Lord's wish to have those monks slaughter me? Excuse me, grandpa, but those forefathers of yours must have been awful milksops."

"Milksops! The words they use nowadays!"—the old gentleman fumed, then turned towards me. "Have you ever seen such scandalous behaviour, sir? And it's for his like that we made the State. Aren't they horrible?"

"They certainly are horrible. Bless them!"

[TRANSLATED FROM THE HEBREW BY YOHANAN GOLDMAN]

---

1 "Shegetz"—that is what the observant Jew calls the young ignorant who is concerned only with worldly matters. Time was when to be called that was an almost mortal insult, but the sabras have heard themselves called so often "shegetz" that they no longer care.

3

Love and Marriage

Blessed art Thou,
O Lord our God,
King of the universe,
who hast created joy and gladness,
bridegroom and bride.

(Wedding Service)

CHAIM NACHMAN BIALIK

Two Steps from My Garden Rail

Two steps from my garden rail
Sleeps my well beneath its pail:
    Every Sabbath comes my love
    And I let him drink thereof.

All the world is sleeping now
Like the fruit beneath the bough.
    Father, mother, both are gone
    And my heart wakes here alone.

And the pail awakes with me,
Dripping, dripping, drowsily:
    Drops of gold and crystal-clear . . .
    And my love is drawing near.

Hist! I think that something stirred;
Was it he, or but a bird?
    Dearest friend, my lover dear,
    There is no one with me here.

By the trough we sit and speak,
Hand in hand and cheek to cheek;
    Hear this riddle: Can you tell
    Why the pitcher seeks the well?

That you cannot answer, nor
What the pail is weeping for?
    Morn to even, drop by drop,
    Fall its tears and cannot stop.

This then tell me, why my breast
Daylong, nightlong is oppressed.
Spoke my mother truth in saying
That your heart from me was straying?

And my lover answered; See,
Enemies have slandered me.
Ere another year be gone,
We shall marry, foolish one.

On that golden day of days
Shall the summer be ablaze.
Fruited branches overhead
Shall in benediction spread.

Friend and kinsman, young and old
Shall be gathered to behold,
And with music and with mirth
They shall come to lead us forth.

And the bridal canopy
In this place shall lifted be.
I shall slip a ring of gold
On this finger that I hold,

And pronounce the blessing: "Thee
God makes consecrate to me."
And my enemies shall there
Burst with envy and despair.

[TRANSLATED FROM THE HEBREW BY MAURICE SAMUEL]

IRVING FINEMAN

Boaz Makes Up His Mind

The following is based on the story of Ruth in the Bible: Ruth returns from meeting Boaz and tells her mother-in-law all that had transpired.

Naomi says, "Sit still, my daughter, until thou know how the matter will fall; for the man will not rest, until he have finished the thing this day."

Ruth 3:17

When Ruth left him there was just one thin, pale streak, low on the eastern horizon, to show the dawn was coming. The darkness of the autumn night still lay like a tired sleeper in the fields; and within on the threshing floor, among disordered sheaves of grain, the sprawling, shapeless forms of sleeping men were barely discernible.

How like a dream it had been! As if in a dream she had come to him in the night. In the soft, bewitching, autumn night they had stood together, whispering. Whispering lest the sleepers be roused. What ineffable joy and pride in her love and faith had come to him—uncalled—as if out of the opulent night. And then, just before the dawn, he had sent her away, with his promise to see the kinsman.

Silent he stood, as if enchanted, watching Ruth as she descended the low hill through the pasture to the road; her white feet glimmering among the dark grasses, her shapely hips swinging gracefully, her sturdy shoulders bowed under the burden of his generous gift; he watched until her dark form merged with the shadows of the trees by the roadside. There was no sound from the shadowy fields. Behind him Boaz heard only the measured breathing of his sleeping men. How like a dream!

The sun came up, and with it the host of familiar sounds of a workaday world: the incessant twitter of birds from field and wood, the crowing of cocks from the barnyard, the lowing of cattle, the bark of dogs, the stir of waking men from the threshing floor. The sun came up like a clamorous brazen shield, dispelling the enchanting darkness from the land, and the seductive visions from the mind of Boaz. He watched its rays glittering on the waters of a stream that ran gaily down the valleys to the west—ran heedlessly down and away to the Dead Sea. And into the mind of Boaz crept a faint perturbation, seeped in and eddied about and rose—until it swept away all the joy of the night in a flood of anxiety. Doubts assailed him like a multitude of darting arrows—the immortal doubts of a man in the face of marriage.

Before him the sun, shining on his wide fields, drew up to his nostrils the smell of the rich warm soil. From behind him drifted the acrid smoke of a crackling fire and the noise of his young men preparing their food—with their hearty laughter and their free talk, boasting of their prowess in the harvest, in combat, in amorous conquest.

The devil! thought Boaz. Whatever had possessed him in the night? Bewitched, he must have been. . . . After a hard day's work with the harvest—as fine a harvest as any in Judah—he had bathed, eaten with gusto and drunk heartily; he had made merry with his men and lain down to rest, satisfied, without a care—as carefree as the youngest of them. And here he was—overnight—in a fair way to lose this precious freedom. . . .

Bewitched!—overnight. Well, there was no denying she had been a good deal in his thoughts since she first appeared gleaning in his fields. He had been impressed, immensely, at first sight of Ruth. So different, this woman of Moab, from the women he knew—the women of Bethlehem. A magnificent creature, handsome and strong and self-possessed. And when he learned who she was, and heard the tale of her loyalty to old Naomi, he was indeed very much taken with her; he had shown a kindly interest in her welfare, in protecting her from the crude men in his fields. Courageous creature. Other women, to be sure, gleaned in his fields, poor wretches. But Ruth was the widow of Mahlon, the son of Elimelech, of good family. The women of Bethlehem of her class, who considered all labor beneath them, would have died rather than stoop. . . . Boaz grimaced at the thought and looked up over his olive trees at the walls of the town, glittering in the morning sunlight.

Those gossipy matrons of Bethlehem with their marriageable daughters: senseless girls with not a thought in their giddy heads but to make a good match, their one ambition. Old and young, always angling. Boaz knew that in the town he had long been marked as the great catch: a well-made, valiant fellow, rich, with many broad acres in wheat and barley. And the stratagems, the wiles they had tried upon him. Mothers of the first families of Bethlehem waylaid him in the foyer of the Temple after services: "You poor lonesome man! How you must want a good home-cooked dinner. You must come over and let me and my Sara give you a delicious meal. Sara is a perfect housewife and would just love it. You haven't met my Sara. Sara, dear, this is . . ." And their fathers, grasping merchants, meeting him in the market place, treating him with unwonted generosity, plying him with patronage and with invitations, dropping hints of dowries that smelt, to Boaz, of barter in cattle. And when he had once been inveigled into calling, how carefully the younger Hannah was hidden from his view while the tiresome Sara was blatantly paraded before him. And finally when he had failed to respond to the lure of Sara, how desperately the younger Hannah was thrown at his head. . . . He despised them all, did Boaz: the crafty, unscrupulous parents, and their dumb daughters with their made-up prettiness, their avaricious eyes, and their dull virtues.

And for years he had escaped them: had eluded their wiles; had continued to live his free, robust life, in his broad fields among his men. And now, in the harvest, this miracle; overnight—captured. That was it, taken by surprise. How startled he had been, aroused in the night, to find Ruth at his feet. Strange, courageous woman. With her sturdy bearing, the fine undaunted eyes in her brown face, the roundness of her warm, sunburnt arms. How those cats in the town would talk if they knew she had come to him in the night, alone. . . . She had followed the honest prompting of her heart; in her straightforward manner, she had come to him, without evasion. "I am Ruth . . ." she had whispered in the night, and swept him off his feet. Carried away like a callow youth, he thought . . . and the flood of doubts came back to plague him. What would they not say in the town? Had he resisted the women of Bethlehem only to fall a victim to the bold proposal of this strange penniless woman of Moab? . . .

The devil! he muttered, and turned to his ablutions. The cool water seemed, for a moment, to clear his vision. After all, nothing had been settled finally. He had still to see the kinsman. This kinsman Boaz knew well—a thin, beady-eyed, stiff-necked merchant whom he disliked and distrusted: a man, like many in the town, who made nothing with his own hands; who bought and sold, traded with the produce of others; who gilded his fingers, as it were, handling the treasures of others. This kinsman Boaz knew for a shrewd bargainer. Let Boaz but show an interest in the worthless, neglected property of Elimelech, and the kinsman would surely hold out for a profit on his right to redeem it. That, thought Boaz, would let him out. But instead of relief in this thought, he found himself still recalling and debating, over and over, in his disordered mind. . . . Her upturned face, the graceful swing of her hips as she walked, her glimmering feet in the dark. . . . And again the pricking doubts —this woman, an alien, what did he know of her strange ways and desires—upsetting his life, his freedom. . . . Only yesterday his mind had been at peace, and now . . . The devil! He had given his word; he would see it through; anyway he would see the kinsman. And Boaz turned his face to the threshing floor where the beat of the threshers had begun and the chaff rose up in a turbulent cloud.

"It appears that love," said the kinsman maliciously, "is not only blind but deaf."

Boaz, holding the shoe the other had given him as a token of the exchange, had a sudden impulse to fling it at the kinsman's head. But curiosity overcame his irritation, and Boaz kept his peace. His meeting with the kinsman before the elders at the city gate had begun just as Boaz expected. No sooner did he mention his interest in Elimelech's property than the avaricious kinsman said he would redeem the land. But then, unaccountably, Boaz found his heart heavy in his breast. Perversely, in that moment when it appeared that release was in sight, it seemed that, freedom or no freedom, he wanted Ruth. He perceived in a flash that he had not really come to escape the enchantment she had put upon him, but ready to pay dearly for the privilege to this hateful kinsman of hers. How great then was his astonishment and his relief to see the kinsman suddenly lose all interest in the matter, as soon as Boaz announced that the hand of Ruth was involved in the redemption of Elimelech's property. Yet as he watched the kinsman quickly unlace his shoe, the sign of his renunciation, surprise and relief turned to wonder. Boaz became curious; there was something about this too sudden victory; there was something in the mean eye of the kinsman. . . . It was curiosity that prompted Boaz to suggest they seal the bargain with a drink at the inn by the city gate.

Over his wine the kinsman proved only too ready to be drawn out—to air his views; and the more he talked the more he disturbed Boaz, irritated him with his self-righteousness, his mean innuendo.

"Blind and deaf," he repeated, staring malevolently at Boaz over the edge of his goblet. "Every man to his taste, of course," he went on after a pause, "but not for me . . ." He shook his head and pursed his thin lips. Boaz could have wrung his stiff skinny neck. "Too independent," he added crisply. "Woman's place, my dear Boaz, is in the home; and if I had my way," he leaned forward, licking his lips, "it would be in the harem."

Boaz stared at him in amazement.

"They do things differently, it seems, in Moab. But this young woman has got herself talked about in Bethlehem with her independence, boldly running about doing a man's work. Immodesty some people call it, and I may as well tell you that people have been saying things; only this afternoon I heard that late last night she had been seen . . . Well really, my dear Boaz, I mean no offence; only telling you what is being said." He hastily moistened his dry lips and Boaz subsided. "That may all be women's gossip. Anyway I don't mind saying she is not my type. Too sturdy. Personally I prefer them like our Bethlehem girls, soft—you know. That, I admit, my dear Boaz, is a matter of taste. But aside from that, I must say," he continued, "I do not see how you can look with joy on the prospect of old Naomi as your mother-in-law. I am not saying she is not a noble old woman, has had a hard time and all that; but much too crafty. Of course, she cannot be blamed for wanting a good home; and when a man is in love he doesn't mind so much being taken in; but really, my dear Boaz, the way she set out to get a good match for her outlandish daughter-in-law . . . egging her on. . . . Everyone has been talking about it. It may be a romantic accident, my dear Boaz, that the Moabitess came to glean in your fields, but there are people in town, I must tell you, who think differently. Of course, I would not go so far as to say, as some do, that Naomi induced her to come to Bethlehem for the sole . . . Why! my dear Boaz!" For Boaz had flung the shoe, narrowly missing the kinsman's head, and stood up before him in a towering rage.

"You may keep the rest of your slanders for your mean-minded friends—weak, despicable creatures, afraid of strong women. . . ." Yet, even as he spoke, conviction failed him, and, in his wrath, words too. He turned and went out. Out of the inn and out of the city gate he strode, and down the road, kicking the dry dust into clouds that rose in the dusk behind him.

Hooked! Boaz muttered. That's what he had been—hooked. It seemed now that he had suspected it all along; that it was this that had troubled him. They were no better than the rest—scheming women. All the same. Setting their traps first to catch a man's eye and then his heart. Scheming all the time. What of the night before? The dream of felicity and faith turned to a nightmare of suspicion. The plaguing doubts became horrid certitudes. . . . Naomi preparing Ruth for the visit—instructing her—"Wait, my daughter, until he has eaten and drunk and his heart is merry, and then . . ." That damnable kinsman was right; he had been blind and deaf. But he would not let himself be taken in. He would go to these women now and charge them openly; they would not dare deny. . . He could have wept for the peace of mind of yesterday that had been changed to this gnawing rancor.

Nor could Boaz have said, even then, whether his spirit was harassed by the knowledge that he had been enslaved by the charms of Ruth, or by the fear that this suspicion of intrigue was taking her from him.

Thus distracted, Boaz suddenly found himself standing at sunset before the rude house that sheltered Ruth and Naomi. He hesitated; the door was open in his hand. The calm of the autumn evening seemed to fall like a balm on his fevered spirit. From within came the voice of Naomi: "Be assured, my daughter," she was saying, "he will not rest until he has settled the matter . . ." Crafty old woman, thought Boaz, it was indeed true; he had not rested. And it seemed to Boaz he had never wanted anything so much as he now wanted rest, and peace from the tormenting business of this day. He entered and Naomi was silent.

She sat by a lamp whose dim light deepened the lines in her face, furrows worn like tracks in an ancient road, as if ridden by recurring sorrows. Boaz, looking down into her patient old eyes, saw there little of craft, but much of wisdom—of the needs of man, and of the perversity of his proud nature. To Ruth, who was bent over the glowing oven, she said, "Boaz is here; come and talk with him"; and went to draw him a cup of wine. He could hear it gurgling from the cask in a dark corner.

About the room hung the pungent, the satisfying aroma of fresh-baked bread; and to his nostrils rose the sharp fragrance of the new-drawn wine Naomi set quietly before him. "Drink, Boaz, and rest," she said; and as he sipped, the plaguing doubts of the day seemed to slip like evil spirits from the heart of Boaz, to lose themselves in the shadows of the quiet room. The devil! he thought, and chided himself. This patient woman, who had been a good mother to her sons and a faithful wife to Elimelech, who had gone bravely with her men to a strange land in their adversity, and suffered there, did she not deserve to find a resting place in her old age? . . . And there before him stood Ruth, silent, expectant, wiping her brown hands on the coarse apron she wore. Ruth with her brave, undaunted eyes, her deep breast, her firm body—sturdy and straight as a cypress. Where was her like in all of Judah? The spell of her eyes, deep, dark and soft as the autumn night, was again upon him. The devil! he wondered; why had he resisted? A mate for a prince! He took her hands; joy and a great peace enfolded him like a cloak; for Boaz had made up his mind.

"She is better to me than seven sons," Naomi murmured; and Boaz answered: "She is worthy to be the mother of kings."

CHAIM NACHMAN BIALIK

The Way of a Man with a Maid

King Solomon had a daughter who was more beautiful than any maiden in the land. He cherished and loved her as he loved life itself; she was the apple of his eye.

In her childhood, she was different from others of her age. As she grew up, she became more shy, disliking the glamour of the palace and avoiding its pleasures. She chose to stroll in the royal garden, for she preferred solitude. Sometimes she would go out into the country in the early morning, and wander aimlessly along its paths. Her heart hummed its own secret; no young man had captured it.

When she was of marriageable age, princes from far and near came to seek her hand. But the king's daughter showed no interest in them; at times she even refused to see them. They went away embarrassed and frustrated. As time passed, the girl became more withdrawn and the eligible princes gradually put her out of their minds.

Solomon became so greatly concerned about his daughter that he decided to consult the stars and learn which prince was destined to be her mate, and when he would appear. One night, the king went up to the roof of the palace, consulted the stars for the heavenly signs, and divined that the bridegroom ordained by the Almighty was not a prince at all, but a poor boy of lowly origin, who would come as predestined and marry his daughter.

This shocked and disturbed him to such an extent that he thought of various schemes to thwart the heavenly decree. Finally, he decided that the surest way to nullify the edict would be to hide the girl on an island until after the appointed time.

King Solomon chose a remote island, so far from human habitation that no ships passed it. Here he built a tower with many rooms and royal chambers, encircled and fortified it with a strong wall, and therein brought his daughter. He assigned seventy eunuchs, elders of Israel, to watch and serve her. He stored up an abundance of provisions in the tower, the finest of food and drink, so that the princess would lack for nothing. The king barred the doors and gates with iron bolts and locks so that no one could enter or leave. And he thought, "Now I will observe God's plan and see whether or not the prophecy of the stars will be fulfilled."

The princess lived in this tower with the seventy eunuchs watching her day and night. They hovered over her anxiously, hastening to please her every whim. No pleasure was denied her, for the king had instructed the elders to keep her from brooding and to encourage her to enjoy herself as much as possible. One thing they could not give her—freedom to leave the tower. It was shut so tightly on all sides, that none could leave and none could enter. Whenever the princess, oppressed by her confinement, would long for some fresh air, she would go up on the roof of the tower, walk around the parapet or lean over it, look out across the endless sea, listen to the breaking waves and find peace.

A sentinel was stationed day and night on the wall of the tower to keep watch in every direction and guard against any vessel that might approach the island. Twice a day, morning and evening, at a distance of a bow's flight from the island, a tiny craft would appear upon the water and silhouette a human form. This was the king's messenger sent to bring a report of the girl's well-being. He would wave a white flag signalling, "Is all well with the girl?"

The sentinel on the wall would wave a white flag in response which meant, "All is well." Then the boat would turn back and disappear over the horizon.

As the time fraught with anxiety for the king drew near, the eunuchs multiplied their vigilance and increased their guard at the gates. They kept their eyes wide open, their ears perked, their nostrils quivering. The buzzing of a fly on the window pane alarmed them; the sound of a weasel burrowing in the wall frightened them; for the men were very loyal to the king and carried out his orders to the letter.

At that time, a poor boy of a good family of scribes, feeling stifled in his father's crowded house, left home to seek his fortune. His only possession was the wanderer's staff, yet he knew neither care nor sorrow, for he was filled with the exhilaration of youth, pride in his manly strength and confidence in the future. He walked with a firm tread, singing all the way. He enjoyed watching the jumping grasshopper, the fluttering bird, the scurrying rabbit, the darting lizard. He was drawn to every growing tree and to every deserted hut in an abandoned vineyard. He lived like a bird on gleanings left in the fields by kind people. His bed was the ground; his pillow a stone. In his wanderings through village and city, his ear was attuned to the talk of passers-by. He stored in his memory every wise saying and parable he heard from the lips of city elders or country folk. He recited them to himself during his lonely hours and found solace.

One day as the sun was beginning to set—it was during the rainy season—the boy found himself in a deserted field. He was barefoot and in tatters, cold and hungry, and lacked the strength to go on. He looked about him for some shelter and noticed a skeleton of an ox decaying in the open field. The lad was overjoyed and thought, "Thank God for providing me with a bed in this desolate place. I'll crawl in and perhaps it will give me protection from the rain." He wriggled inside the skeleton's ribs and fell into a deep sleep.

During the night, a mighty eagle swooped down, lifted the skeleton and its sleeping occupant in its beak, flew to the princess' tower, deposited its burden on the roof, and started to peck at the skeleton's remaining scraps. The boy awoke, jumped out and drove the eagle away. He remained on the roof exhausted and shivering the whole night long. By morning, the skies had cleared and the day was sunny. The princess went up to the roof as was her daily habit and spied the stranger. She stepped back astonished and asked, "Who are you? Who brought you here?"

The boy answered, "Don't be afraid, damsel, and please don't be angry with me. I am a poor Hebrew from Acre. Yesterday, the rain got the best of me in the field. I was hungry and cold and had no covering, so I lay down in the skeleton. An eagle lifted me and brought me here. I have no idea how to get out of this place, for the sea is all around us and there is no sign of a boat."

The princess pitied him and brought him stealthily to her room. She found clothes for him and showed him where to bathe and dress. When she saw how handsome and how charming he was, she was delighted to have him for a companion. She kept secret his presence in the tower so that the eunuchs, who did not enter her room without permission, had no inkling of him. The princess would now appear outside her apartment twice each day, stay long enough to show the elders that she was well, and return to her room. They considered this of no significance and continued their diligent watch. Each one remained at his post with peering eyes, cupped ears and sniffing nostrils. They were trusty servants, indeed, who carried out the king's wishes to the smallest detail.

The princess was delighted with the boy's intelligence and admired his fine character. She fell madly in love with him.

One day she said shyly, "Do you like me well enough to marry me?"

The boy was startled. "What a question to ask me, who could hope for nothing more than to be your humblest slave!"

Then the girl confessed her deep love for him; told him that she preferred him to all the princes of the world; that God had brought him to her on eagle's wings; that the moment she saw him she fell in love with him; that life would be empty without him. She talked on and on in this way. He responded by revealing his love for her. His words of endearment were seventy times seven more loving than hers, now that he felt free to say them. They made a covenant of everlasting love. The boy drew blood from his arm and with it inscribed the words of the covenant in a scroll. He wrote and sealed it, betrothing himself to the princess in accordance with the law, saying, "God brought us together. The archangels Michael and Gabriel are our witnesses."

The eunuchs, honest and loyal servants though they were, knew nothing of these happenings. They were very busy, night and day watching at their posts more diligently than ever.

When the appointed time revealed to Solomon had passed, the king considered it safe to free his daughter and bring her home. He reached the island by boat, examined the doors and gates of the tower, and found the locks and bolts untouched and untampered with. He ordered them sawed off, and the gates opened so that he might enter. The elders trembled as they rushed to greet him.

"Is my daughter well?" the king asked. "Where is she?"

"She is well and happy, our lord and king. She is in her royal chamber."

The king walked to his daughter's room followed by the elders. Lo and behold! When they opened the door, a handsome youth was in the room with the princess! Panic seized the elders. Their hearts almost stopped beating. The king turned to them with anger and shouted, "Who is this?"

Petrified with fright, they could not answer. All they did was stand there, pale as ghosts. Solomon stamped his foot and cried, "Answer! Or I will have you torn limb from limb!"

The elders prostrated themselves and stammering with fright said, "Pray lord and king! We have no words with which to defend ourselves. The lord is our witness that we have watched the princess with every ounce of our strength. We are puzzled as you are, for we have no inkling of how the youth could have come here."

The king turned to his daughter and thundered, "Wanton! What is the boy doing here? Who brought him?"

The girl fell at her father's feet and cried, "Please don't be angry, Father. It was God's doing. He sent an eagle as his messenger to bring me this wonderful lad, and I have become his wife. Please, Father, accept him and give us your blessing."

Addressing the youth, the king asked, "Who are you? How did you come?" The boy stood up before the king and spoke with no trace of fear. He told the whole story, just as it had happened. The king engaged him further in conversation, for the boy had impressed him favorably. He became convinced that the youth was ten times as intelligent and learned as any scribe or scholar in his kingdom. Solomon asked him about his home town and his parents. The boy answered simply and to the point. He told of his poverty and his wanderings, the fantastic tale of how the eagle had brought him to the tower, how the girl had received him kindly, and he showed the marriage scroll that he had written and sealed with his blood.

Solomon listened to this strange and wondrous tale from beginning to end. He realized that this youth was the very one he had seen in the stars.

"Now I know," said the king, "that there is no wisdom or counsel that can stand up against the will of God."

When the eunuchs saw that the king's anger had subsided, they began to breathe more freely. They arose, lifted their hands to the heavens and said, "Blessed is the Lord who ordains wife to man."

Solomon brought his daughter and her husband to Jerusalem, where he rejoiced and feasted with them for seven days. After the celebration, he called the young groom to him and said, "Now you are the son-in-law of a king. I have a very large kingdom. Choose any important post and it is yours."

The bridegroom answered, "My lord the king! My forebears were scholars and scribes. I have learned to be a scribe in my father's house. My folks are poor and have no interest in courtly pleasures. You would make your humble servant most happy if you would grant him a home somewhere off near the sea, where it is quiet and peaceful. I would be content to live there with my wife, engage in the profession of my father, and ponder upon God's ways."

Solomon granted his request and appointed him Chief Scribe to the king. He occupied himself by gathering all that he heard from the king's lips and he wrote them in a scroll. To this, he added parables and bits of his own wisdom that he had acquired through meditation and observation. They are known to this very day as the words of Agur, son of Jakeh. One of the proverbs that he recorded reads:

> There are three things too wonderful
> Nay, four, that I do not comprehend!
> The way of an eagle in flight
> The way of a serpent on a rock
> The way of a ship on the sea,
> The way of a man with a maid.

[TRANSLATED FROM THE HEBREW]

LEO W. SCHWARZ

Of Love and Faith

A LEGEND

I

There once lived in Jerusalem a plantation owner named Kalba Shebua. He was fabulously rich and exercised his power over numerous workers and his own family like a proud tyrant.

He had one daughter whose loveliness was like the sunset over the hills of the city, and whose wisdom made her precious among the daughters of Israel. But, to her father's dismay, she spurned proffered matches with some of the richest tradesmen of Jerusalem and the wealthiest merchants of Babylonia; for she had fallen in love with Akiba ben Joseph, one of her father's shepherds. He was a poor but noble man, the best of the shepherds in the country. One day, after singing and piping melodies to the girl near his beloved flocks, he revealed to her his love in the golden words of Solomon's rival:

> "Ah, you are beautiful, my love;
> Ah, you are beautiful;
> Your eyes are doves.
> Like a rose among thorns,
> So is my beloved among the maidens."

And after she acknowledged her love for him, saying that his fruit was sweet to her taste, she betrothed herself to him on his promise to leave the fields and devote his life to study and teaching. Then, enfolded in his strong arms, she sang to him:

"Set me like a seal upon your heart,
Like a seal upon your arm;
For love is as mighty as death,
As strong as the grave;
Many waters cannot quench love, nor rivers overcome it;
If one were to offer all the substance of his house for love,
it would be utterly contemned."

When Kalba Shebua heard of the betrothal, he became violent and drove her out of his house. The girl lived with Akiba's mother, and because she belonged to a family of high standing, the neighbors would bring her work secretly while she sent part of her earnings to Akiba, who was studying at the Academy. Despite the drudgery of her position and the sarcasm of the townspeople, she was not discouraged. Did she not smile goodheartedly at a cripple who said to her, "Your hair will turn grey before that shepherd will become a scholar."

Akiba, however, was not certain of attaining his goal, for he was about forty years old when he began his career as a student: he did not believe that he would succeed in swimming safely through the rough seas of Jewish Law. But his wife showed him by practical example how people laughed only once or twice, and then respected a person's conviction. Once he was sitting before a fountain in Lud and saw a large stone with a cavity in the center. When he asked who bored the hole and was told that it had been caused by the rope, with which the bucket was lowered, pressing along the stone, he said to himself: "If such a soft material can dissolve stone, why should not the words of the Law, which are as hard as iron, make an impression on my heart, which is flesh?" So he devoted himself heart and soul to the study of the Law.

After twelve years Akiba returned to Jerusalem. He was now a renowned scholar and two thousand pupils and disciples followed in his train. All the people crowded the streets to get a glimpse of Rabbi Akiba. Among those who appeared was Kalba Shebua who was presented to the sage. He asked him what he should do with his daughter whom he had driven away from his home. He had made a vow not to support her, but now she was starving and he wanted the great Rabbi to release him from his vow. Akiba asked him the reason for this vow. He said,

"She betrothed herself to an ignorant shepherd who could not even say the blessing over the meals."

"But if he has since become a scholar?"

"If he only knew the blessings," Kalba Shebua replied, "I would give him half my fortune."

"I am the man," said Akiba.

His father-in-law immediately arose, kissed him and thanked the Lord for His generosity and mercy.

As Akiba drew near to his house, his wife came to meet him, fell at his feet and wanted to kiss the hem of his garment. The pupils, not knowing who the woman was, were about to push her aside when Akiba said,

"Leave her alone, for all that you and I know is due to her, for it is the wisdom of the women that builds up the house."

And he had a large tiara, set with many precious stones, made for his wife. When the children asked why he always gave her such valuable presents, he replied that he could never repay her adequately for her love and devotion.

II

Now Rabbi Akiba lived in the most calamitous times. The land of Israel groaned under the iron yoke of the

Romans who, attributing the heroic resistance which the people had made against them to the spirit of the Jewish religion, attempted to abolish it by forbidding the observance of the festivals and the study of the Law. Akiba, however, continued to instruct the people in their religious duties, and to teach the Law publicly.

One day, while he was teaching his disciples, Papus ben Judah, a man well known for his learning, took him to task for endangering his life by disobeying the Roman decrees.

"Akiba, are you not afraid of the Romans?" he asked. "Are there not times that require us to yield to circumstances?"

"Papus, are you the man whom people address as a sage? Surely, your questions indicate that you are a fool. When the Law says, "Thou shalt love the Lord, thy God, with all thy heart, and with all thy soul,' does it not teach us that, when our religion is threatened, we must not, under any circumstances, yield to expediency? Now listen to this fable.

"A fox once took a walk by the side of a river, and observed the fish hurrying to and fro, in the greatest agitation and alarm. Anxious to know the cause of this confusion, he addressed himself to them as follows.

" 'Friends, may I be so bold as to ask why you are so agitated?'

" 'We are attempting to flee from our enemies, and avoid the many nets and snares which they have prepared for us.'

" 'Oh! oh!' said the cunning fox, 'if that is all, I can tell you of an easy way to secure your safety. Come along with me on dry land, where we may dwell together in peace, in the same manner as our ancestors did before us.'

"The fish, perceiving the treachery of their advisor, said to him.

" 'Fox! fox! So you are considered the most sagacious of animals! Surely, your advice proves you are a fool. If, even in our natural element, we are beset with so many dangers, what security can we expect to find in an element so antagonistic to our nature, and so contrary to our habits?'

"It is even so with us," continued Akiba. "If even by partially observing the Law, which is our very life, we experience so much distress and oppression, what do you imagine our lot would be if we entirely abandoned it?"

Akiba was thrown into prison by the Romans. Not long afterwards, Papus was placed in the same dungeon with him. When Akiba saw him, he asked,

"Well, Papus, what brought you here?"

"Blest are you, Akiba," replied Papus, "for you suffer for the Law. Woe to me, who suffers for vain things."

Akiba finally suffered martyrdom. By the order of the emperor Hadrian, he was publicly flayed alive with blazing iron tongs. Before he breathed his last, he cried aloud,

"All my life I have repeated and fulfilled the commandment, 'Thou shalt love the Lord with all thy heart, and with all thy might.' Now I know what it is to love him with 'all my soul.' "

SHOLOM ALEICHEM

A Page from the Song of Songs

Buzie is a name. It is a diminutive of Esther-Libbe. First Esther-Libbe, then Libuzie, then Buzie. She is a year older than I, or maybe two years, and together we are not quite twenty years old. Now, I ask you, how old am I and how old is she? But that is not important. Instead let me give you a short sketch of her life.

My older brother Benny lived in a village, where he owned a mill. He was a wonder at shooting, riding and swimming. One summer day while bathing in the river, he drowned. Thus the old adage that the best swimmers drown was borne out. He left the mill, two horses, a young widow and a child. The mill was abandoned, the horses were sold, the widow remarried and moved to some distant place, and the child was brought to us.

That child was Buzie.

That my father should love Buzie as his own is easy to understand, and that my mother should watch over her like an only daughter is natural. In her they found a comfort for their great sorrow. But that has nothing to do with me. Then why is it that when I come from *cheder* and find Buzie not at home my food is flat and tasteless? And why is it that when Buzie comes in, the darkest corners are suddenly lit up. And when Buzie laughs at me I weep?

And when Buzie . . .

All through the winter I had been looking forward to the Passover holidays. Then I would be free from *cheder,* free to play with Buzie, free to run outdoors with her. We would run down the hill to the river's edge, when I could show her how the ducklings learn to swim. When I try to tell her about it she only laughs at me. Buzie doesn't believe a thing I tell her. She doesn't believe that I can climb to the top of the highest tree—if I only wanted to. She doesn't believe that I can shoot—if I only had a gun to shoot with. She never says she doesn't believe, she only laughs at me. And I hate nothing more than to be laughed at. But when Passover comes, the beautiful, free days of Passover, when we can run outdoors away from the watchful eyes of my parents, then I will show her such wonders that they will take her breath away.

The wonderful time, the most joyous time of the year, has come.

Buzie and I are dressed in our holiday clothes. Everything we have on twinkles and shines and crackles. I look at Buzie and I am reminded of the *Song of Songs* which I studied before Passover with my rabbi. Verse after verse, it comes back to me:

"Behold, thou art fair, my beloved, thou art fair; thy eyes are as doves, thy hair is a flock of goats that comes down from Mount Gilead.

"Thy teeth are like a flock of white lambs that come up from the river, all are alike; the same mother bore them.

"Thy lips are like a thread of scarlet; thy speech is full of sweetness."

Why is it that when you look at Buzie you are reminded of the *Song of Songs?* Why is it that when you study the *Song of Songs* Buzie comes into your thoughts?

We are ready to go. I can hardly stand still. My pockets are full of nuts. My mother gave us all we wanted. She filled our pockets and told us we could play with them to our hearts' content. But she made us promise not to crack any before Passover.

"Are you ready?" says Buzie.

I jump for the door. Away we go. The nuts make a drumming sound, they rattle as we run. At first we are dazzled by the brilliance outside. The sun is high up already; it is looking down on the other side of town. The air is free and fresh, soft and clear. Here and there on the hill beyond the synagogue there sprouts the first grass of spring—tender, quivering, green . . . With a scream and a flutter of wings a straight line of swallows flies over our heads and again I am reminded of the *Song of Songs*: "The flowers appear on the earth; the time of the song of birds has come and the voice of the turtle is heard in our land."

I feel strangely light. It seems to me that I have wings. Any minute now I will rise into the air and fly.

From the town strange sounds arise—a roaring, a boiling, a seething. It is the day before Passover, a rare and wonderful day. In one instant the world is transformed. Our yard is a king's court. Our house is a palace. I am a prince and Buzie is a princess. The logs of wood piled about our door are the cedars and cypresses that are mentioned in the *Song of Songs*. The cat that lies near the door warming herself in the sun is a roe or a young hart that is mentioned in the *Song of Songs*. The women and the girls who are working outdoors, washing and cleaning and getting ready for Passover are the daughters of Jerusalem mentioned in the *Song of Songs*. Everything, everything is from the *Song of Songs*.

I walk about with my hands in my pockets and the nuts rattle. Buzie follows me step by step. I cannot walk slowly, I am treading on air. I want to fly, to swoop, to soar, like an eagle. I start running and Buzie runs after me. I leap onto the pile of logs and jump from one log to another. Buzie jumps after me. I jump up, she jumps up; I jump down, she jumps down. Who will get tired first? I guessed it.

"How-long-will-you-keep-it-up?" asks Buzie all out of breath.

And I answer her in the words of the *Song of Songs*:

" 'Till the morning breeze come and the shadows flee away.' There! You are tired and I am not!"

I feel proud that Buzie cannot keep up with me. I gloat over her and at the same time I am sorry for her. My heart aches for her, because I imagine she is unhappy. That is Buzie—full of gaiety one moment, and the next she is hiding in a corner, quietly weeping. At times like these nothing helps. No matter how much my mother tries to comfort her, how much my father caresses her, she continues to cry. For whom does she cry? For her father who died when she was a baby? For her mother who married and went off without as much as a goodbye? Ah, that mother of hers. When you mention her mother her face turns fiery red, as though she were ashamed of her. She never says an unkind word about her, but she looks unhappy. I cannot bear to see Buzie looking so wretched. I sit near her on the logs and try to distract her thoughts.

Rolling a few nuts about, I start:

"Guess what I could do if I wanted to."

"What could you do?"

"If I wanted to, all your nuts would be mine."

"No. We wouldn't even start playing."

"Well then, would you take them away from me?"

"No. They would come to me by themselves."

She raises her eyes to me, her blue eyes, eyes straight out of the *Song of Songs*. I say, "You think I am joking, well, I know a certain language, I know some magic words . . ."

She opens her eyes wider. I explain, feeling grown-up and important, all puffed up with pride. "We boys know a lot of things. There is a boy in *cheder*, Shaike, who is blind in one eye—he knows everything. He even knows *Kabala*. Do you know what *Kabala* is?"

"No. How should I know?"

I am suddenly lifted to the seventh heaven because I can give her a lesson in *Kabala*.

"*Kabala*, silly, is a useful thing. By means of *Kabala* I can make myself invisible. With *Kabala* I can draw wine from a stone and gold from a wall. With the help of *Kabala* you and I, just as we are sitting here, could rise to the clouds and above the clouds . . ."

To fly up to the clouds with Buzie and above the clouds, and fly away with her, far, far off over the ocean—that has been one of my fondest dreams. There, beyond the ocean, begins the land of the dwarfs who are descended from King David's time. These dwarfs are kindly little people who live on sweets and almond milk, play all day long on little flutes and dance in a ring, are afraid of nothing and are kind to strangers. When someone arrrives from our world they give him food and drink and shower him with costly garments and gold and silver ornaments, and before he leaves they fill his pockets with diamonds and jewels which lie about in their streets as trash does in ours.

"Really? Like trash in the streets?" asked Buzie, wonderingly, when I once told her about the dwarfs.

"Don't you believe it?"

"Do you?"

"Why shouldn't I?"

"Where did you hear about it?"

"In *cheder*, of course."

"Oh, in *cheder*!"

Lower and lower sinks the sun, painting the sky a fiery gold.

. . . The gold is reflected in Buzie's eyes. They swim in molten gold.

I want very badly to impress Buzie with Shaike's ability and with the wonders I can perform by means of *Kabala.* But Buzie won't be impressed. Instead she laughs at me. She looks at me with her mouth half-open and all her pearly teeth showing, and laughs.

Annoyed, I ask, "Don't you believe me?"

Buzie laughs again.

"You think I am boasting. That I am making up lies."

Buzie laughs harder. I have to repay her for this. I know how, too.

"The trouble with you is that you don't know what *Kabala* is. If you knew, you wouldn't laugh. By means of *Kabala,* if I wanted to, I could bring your mother down here. Yes, I can. And if you begged me very hard I could bring her tonight, riding on a broomstick."

At once she stops laughing. A cloud crosses her lovely, bright face and it seems to me that the sun has suddenly disappeared and the day is done. I have gone too far. I have wounded her tenderest feelings. I am sorry I had ever started this. How can I make up to her now? I move closer to her. She turns away from me. I want to take her hand and speak to her with the words of the *Song of Songs*: "Return, return O Shulamite, turn back to me, Buzie . . ."

Suddenly a voice calls out, "Shimek, Shimek!"

Shimek—that's me. My mother is calling me, to go to the synagogue with my father.

To go with Father to the synagogue on the Eve of Passover is one of the pleasures of life. Just to be dressed in perfectly new clothes from head to foot and to show off before one's friends. And the service—the first evening prayer, the first benediction of the holiday season! What delights the Lord has provided for his Jewish children!

"Shimek! Shimek!"

My mother is in a hurry. "I am coming! I am coming right away, I just have to tell Buzie something, just one little thing!"

I tell her just one thing. That what I told her was not true. To make other people fly by means of *Kabala* is impossible. But I myself—I can fly, and I will show her right after the holidays. I will make my first attempt then. I will rise up here from those very logs where we are now sitting, and in one moment I will be above the clouds. From there I will turn to the right—there, see—there where everything ends and the Frozen Sea begins . . .

Buzie listens, absorbed in my story. The sun, about to sink, sends its last rays to kiss the earth.

"What," asks Buzie, "do you mean by the Frozen Sea?"

"Don't you know what the Frozen Sea is? That's far in the north. The water is as thick as jelly and as salty as brine. Ships cannot go there, and people who are caught in it never return."

Buzie looks at me wide-eyed. "Then why are you going there?"

"Am I going to touch the sea, you silly thing? I'll fly high up over it, like an eagle, and in a few minutes I shall be on dry land. That is where the twelve high mountains begin that belch fire and smoke. I shall stop on the tip of the twelfth mountain and walk from there for seven miles till I come to a small lake. I shall swim across the lake and count seven times seven. Out of the ground will spring a dwarf with a long white beard. He will say to me, 'What is your wish?'

"And I will say to him: 'Lead me to the Queen's daughter!' "

"Which Queen's daughter?" asks Buzie, startled.

"The Queen's daughter," I explain, "is the beautiful princess who was snatched away from under the wedding canopy, bewitched, and carried far, far away and locked up in a crystal palace for seven years . . ."

"What is she to you?"

"What do you mean—what is she to me? I have to set her free, don't I?"

"You have to set her free?"

"Who then?"

"You don't have to fly so far, believe me. You don't have to fly so far," says Buzie, and takes my hand. Her small, white hand is cold. I look into her eyes and see in them the last faint reflection of the gold that is draining from the sky.

Slowly the day is going, the first beautiful day of spring is passing away. Like a spent candle the sun goes down. The noises that we heard all day are dying too. There is hardly a person to be seen in the street. From the windows of the houses there wink the flames of candles lit for Passover Eve. A strange, a holy stillness surrounds us, and Buzie and I feel ourselves slowly merging with this stillness.

"Shimek! Shimek!"

This is the third time my mother has called me. As if I didn't know myself that I had to go to the synagogue! I'll stay only another minute, not more than a minute. But Buzie hears her too, pulls her hand out of mine, jumps to her feet and begins to push me.

"Shimek, your mother is calling you. You'd better go. It's late. Go."

I am getting ready to go. The day is done, the sun has been snuffed out. All the gold has turned to blood. A cool breeze has sprung up. Buzie keeps pushing me toward the house. I throw a last quick look at her. Her face has changed and it has a different, an unearthly beauty in the twilight. The thought of the bewitched princess flits through my head. But Buzie won't allow those thoughts. She keeps pushing me ahead. I start slowly to go and I look back just once at the bewitched princess who has now completely merged with the weird Passover twilight, and I stand rooted in one spot. But she waves her hand at me, bidding me to go, to go quickly. And it seems to me that I hear her speaking in the words of the *Song of Songs*:

"Make haste, my beloved, be thou like a gazelle or a young hart upon the mountain of spices."

[TRANSLATED FROM THE YIDDISH BY JULIUS AND FRANCES BUTWIN]

MIRIAM SHOMER ZUNSER

The Wedding

Early in the month of March, in the year 1866, at a wayside inn in the hamlet of Ploskin, my mother, Dinneh Bercinsky, and my father, Nochim-Mayer Shaikevitsch, were married.

At three in the afternoon the *kalleh* was dressed in her veil and wedding gown of black moire silk with its long train. She sat and watched her girl friends making merry about her. She herself was a little faint, because, following the traditional custom, *chossen* and *kalleh* had to fast on the day of their wedding. But the fiddlers, drummers, and clarinetists struck up a merry tune, and away went her gaily-dressed girl friends in a merry dance. My mother says that they danced the quadrille and the lancers, which were the fashionable dances of the day. But that was before they really warmed up, before they broke into the honest, traditional Jewish dances. Then they plunged into the *Brayges Tanz,* the *Patch Tanz* and many other Jewish folk dances. Just now the girls were gleefully putting on a dance of mock distress, illustrated by necessary gestures of despair. They sang:

Vosshe vell ich ton	What will I do
Vosshe vell ich ton	What will I do
As der Baal Choiv	When the creditor
Vet kummen monen?	Comes for his money?
Az der Baal Choiv	When the creditor
Vet kommen monen?	Comes for his money?
Vell ich hoben	If I have it,

Vell ich geben,	I will give it,
Vell ich nit hoben	If I haven't,
Vell ich nit geben.	I won't give it,
Ain vort ich hob nit!	In a word—I haven't
Ain vort ich hob nit!	In a word—I haven't.

But right here the *marshaloch,* the wedding-bard, appeared ready to remind the *kalleh* in rhyme of the importance of the step she was taking. He placed her in the middle of the room, while all the women, gathered around her with their handkerchiefs in hand, ready for the eventual weeping that would follow. The wedding bard then began to harangue the poor bride as only a man paid for the service could. He portrayed to her her youth, her happy life with her father and mother; he warned her that these days of happiness were now at an end, and he tormented her with horrible speculations on what might be in store for her. He wailed over her as one bewails the dead, except that it was done in rhyme. The women and girls, hearing his cries and the heartrending fate that might befall the fair young bride, broke out into loud weeping. Fortunately, Dinneh was a strong girl and did not faint, as many another young bride would and did. She was dissolved in a flood of tears, however.

But now, in through the door, to the merry tune of the *klezmer* (a band of lowly musicians), came the wedding procession led by Nochim-Mayer escorted by his father, mother, grandmother and friends. A hail of rice, sugar and oats fell upon the young man, thrown by the gathered throng. Rice and oats for fertility, sugar for the sweetness of life. The gay, yet solemn, procession advanced to the *kalleh's* chair, all except Nochim-Mayer, carrying lit candles woven of many colored strands. Dinneh was now surrounded by her kinsfolk, these too bearing flaming candles. The *chossen* and his party arrived and halted in front of her chair.

Nochim-Mayer looked at the radiant girl to whom he had written his fervent letters, and dropped the veil over her face.

To the accompaniment of gay music he and his party then made their way to the open field where the marriage ceremony would take place, and where now the *chuppe*—the wedding canopy—was held high by four men, each supporting one of its poles. There Nochim-Mayer was stationed to await the *kalleh* and her train.

Up across the field they came, Dinneh in the forefront escorted by her father and mother. The music played. Eagerly the throng pressed forward, the lighted tapers held aloft. At last the *kalleh* too was under the *chuppe*. Slowly she circled about Nochim-Mayer, seven times.

Now it was the officiating rabbi's turn to perform his duty. He greeted and blessed *chossen* and *kalleh* and their kin eloquently. Then he said a prayer in memory of the dear departed whose presence was missed at the union of these two. Naturally everybody wept at the mention of the beloved dead. The rabbi then placed a little glass under the *chossen's* heel for him to smash. There are two popular interpretations of this ceremony: one, to remind the celebrants of the destruction of Jerusalem; two, to prove that the bridegroom is a virile man. The wine was then sipped from a common cup by bride and groom, the ring was placed on Dinneh's finger and the two were pronounced man and wife according to the "law of Moses and Israel."

From the time it began until this juncture, in its procedure, the marriage ceremony had been a solemn affair for principals and wedding guests alike. But now, upon the pronouncement of the union, a new, joyous note was sounded, and people cried, *"Mazel-tov! Mazel-tov!"* "Good luck! Good luck! Then there was a burst of music, while the bride was kissed by the women, the bridegroom by the men. Then the women kissed each other and the men did likewise and everybody started to dance.

A word about this dancing at a Jewish wedding: there is nothing at all that I can compare with it to convey its spirit. You dance not because you know how, but because the spirit moves you. Outside of the prohibition of men dancing with women there are no restrictions or prearranged or practised steps or forms. Women may dance with women and men with men if they so choose, but that, too, is not necessary. There is no order about the dance. Each person, as the impulse moves him, gets up and dances. Old and young, great and small, dance separately, or opposite each other. When the fiddles strike up a merry strain, and the cornet blows, when the drums boom and the tambourines jingle, then all stamp their feet, clap their hands. lift their skirts and make steps—any kind of steps! If you are a man, you lift your coat tails and hop around. If you are a woman, you grab a neighbor, whirl about with her, or go backward and forward in front of her, improvising as you dance. A group of people will form a ring and dance in a circle, each one creating his own steps, just so long as he keeps time with the music. If you are somebody of any importance at the wedding, the dancing ring will probably form around you. Dancing at a Jewish wedding, (not a modern American one, of course) means a bodily expression of joy. And, indeed, if one cannot or will not for some reason move one's body or feet, one can of a certainty carry on with one's hands. Waving arms and snapping fingers were very acceptable substitutes for dancing.

So much for general dancing. There were also special dances, such as the *Kosher Tanz, Mitzvah Tanz, Heidim-Deidim* and the *Brayges Tanz* and *Patch Tanz* which I have already mentioned. Even for these one needed no special instruction. All you needed was to get the idea of what the dance was about, and then you would surely be all right.

In a *Brayges Tanz*—a "Sulky Dance"—two women pretend that they have had a quarrel, that one is sulky in consequence and that the other is very eager to make up with her. The offended one dances about keeping her face averted from her anxious friend. In vain the suppliant does everything possible to get the sulky girl's attention and to look into her eyes. In pantomime she offers the offended one gifts: her earrings, her ring, her bracelet or any other treasured thing she happens to have. At each refusal the suppliant wrings her hands and makes gestures of despair. Finally, the offended girl relents; the two then throw their arms about each other, the music screams with joy, and the women dance happily together.

The *Patch Tanz* is a "Clap Dance" in which no dignified person indulges. The crowd dances in a jolly ring, stopping at intervals to clap their hands and stamp their feet in a given measure. The ring is then resumed to be broken up again and again by the stamping and clapping.

A *Heidim Deidim* is danced by men. It consists simply of two men whirling about after entwining their right arms so that each man's hand rests on the other man's shoulder. Many such couples, with their arms so entwined, dance about the room, lifting their legs as high as possible, while the music plays traditional melodies and everybody, including the dancers, sings *Heidim Deidim*—which means nothing in particular. The dancers then change to their left arms and spin about again, their heads thrown back, their free hands up in the air, their fingers snapping in ecstasy. In variation the free hand holds aloft the flying skirt of the *caftan* or gabardine.

A *Kosher Tanz* is a wedding dance for two, generally confined to the principals of the occasion and those very close to them. It is, I believe, the only dance in which a man and woman were allowed to dance together. Thus, the bride's mother will dance a *Kosher Tanz* with the bridegroom's father, or the bride's father with the bridegroom's mother. Grandmothers and grandfathers, too, may have the honor of this dance, and the bride may be the partner of any one of the mentioned dignitaries. On rare occasions the rabbi himself will participate in its dignified steps. Since the *Kosher Tanz* is a dance of honor, all other dancing ceases when this one is in progress. The assembled guests gather about the dancing pair. The man and woman step out gravely into the middle of the room; since holding hands by men and women is strictly avoided, each takes hold of one corner of a large handkerchief and the two move slowly around in a circle, keeping step with the music.

A *Mitzvah Tanz,* a dance of "Good Deed," is one in which the bride dances with all the guests and even with beggars who have come to attend the wedding. It is also the dance performed by one woman, who trots backward before the bride and groom as they emerge from under the *chuppe.*

But, to return to Dinneh's and Nochim-Mayer's wedding out in the field in the hamlet of Ploskin. . .

After the spontaneous outbursts of merriment, the crowd made its way to the main house of the inn where the wedding feast was waiting. Across the field the dancing procession moved, headed by Nochim-Mayer and Dinneh, who were now man and wife.

All went well until they reached the door of the inn. There a sudden commotion arose. Hodes was defending her Nochim-Mayer's right to be the first to enter the house by trying to push him through the door. But Dinneh's friends were claiming the right for her by urging her forward at the same time. It was generally believed that whichever one of a newly married couple was the first to cross the threshold would have priority and be dominant in the life they were to begin together. The pushing argument at the door was therefore real and earnest; but it did not last very long, for the young husband gallantly stepped aside and allowed his wife to be the first to step over the threshold.

The wedding feast was a sumptuous one, both for wedding guests and beggars. The latter, numbering several score, were fed plentifully at tables set out for them in the open field.

But no matter how gay the atmosphere, how bright and brilliant the gathering, how grand the banquet, the young couple were uneasy. They well knew that following the feast they would have to go through a most embarrassing ceremony: that of being escorted to their nuptial bed, as indeed they were. Whispered advice was given to the bridegroom by Berel, Reb Michel's brother, while Dinneh received instructions from Sprintze, the respected old woman who had charge of the wedding. The two young people were horribly uncomfortable and utterly helpless; but they had to submit to the traditional custom and make the best of it.

I have noted before the fact that Dinneh's dislike for Hodes was engendered at the time of the betrothal when the older woman showed her impatience at Nochim-Mayer's request to see his bride-to-be. That dislike was deepened when Hodes disputed Dinneh's right to cross the threshold, but it grew into positive hatred when Hodes, during the week which followed the marriage, would not permit the bride to sit in daylight at her husband's side, warning her that the years of her life would be cut short if she did so.

At the end of the long wedding festivities Nochim-Mayer bade goodby to his parents, to his Bobbe Sorke and to all the good people of Nesvish who came to attend his wedding. He was leaving them to go to Pinsk to live at the house of his father-in-law, Reb Michel Bercinsky, where he was to have three years *kest*. But before he left the wayside inn and its memories, he went out at the dawn of day into the field, and there, upon a lonely tree, carved the name of his bride entwined in that of his own. He was indeed a romantic young man!

SOLOMON REICHENSTEIN

The Wedding on the Hill

Tuvya walked to the opening in the tent and lifted the curtain. But, instead of leaving, he half turned towards his friends, cast his eyes down, and stammered.

"The point is . . . well . . . you know, I came to talk to you. That is . . . you must have heard . . . I want a favor of you . . . In a week, the threshing will be done . . . I want you to ride into town with me . . . well?" He was blushing.

"To town?" Raphael and Naomi asked in surprise.

"You see . . . it is pertaining to the same matter . . . Rachel insists. She wants us to go to a rabbi . . . Rachel won't have it any other way."

"Really? No one but a rabbi will do?" Naomi was shocked.

Raphael looked away. He felt uncomfortable at his friend's embarrassment. Big, proud Tuvya, he thought: without his sanction nothing happens on the Hill. Now he is trembling like a poor child . . . So that's why he came over.

"Don't worry!" Naomi tried to comfort Tuvya, "I'll have a talk with her."

"No! Don't bother. It'll be of no use. I've already tried everything. She is adamant on this point; won't have it any other way," Tuvya mumbled.

"So we'll go," Naomi agreed all too readily.

"We would be pleased if you would join us at the ceremony. Rachel would like it, too. And I would appreciate it." With these words, Tuvya bent down and went out into the night.

The four of them wended their way through the streets and alleys of the peaceful little town, arousing the curiosity of the idle shopkeepers. Rachel was wearing the holiday dress that she had brought with her from her parents' home, and Tuvya, at her insistence, had put on the best clothes he could find in the common storeroom at the *kevutzah.*

The small wedding party found its plodding through the town very tiresome. Tuvya, accustomed to the fields that stretched out as far as the eye could see, was glum. He felt as if he didn't belong among the stifling walls. "We'll get it done and over with," he thought.

They entered a narrow alley and met a pale-faced boy with stringy earlocks dangling down his sallow cheeks.

"Where does the rabbi live?" Naomi asked.

The boy, startled, lowered his eyes, turned around and ran away.

"Ha, ha! We scared him! We apparently don't look like normal people," Naomi laughed.

A window in an upper story opened; a woman stuck her unkempt head out, and asked in Yiddish, "What do you want?"

"Where does the rabbi live?" Naomi asked in Hebrew.

"Talk Yiddish! I don't understand you," the woman quacked, testily.

"A rabbi," Raphael came to the rescue in Yiddish. "Where does he live?"

"There!" And a finger pointed to a house opposite.

They knocked on the door. An old man with a long beard and innocent blue eyes greeted them.

"Does the rabbi live here?" Raphael asked.

"Yes! Oh, yes! Please come in, children." He spoke in fluent Hebrew.

When he learned the reason for their coming, his eyes twinkled, brimming over with love.

"Sit down, children . . . here, sit! Where are you from?"

The venerable rabbi was obviously well-informed about the Hill that was established in the wilderness. He showed great interest in their lives, asked all sorts of questions, and wanted to know if they were harassed by the Arabs.

"Neche, come in," he called toward the drapes that separated the room they were in from the one adjoining.

The rabbi's wife, an old woman with a wrinkled, yellow face, hobbled in on a cane.

The rabbi told her who they were and why they had come. "I always said," and his big blue eyes sparkled with kindness, "there is no measuring the depth of the Jewish soul. These dear children, scorched by the sun and exposed to barbaric attacks by Arabs, have come to the rabbi. I knew it! I always knew that they'd come." His enthusiasm grew as he talked and his face shone.

"They are precious children, flesh of our flesh . . . There is no limit to the magnitude of the Jewish spirit. What did I tell you, Neche?"

The old woman patted Rachel and Naomi on their arms, cheeks and throats, with a trembling, withered hand. "Precious children," she repeated, in a voice cracked with age.

Tuvya wanted the wedding ceremony to take place at once. They had to return to the Hill that very day.

"Immediately!" said the rabbi. "I'll call a *minyan*. The neighbors will be happy to come. Did you bring wine . . . some refreshments?"

"Devil take it!" muttered Tuvya. "I completely forgot about that," he thought. "The work in the fields and all the other responsibilities made me forget many things. The struggle to conquer the Hill has shut out memories of my childhood. One would think that I didn't come from a home steeped in Jewish tradition. And now, this new development . . . this new experience in my life . . ."

"Go out and buy some wine and cakes," Rachel prompted. Tuvya quickly complied.

The old woman kept on caressing the bride. She had so much to say to her, so much advice to give her! As Rachel listened to the quaking voice, she saw in her mind's eye her father's house. There was a quivering in her heart and a tightening in her throat.

The heat in the alley where Tuvya bought the wine and cake was suffocating. He felt very uncomfortable in his pressed clothing—hadn't dressed like that since he had come to Israel. The clothes stuck to him, causing beads of perspiration to roll down his body. The bottles of wine in his pocket knocked against each other with a hard thin ring that awakened a strange anxiety in him. How did he happen to come here, among the stifling houses, where the trapped rays of the blistering sun scorched his eyes and blurred his vision? Who were those people who were revolving before him? Wasn't that his mother with the melancholy eyes? And the man at her side, with the black beard and the somber expression, wasn't that his father? That look of impatience . . . those accusing eyes . . . what were they doing there in the fields, in the oppressive heat? Why did Father hurry so, pulling poor mother along the rough ground? Where were they rushing?

Tuvya rubbed his eyes in a desire to erase the vision. He walked faster, while the clanking of the bottles in his pocket beat against his temples. "I'll hurry and get it over with," he thought.

"Speak up, son," the venerable rabbi encouraged the groom. "Say in a loud voice, 'Behold thou art consecrated unto me, in accordance with the law of Moses and Israel!' "

Tuvya repeated after him, word for word. He tried to keep calm with the thought, "The quicker it's over with, the better."

And what about Rachel, the one in charge of the main tent on the Hill? Rachel, who could stand up to anyone? Her eyes filled with tears that gushed down her cheeks in two streams. Her face contorted in her effort to control her weeping; her shoulders and with them, her whole body shook. Naomi's beautiful eyes tried to comfort her.

And Raphael—he just stood and stared at the window frame of a house across the street. "The frame of that window is set in crooked," he kept on repeating to himself.

In the late afternoon, when they returned to the Hill, all their comrades were out in a crowd to greet them. Chayim had surmised the reason for their going into town and had spread the good news. The pranksters were out in full force, with Yeheskail in the lead. He jumped and hopped before Rachel and Tuvya, grimaced and screamed at the top of his lungs, "Bride and groom, good luck! The drummers beat on their tin cans and everyone joined, shouting, *"Mazel Tov,* bride and groom!"

A complete wedding celebration was enacted on the Hill. Rachel's protestations that the wedding had already taken place in town were disregarded. Yeheskail called himself "rabbi" and "decreed" that only he was permitted to perform marriages on the Hill.

"Idiots!" he exclaimed. "They had to go to town! We'll show them how to arrange a wedding and how to give the bride and groom a good time."

The main tent was decorated and the long tables were set with holiday fare. Yeheskail acted as toastmaster and read a long series of rhymed jests, in a whining, weepy voice. Chayim had prepared congratulatory and humorous telegrams. His reading was greeted with much laughter and applause. The noisy celebration continued for hours.

"Now we'll go out," Yeheskail announced.

They put a white sheet on four guns to serve as a canopy, pushed Tuvya and Rachel under it, and forced Tuvya to say, "Behold, thou art consecrated unto me . . ." all over again, and at the conclusion, the rifle shots pierced the silence of the hot, summer night.

To the accompaniment of tin drums and raucous singing, the couple were escorted to their tent that had been thoughtfully decorated for them.

Rachel glowed with happiness. The singing and shouting of the girls and the fellows had driven away her every sad thought and pensive mood.

Tuvya was at her side, his eyes laughing, embarrassed. But the eternal flame shone in them and threw off sparks. Here, on the Hill, he was at home.

[TRANSLATED FROM THE HEBREW]

4

Home and the Woman

Moses gave the Torah first to the women. For it is said, "Thus shalt thou say to the House of Jacob and tell the Children of Israel" (Exod. 19, 2.) "House of Jacob" refers to the women, for they make the home. They are the greatest influence in the education and upbringing of their children. They encourage them to study the Torah and train them from childhood to go in the ways of the Torah.

Cradle Song

Under the cradle of my small son,
Stands a kid, a wee, white one.
Soon to market will he hie,
Raisins and almonds will he buy.
What are the best goods to be had?
The study of Torah for my lad.
Torah study for my son
And to be a rabbi when he's grown.

[TRANSLATED FROM THE YIDDISH]

A FOLK TALE

Elijah and the Three Sons

Once there lived a pious man who had three sons. When he grew old and knew that he was about to die, he called his sons to his bedside and said, "I have always taught you to fear God and to follow His commandments. Promise me that you will never quarrel among yourselves, as quarreling leads to sin.

"I have very little to leave you—just this house and the spice garden which I have planted and cultivated. Continue to care for the garden and live together in peace."

Tearfully, the sons listened to their father and gave him their word that they would carry out his wishes.

One night, after their father had died, the oldest son came to the garden to watch it. Suddenly, Elijah, the prophet, appeared before him and said, "Do not be alarmed by my presence. Because you have been a dutiful son and are obeying your father's wishes, I shall give you a choice of three gifts. The first gift is wealth, the second is scholarship, the third is a beautiful maiden."

"I choose the first," said the oldest, "I want to be rich."

Elijah placed a coin in his hand. The son glanced down to see what the prophet had given him, and when he looked up, Elijah was gone.

The following night, the second son went into the garden. Elijah came to him as he had to his brother, and repeated the offer of the three gifts.

"If I have a choice, I want to be a scholar," said the second son.

The prophet gave him a book and disappeared.

On the third night, the youngest son spent the hours in the garden, and Elijah came and gave him a choice of a gift.

"I want a beautiful and good wife," said the youngest.

"Come with me," the prophet told him, "and your wish will be fulfilled."

It was morning when Elijah and the youngest son started on their journey. They walked past fields and farmhouses until the sun began to set and they stopped at an inn. The young fellow was tired and fell asleep immediately, but Elijah, who understood the languages of all God's creatures, lay awake listening to the clucking of the hens and the cackling of the geese.

"He looks like a fine fellow," said the hens, "but you can't tell by appearances."

"Of course not," said the geese. "He must be an awful sinner if he is destined to marry the innkeeper's daughter, for her father is dishonest and her mother is a shrew."

"They are worthless people," the hens agreed, "and their daughter is haughty and vain."

Before sun-up, Elijah awakened the lad with, "We must leave at once," and hurried him out of the inn.

They stopped again, in the evening of the second day, to spend the night at an inn. Here, too, Elijah heard the chickens and the geese gossiping about their masters.

"What lawless people!"

"And their daughter is following in their footsteps."

Early in the morning, Elijah awakened the lad and off they went. They trudged along until nightfall, when they came to an inn. Here the chickens and the geese said, "What a handsome lad! If he is as honest as he is comely, it would be right for him to marry the innkeeper's daughter. Her parents are pious and she is as good as she is beautiful."

In the morning, Elijah said to the lad, "We will remain here for a few days. I have to attend to some business," and he went to speak to the innkeeper who was gathering firewood out-of-doors.

The young fellow looked out of the window and noticed a beautiful girl, the innkeeper's daughter, feeding the geese and the chickens and speaking softly to them.

"Eat, my pretty ones; I know you are hungry."

She came indoors and dusted and tidied the house. She smiled often and when she did, her face lit up and it was as if the sun had entered the inn. The boy fell in love with her and decided to tell Elijah. At that very moment, the prophet was talking to the innkeeper about arranging a marriage between the boy and the girl.

"The lad is of fine character, and his parents were pious people," Elijah assured him.

The innkeeper was very well pleased, but wished to get his daughter's approval before he gave his consent. The girl had already seen the lad, had fallen in love with him, and a wedding was arranged. Elijah performed the ceremony and disappeared immediately thereafter.

The young couple bade goodbye to the girl's parents, and left for the groom's home. Barely had they entered the house, when the brothers upbraided him.

"What right did you have to leave us with the care of the garden? You promised to watch it as well as we did, but as soon as Father died, you ran away, in quest of your own pleasure."

The youngest son was silent, as he did not wish to tell them anything that had happened between him and Elijah. His silence only made his brothers more angry, but the bride spoke up.

"Dear brothers, do not quarrel on my account. I was destined to marry your brother, and that is why he was away from home. We will make up for it, I promise. I will help my husband take care of the garden, so that you shall have much time to do with as you please."

The brothers sulked, but there were no more angry words.

Some days later, the oldest brother, who had become rich, said, "I can't bear to live in a hovel. I have built a house for myself and am leaving."

A few days later, the second brother, who had become a scholar, announced, "I don't want to live with ignorant people," and he also moved out.

The young couple continued to live in the house and were very happy. Together, they cultivated the garden and it became the best of its kind. People heard about it, came from far and near to buy the spices, so that the couple was able to earn enough for their simple needs.

Years passed and Elijah decided to visit the brothers and find out how they had fared. He disguised himself as a beggar and came to the home of the eldest. On the gate was a large sign, "No Beggars Allowed." Dogs were barking furiously; a servant appeared.

"I must see your master," said Elijah.

"Go away!"

"Tell your master that he has something of mine and I came to claim it."

The rich man, on hearing the loud talk, came out and said, "Leave, or I will call the police."

"You are not worthy of the coin I gave you. You have become hard-hearted and greedy."

The man now recognized the prophet. He cried and pleaded with Elijah, promising to reform, but it was of no avail. He was obliged to return the coin.

Elijah disguised himself again, this time as a scholar, and came to the home of the middle brother. In answer to the prophet's knock, the man stuck his head out of the window and in an angry voice asked, "What do you want?"

"I would like to study with you."

"I don't waste my time on riffraff!"

Elijah saw how arrogant the man had become. He knew that he had no pupils, not desiring to impart his knowledge to others, and that he himself, had ceased his studies. A true scholar is humble, for the more deeply he probes into the wisdom of the world, the more zealously must he search for answers to new questions that constantly arise.

"You have come to the wrong place," continued the middle brother.

"No, not to the wrong place, but I have given a gift to the wrong man."

"What? Who—who are you?"

"The learning that you have acquired has come to you from the book and not because of your own worthiness," said the prophet, and he took away the book.

Elijah, disguised as a poor man, appeared at the home of the youngest brother. The brother was out, but his wife came to the door. Two little children were peeping out from behind her skirts. She invited the beggar in, asked him if he were hungry, and set food before him. After he had finished eating, she said, "Rest awhile, if you wish."

"I would like to meet your husband."

"He is working in the garden, but I expect him home soon."

When her husband arrived, Elijah revealed himself.

"Because of your wife's good deeds," said he, "I give you the coin, for I know that you will share your wealth with the poor, and I give you the book, for the scholarship that will shine in this house will also shed its light on others who seek knowledge and truth."

[ADAPTED]

MILTON STEINBERG

Beruriah and Her Sons

From the Talmud comes a moving tale of Beruriah, renowned wife of Rabbi Meir (2nd Century C.E.), retold here by the great spiritual leader, Rabbi Milton Steinberg. Beruriah lived in the troubled times after the Bar Kochba rebellion against Rome. The spirit of the Jews was low. They suffered inhuman persecution from the Roman emperor, Hadrian. Then a dreadful plague struck.

The last echoes of the unresolved conflict in authority between the Sanhedrin and the Roman Government were just fading into inaudibility when a new, graver danger arose to threaten the Jews of Palestine. The plague visited the land. Hearing the report of it, people paled and trembled, each for himself and his own. And when it became apparent that the dread malady was not to be confined to the seaports where it had first appeared, men turned indifferent to their habitual pursuits and ambitions. Bound together in a fellowship of fear, they spoke only of the terror that froze their blood, exchanging with morbid fascination reports of the stricken and rumors of eerie deaths or miraculous cures.

All that Spring no one drew a free breath, so weighted with anxiety was each heart. Then with the coming of summer the incubus lifted slightly. For, though scarcely a town was spared, the disease was obviously not becoming epidemic. Cautiously old interests began to reassert themselves. Life slipped toward normality, without however attaining it altogether. For death still lingered. And as long as it tarried, no one could feel himself secure.

On a blazing Sabbath afternoon during this season of calamity, Elisha and Meir sat side by side in one of the synagogues of Usha. The auditorium baked like the interior of an oven. All that week the sun had glared with a fury, extraordinary even for a Palestinian summer at its height. Outside now not a breath of wind stirred, not a wisp of cloud flecked the dimming sky. But the two men did not feel the heat nor were they attending to the speech of a preacher who droned interminably from the pulpit. They were thinking with unbearable apprehension of Meir's two sons who even then tossed and moaned in their little bedchamber. For the fire within them burned ever higher, parching their skin and glazing their eyes. Physicians, bloodlettings and potions had proved unavailing, and Beruriah, ministering to her children with a hypnotic calm, revealed her desperation only in the pallor of her face and the tonelessness of her speech.

From a corner of the room the sobs of some bereaved woman broke forth, shrill and uncontrolled. Meir shuddered at the sound, and Elisha reached out and pressed his hand. But his gesture of confidence was only a pretense. Too vividly did he remember the deaths of a young disciple, of a burly laborer on the estate, of an old sage, of a Syrian peddler who dropped in his tracks on the highway before the villa.

"God is just and merciful," he murmured, reassuring himself as well as Meir.

The droning of the preacher came to an end. One of the elders of Usha descended the three steps to a depression before the Ark, so constructed that he who prayed for the congregation might literally fulfill the words, "Out of the depths have I called upon Thee, O Lord." In a prescribed chant of great antiquity he called forth the invitation to prayer.

When the brief service was over, the congregants greeted one another hastily and exchanged wishes for a happy week. Then they dispersed, each man to his own home, his own weekday tasks and concerns, or, if so unfortunate, to the sickbed of a kinsman. As Elisha and Meir stepped into the cpen street, the air, still hot with day, rose from the cobblestones to smite them with an angry hand. A white moon illumined the world with an unreal light.

Meir walked so rapidly that Elisha was barely able to keep abreast of him. He led his teacher into the courtyard of his home and climbed the steps with precipitate haste. The room, when they entered, was silent and dark save for such fragments of the universal whiteness of the moon as poured through its windows.

Beruriah rose from the shadows to greet them. "A happy week to you, my master and husband, and to you, my master and teacher." Her face was a shimmering white mask, its expression inscrutable.

"A happy week," the two men responded.

Then Meir burst forth, "How are the children?"

"Better," Beruriah replied and turned to a cupboard to fetch a lamp, a spice box and a cup of wine.

"It is still the Sabbath here," she said monotonously. "When we have discharged our duty to God we shall talk of our own affairs."

Reassured by her calm, Meir kindled the first light of the new week, pronounced a blessing over the wine cup of division between days, sacred and profane, shook the spice box so that Sabbath angels might depart in a cloud of fragance, and uttered the words whereby the week which was about to begin was marked apart from the Sabbath.

The echoes of Meir's last words of prayer had not yet died away when Beruriah began spinning out a parable.

"A man came to see me some years ago," she said in a voice quiet and half-hypnotic. "He left in my care for safekeeping two precious stones. Today, just before you returned, he appeared again. I am loath to part with them. Tell me, must I give them back to him?"

"Of course," Meir responded guardedly. "They never really were your property, no matter how long you have held them. But why is it so still here? Are the children asleep? Why do you talk of such strange matters?" His voice faded to a whisper, word by word. "Why do you say nothing about the boys?"

Without waiting for answer, Meir turned toward the children's chamber, moved as if to enter and then stopped, struck with sudden comprehension. Like one in a trance, he came back until his face was close to Beruriah's. He stood staring into her eyes, waiting for the interpretation of the parable he dreaded to hear.

Beruriah raised both hands to her quivering lips.

"The jewels," she said, through her fingers, "are in that room."

In the feeble light of the lone flame the face of Meir was transfixed. He pushed abruptly into the children's chamber. For a moment there was only silence behind the swaying curtains. Then through it there cut the horrible rasp of rending cloth. Elisha covered his face. He knew that sound. It was the tearing of a garment in the presence of death.

He did not see Meir when he came out of the room. But he heard with intolerable clarity his stumbling steps and uneven breath. When he opened his eyes again Meir was sinking onto a chair before the table. "The Lord hath given," he droned, "the Lord hath taken away. Blessed be the righteous Judge." He bowed his head upon his forearms and wept.

As though the words of ultimate resignation were a command, Beruriah's hands went to her dress, her fingers tugging at it. The cloth tore under her insistent pulling. With the stiff gait of a sleepwalker, she moved silently into the room where life had been born to her and where, together with her heart, it had died.

And Elisha, to whom these children had become as his own might have been, dug his fists into his chest to keep his tortured heart from breaking.

In the shadows of Meir's home the stillness was broken only by the sobbing of a grown man. A hot wind blew through the open door and extinguished the solitary lamp. For a moment all was darkness. Then the unperturbed moon sent in its spectral light and the room was peopled with creeping shadows.

MOSHE PRAGER

The Secret of the Pudding

A Tale of the Warsaw Ghetto

Queen Sabbath has been companion to the Jewish People from their early history. Under its protective wings, the downtrodden Jew becomes transformed into a king, joyous and arrayed in splendor. The Nazis methodically tried to destroy the Holy Sabbath, the very soul of the Jew. But the harassed, oppressed people steadfastly clung to their faith and kept the Seventh Day sacred. They did not neglect it nor did they desert it. They took it along with them into the cellars; they burrowed into the bunkers with it; they watched over its light and did not allow it to become extinguished.

A voice from one of the hidden, gloomy rooms of the crowded ghetto was heard, half pleading, half chanting, "Children, the Holy Sabbath is coming. Don't forget it, in God's name." That was Mother, weighed down with sorrow and compassion.

It was Monday, the day on which one's existence during the entire week depended. It was the day that the tyrants, the oppressors of the ghetto had chosen for handing out the week's ration of bread. Their inhuman plan was simple—the Jews who labored like beasts of burden would presumably consume the bread allotted to them in the beginning of the week, and they wouldn't have anything left for the Sabbath. "Here, take it, hungry Jews," they inplied, divide your bread for the entire week. Toil each day and eat your miserable bread. Count your morsels . . . count your crumbs . . . and if you cannot overcome your hunger and you consume more than your fixed amount for the day, the privilege of dying of starvation is yours."

The older folk were able to withstand temptation and divide their allotment into portions for each day. But the children, who were weak from hunger, clung to their mother and pleaded, "We can't do it! You divide the bread, please."

The mother, the most unfortunate of all the ghetto's miserable creatures, took this heavy burden upon herself and divided the bread of her children for the entire week. How difficult was her task! She cut the bread into as many slivers as possible, weighed the morsels in her hand, and all this time kept the thought in mind that she must leave something for the Sabbath. As she cut it, she spoke to them.

"Remember, children, the days pass quickly and the Sabbath will soon be here. It is almost knocking at our door. Remember, in God's name!"

Poor Mother! How that responsibility weighed upon her! But a more difficult task was that of watching the bread and making sure that it lasted the whole week through.

"Listen, children! I'll take special care of the pieces we set aside for the Sabbath. Each of us can take a little from his daily portion, whatever he wishes. These pieces will add up so that we will have more for the Sabbath."

"We agree!" the children shouted in unison.

One child, who was sick in bed, spoke up hesitantly, "Mother, if all of us give you an extra piece, will you make the delicious pudding that you made for us last Shabbat?"

"If God be but willing! Please, God, be willing!"

"What a wonderful pudding! How did you make it," another child asked.

"That's a secret; I can't tell," Mother answered with a wry smile. She felt ashamed when she thought of how she had made that pudding. Mother did not reveal the secret.

What was there to say? Could she tell them that she took an extra piece off from her own minute portion each day and that these crumbs made the "wonderful" pudding? Now that one child became ill and she gave him some of her own bread each day, how was she to save anything extra for the pudding?

"If God wills it," and Mother's hand trembled as she wrapped the Sabbath portion of bread into a white napkin, "you shall have a pudding this Sabbath also. I promise you! And a very delicious pudding it shall be!"

Mother kept her promise. She made a pudding the likes of which had never been made before. It was a pudding fit for a king. She took potato peelings that she had collected secretly, soaked them in water and washed them thoroughly so as to remove every speck of dirt and grime. Then she dried and ground them. Into the flour she added all kinds of spices—salt, pepper, dried herbs.

And one more ingredient she added—her scalding tears . . .

"May it be your wish, O Lord," was her wordless, silent prayer, "that this dish taste good to my children, that they find in it the savor of manna as did our holy forefathers in the desert. May it be Your wish, dear God, that the work of my hands shall not desecrate the holiness of the Sabbath."

All the time that this unfortunate woman was preparing the pudding, thoughts kept distressing her. Maybe this pudding, a dish made of nothing but potato peelings, will prove to be desecration of the Sabbath. . . . It would be nice to add a few drops of oil to this unusual mixture. Oil would add much to its flavor. But, if I use up the oil for the pudding, how will I light my Sabbath candles?"

Thus, the poor woman debated with herself. "Food and candles . . . both on honor of the Sabbath. . . . What comes first? No doubt, candles come first, for there is a special prayer to say when lighting them . . . a commandment and a blessing. . . ." However, the next moment she changed her mind. "What can a candle do for my sick child when he is dying of hunger? The oil in the pudding may sustain his life."

Her heart was torn with uncertainty.

"This commandment to light Sabbath candles is also of importance to a sick child. The child depends upon the mercy of Heaven and there is no better time for prayer and supplication than at the moment of lighting the candles for the Sabbath Queen."

Suddenly, another thought struck her, a shattering one—she would make the blessing over the candles without oil!

"He who dwells in heaven and sees all and understands our thoughts will know that I am sanctifying the bit of oil for the holiness of the Sabbath. There is consecration in my use of the oil; I will light the candles without it!"

Sabbath eve, at twilight, Mother stood before her candles—wicks without oil—and her lips moved in silent prayer.

"O Lord of the Universe, accept these candles without light. In your infinite mercy, illuminate them with your Heavenly radiance. O Lord in Heaven! Forgive me—a woman rebellious and ashamed, who dares to steal the oil from the wicks, in order to light the joy of the Sabbath in the hearts of her little children who are starving before her eyes. If I have sinned and You cannot accept this prayer, I beg of You, O compassionate Father, listen to the Sabbath songs of the children that will resound in my poor dwelling when I bring this pudding to the table . . ."

When the children ate the pudding, it tasted of Paradise, and they burst out in chorus, "We will sing the Sabbath Song . . ."

And what about Mother? She swallowed her tears, tears of joy and fear. How was she to know that the Sabbath Queen, herself, had spread her pure angel wings over these singing Sabbath children, and was humming a song of her own, "Let us sing a song to the Jewish mother."

[TRANSLATED FROM THE HEBREW]

YITZHAK LEIB PERETZ

The Seven Good Years

The following story took place in Turbin, a small Polish town:

There once lived a porter in Turbin who was very, very poor. His name was Tuvyah. One Thursday, Tuvyah stood in the market place, his coattails tucked over the rope around his hips, and looked about him anxiously for someone who might need his services. The shops were deserted. There were no bundles to carry and no need for porters. He wondered how he was going to earn something for the Sabbath, sighed, and turned his eyes to Heaven with a prayer to the Almighty to keep his wife and children from going hungry, and to prevent sorrow from marring his enjoyment of the Sabbath.

While he was thus absorbed, he felt a tug at his coattail and turned around. Behold! There stood a foreigner dressed like a hunter, with a feather in his hat and green piping on his jacket. The stranger addressed him.

"Listen, Tuvyah! You have been allotted seven goods years—years of prosperity, good fortune, boundless wealth! When do you want them? It is up to you. Say the word and your lucky star can rise and shine this very day, even before sunset! You will be able to buy all of Turbin and its environs. But, at the end of the seven years, you will become as poor as you are now. You may, however, have the seven good years at the end of your days, if you so prefer. In that case, you will die a very rich man."

The stranger, as it turned out, was the prophet Elijah in disguise, who was known to appear miraculously from time to time. However, Tuvyah mistook him for an ordinary magician.

"My dear sir," Tuvyah answered, "forgive me, but I am so poor—may you never experience such straitened circumstances—that I cannot buy a thing for the Sabbath, so how can I pay you for your advice or service?"

The stranger, disregarding Tuvyah's words, repeated his offer of the seven good years and said it a third time, for special emphasis, until it dawned upon the porter that there might be something in what the man was saying.

"If you aren't teasing me just because I am poor, if you are in earnest about the seven good years, I must tell you that I never make a decision without first consulting my wife, Sorel. I cannot give you an answer by myself."

"An excellent habit," said the stranger, "to talk things over with your wife. Go now and ask her. I will wait here for your return."

Tuvyah surveyed the market place once more. There was no prospect of earning a penny. "What have I to lose?" he thought, shrugged his shoulders, adjusted his coattails and started homeward. First he had to walk to the outskirts of town, then into the open country, before he reached the little clay hut in which he lived.

It was summertime and the door was open. Sorel caught sight of her husband through the open door and ran out joyously to meet him. She was sure that he had brought her his earnings for their Sabbath needs.

"No, dear, the good Lord has not assigned any wages to me. But something unusual has happened. A foreigner came up to me . . ." and he told her the whole story from beginning to end, about the seven good years and how he had to decide whether to have them now or before his death.

"Go, dear husband, and tell him that you want the good years to begin now, this very minute!"

"Sorel! Why? After the seven years you'll be poor again, and one who is reduced to poverty has a much harder time of it than one who has always been poor."

"Don't worry so about the future. Take what is offered, take it now and say, 'Thank God for this day.' Do we have a choice? The children are home from school because we haven't paid the tuition. Look at them out there playing in the sand."

That was enough to make Tuvyah run back to the stranger with an unqualified answer—the seven good years were to begin immediately.

"Think it over, Tuvya. Now you are young and strong and can earn a living, more or less. What will you do when you are old and all your money is gone?"

"Listen, stranger. My wife, Sorel, wants it now. In the first place, she says, 'Praise the Lord each day and let the morrow take care of itself!' In the second place, our children have been sent home from school because we cannot afford the tuition fee."

"If that is so," said the stranger, "go home. You'll be rich before you get there."

As we mentioned before, Tuvyah had to walk quite a distance, for he lived in the open country. When he approached his house, he saw his children playing nearby. On coming closer, he noticed that they were digging pure gold from a hole in the ground. Needless to say, the seven lucky years had already begun!

Time flies like an arrow from a bow, and the seven years sped by. Once again the foreigner appeared in the market place and found Tuvyah standing there just as he did seven years before, his shirttails tucked over his belt.

"Tuvyah, the seven good years are up!"

The stranger reminded him that all his money would vanish, not only that which he had at home, but also anything he had hidden elsewhere.

"You had better tell it to Sorel, my wife. She's in charge of the finances."

The stranger accompanied Tuvyah to his home. He still lived in the same old clay hut. His smiling wife, dressed in a plain housedress, met them at the door. The man repeated to her what he had already told her husband.

"My dear sir," she responded, "for us the seven years that you talk about haven't even started. We haven't begun to enjoy the good years, for we never felt that the money was ours to use for our own pleasure. We believe that a man truly possesses only that which he, himself, has earned. Money acquired not by one's own labor is only given in trust. We assumed that the good Lord wanted us to distribute our wealth among the poor. We only took what we needed for the education of our children. Since they are learning God's word, we thought it permissible to spend His money for it. If the good Lord has a better trustee, well then . . ."

Elijah the prophet listened closely to the woman, and disappeared to bring her words to the Court of the All Highest. Its verdict was that no better guardian for the money could be found.

And so, for Tuvyah and Sorel the seven good years lasted all the days of their lives.

[TRANSLATED FROM THE HEBREW]

BELLA CHAGALL

The Bath

Jewish communities in Eastern Europe had their own mikvahs *(ritual baths) that were built and maintained by communal funds. Since bathtubs in private homes were practically unknown, a mother would often take her little daughter with her to the* mikvah. *The following is the recollection of such an experience.*

In the frame vestibule we bump into the ticket seller, wrapped up like a bale of goods. At first she does not stir from her place. One sees only the end of her nose and the tips of her fingers. Next to the tickets there is a glazed apple and a pear. A bit of blue kvass—blue probably from the frost—bubbles in a bottle.

The cashier, as though absorbing our warm breath, slowly undoes her half-frozen mouth and gives us a cold smile.

"It *is* cold to sit here the whole day," she says, beginning to revive. "The wind is blowing from all sides. A little more of this and one would freeze to death before at last a living being came."

Mother encourages her with a smile and takes from her an apple or a pear for me.

We push at the little door leading to the bath itself. The noise of the latch being raised arouses a couple of naked women resting under their shawls. Like startled flies they jump up from their benches and hum around us.

"Good evening to you, good evening, Alta, my dear! So late! How are you, Alta? Are all the children well? How are you, Bashinke?"

The women touch me from all sides.

"Ah, you're growing up as on yeast—may the evil eye spare you!"

They are warmed up, they have not waited in vain. The shawls like black wings fall from their backs. Before me there flashes the whiteness of their bodies. Everything becomes purer, brighter, all about.

The heat of the anteroom leading to the bath mingles with the cold outside air that has blown in. I can hardly recognize the bath attendants, although they are always the same. I used to think that every Thursday they had grown older, uglier. The younger one, who still smells of her moldy shawl, seizes me at once with her bony hands. "It's cold, isn't it?" she says. "Well, have you unpinned your dress? Have you got another one with you? Well, we'll put it in the box. Now, hold out your leg—come on!" She urges me as if I were a colt.

And before I have time to look around me, all the buttons of my shoes are unbuttoned, and the shoes with my twisted stockings fly into the black box on which I sit. My buttocks rise and fall with the lid of the box. I have not even had a chance to see what goes on inside the box, into which my belongings are tossed as into a dark pit.

From the frosted window panes, coated over with snow like a pair of blind eyes, a wind blows. I shake from cold. The bath attendant snatches up my sheet and wraps me in it. "Well, wait awhile!" she says. "In a minute you'll be warm! See, we are going to the bath at once."

I feel giddy. She drags me like a bewildered captive straight over to the little door. "Do not fall, Bashinke, God forbid," she says, pulling me with her steely hands. "Walk slowly, it's slippery."

In the doorway to the bath my breath is cut off and I allow myself to be dragged along, half in a faint. A dense cloud veils my eyes. A little tin lamp hangs from its bent hook high above the door. Its chimney, tiny as it is, is still too large for it, and it wobbles in all directions as soon as one touches the door.

I remain glued to the spot. I am afraid to move. The floor is slippery, full of water. Water drips on my feet, drips from the ceiling, from the walls; the whole of the little house is sweating from the heat.

The attendant rushes to the buckets and rinses the slippery bench on which I am supposed to sit. She has no time to say a word to me. Her glistening, scrawny rump twists like the tail of a cat.

Boiling water is poured out, seething. The buckets near me immediately breathe their heat into my face.

The warmth of the bench soothes me and I allow the attendant to put my legs into a bucket of luke-warm water. The woman comes closer to me. Her breasts hang before my eyes like deflated windbags, and her belly, with its skin taut like a drum, comes just under my nose. I am penned up between the buckets and the attendant's belly. I cannot turn, I cannot even think of turning.

Her scratchy fingers gather up my long hair. With one motion she heaps it on my head and begins to rub it with a big cake of Zhukov soap. She pushes the soap back and forth as though she were ironing clothes with it on my head.

Buried under hair, my head whirling, I have no time to think of crying. Smothering my tears, I pull out the bits of acrid soap that cut and bite my eyes. Soap gets into my ears, my mouth. Blindly I dip my fingers into a bucket of cold water beside me.

I get down from the bench only when my hair is rinsed. Long drops of water roll down into my eyes and heal them. I catch my breath, straighten my back; my eyes open.

I hear a creak of the door and on the threshold I see my whitely nude mother. She is immediately enveloped in the cloud of hot steam. Two attendants hold her at either side. Little tears of sweat drip from their hanging breasts and bellies. A thin little rain of drops, condensed from the steam, suddenly trickles from their hair behind their ears.

Silent and embarrassed, mother stands at the door. Her attendants rush to the buckets, open wide all the taps. They pass steam over the bench for her.

Mother calmly sits down and her body occupies the whole bench. Exhausted from being scrubbed, I hardly see her from where I am. She is ill at ease even before me and lowers her eyes as soon as my glance rests on her hair. Instead of her accustomed thickly curled wig, I see her own short, scraggly hair. Smothered for years without air under the heavy wig, it has thinned out. I become sad, suddenly losing my own strength, and allow myself to be washed without resisting.

My attendant seizes my body, she even lays hands upon my soul. She places me on the bench like a piece of dough and begins to rub and pinch me; she might be trying to knead a challa out of me.

I turn over on my stomach, and she gives me such a whack on my bottom that I jump up.

"Well, what do you say, Bashinke? It's good, isn't it?" says the attendant, suddenly recovering her speech. "Look, how red you have become! It's a pleasure to pinch you!"

Exhausted, I wait till I am rid of her. Suddenly I am frightened by a flood of water poured on me from behind. For a moment I am engulfed in the stream, the water lifts me and carries me as though I were in a river. This is the attendant rinsing me. From delight and heat, I melt like white wax.

"Oof!" sighs the attendant, wiping her nose with her wet hands. "You're shining just like a little diamond, Bashinke!

May this give you health, my child!" She looks at me with her glassy eyes, faded by the water, and quickly wraps me in a warm sheet.

Surely she will at last dry herself off a little. She slowly encircles me with her two arms as if I were her white Sabbath candles that she must bless.

From a distance I watch what is being done to my mother. Surely she has been soaped and rubbed just as I have been, and surely she too has taken delight in the buckets of lukewarm water. But she is not through as quickly as I.

After the scrubbing the older attendant pushes a low stool up to my mother and sits at her feet. She puts a brass candlestick on a little box and lights the piece of candle that is stuck in it. She fans the little flame and begins to complain to mother about her hard life. Her back sinks heavily, as though all her troubles were heaped on it; her drooping head is at mother's feet. "May God have mercy upon us and deliver us from all pain," she says, lifting her eyes from the ground. "So be it, Lord of the Universe!"

She must be trying to forget her own thoughts as she picks at mother's toes. The little flame burns brightly with each blessing she murmurs before cutting the nail. And her heart becomes more serene, it seems, with each blessing. Mother, with lowered eyes, watches what the attendant does to her feet, listens to her patter. Behind the burning candle both are fenced off from the dark bath chamber as within a crown of light. Their heads are close together, their white faces shine in a sort of purification.

Having cleaned mother's toes, the old attendant raises her head and says in a low voice: "Now, Alta, let us go to the mikvah!"

Mother swallows her breath as though the attendant had told a secret. The two rise slowly, straighten their backs, sigh deeply, take a long breath as though preparing to cross the threshold of the holy of holies. Their white shadows vanish in the darkness.

I am afraid to go too. One has to pass a hot chamber where writhing souls lie in torment on long benches. Steaming besoms swing out of the air and lash them and spatter them with drops of hot water. Heavy breathing comes from the benches, as though all of them were being burned on hot coals. The heat presses into my mouth, seizes me by the heart. "This must be a hell for those who have committed many sins!" I think to myself and run after my mother to the mikvah.

I stumble into a black chamber like a prison. On a staircase stands the old attendant. In one hand she holds the burning candle, from her other arm dangles a large white sheet. Mother—I have been so fearful about her—quietly descends the four slippery steps and goes into the water up to her neck. When the old Jewess cries out a blessing, mother is frightened. Like one condemned, she holds her nose, closes her eyes, and plunges into the water as though forever—God forbid!

"Ko-o-sher!" cries the attendant, with the voice of a prophet.

I am startled as by a thunderclap. Trembling, I wait—surely now lightning will strike from the black ceiling and slay us all on the spot. Or perhaps a deluge will pour from the stone wall and drown us in the dark mikvah.

"Ko-o-o-sher!" the attendant cries out again.

Where is mother? The water does not splash any more. But suddenly the pool splits open and mother's head emerges. She shakes off water as if she were coming up from the very bottom of the sea.

Three times the attendant cries out, and three times mother sinks into the black water.

I am desperately waiting for the moment when the attendant will stop shouting, so that mother will no longer have to disappear in the water. After all, she is tired by now. Water streams down from her hair, from her ears. But she is smiling. Contentment spreads over her whole body. She walks from the water as from a fire, clean and purified. "May it do you good, may it give you health," the attendant says, smiling too.

Her long, thin arms lift the sheet up high. Mother wraps herself in it as in a pair of huge white wings, and smiles on me like a white angel.

Dressed, all finished with my steaming, I chew my glazed apple, which has long since melted from the heat, and wait for mother. At once she begins to hurry, as though she recalls suddenly that it is a weekday, that the shop is still open. The sanctity and the warmth of the bath slip from her. She is in a hurry to get dressed. The women tell her their last tales of trouble, while one hands her dress to her, the other a shoe. They are probably afraid to leave anything untold, lest they should have to wait until the following Thursday to unburden their hearts. With trembling hands they wrap up our bundle of linen, and they wrap me too like a bundle. Swollen with warmth, I can hardly move.

Mother distributes her tips and listens to the long benedictions with which the women send us off.

"May it give you health, dear Alta! Till next Thursday, if God wills! Keep well, Bashinke! May it do you good!" One woman shouts louder than another, and all of them quickly cover themselves with their shawls.

The door opens as of itself. For a moment we stop on the threshold. What cold! Snow is falling from the black sky. Stars glimmer, and snowflakes. Is it day or night? To my eyes all is white and cold. The driver and his horse have grown into a high white mountain. Are they frozen? "May you have health!" the driver says with a smile.

His wet mustache comes unglued from his mouth. Little lumps of snow fall from his thick eyebrows. The horse awakens to life and begins to neigh.

"God speed you!" Voices call to us from the door of the bathhouse.

The sleigh starts.

"Hup, hup!" The driver lashes at his thin horse.

Even faster than when she left, mother runs in at the front door and leaves her bundle of linen there. The smell of our apartment and of the shop hits her in the face.

"God alone knows what has gone on here in my absence!" With a look of guilt, she hastens to wash her reddened face and then hurries to the shop.

I am regretting that the warm bath has ended so soon.

[TRANSLATED BY NORBERT GUTTERMAN]

5

Love Thy Neighbor

Let the honor of thy fellow man be as dear to thee as thine own.

Pirke Avot (Sayings of the Fathers)

MOSES GASTER

Rabbi Joshua Ben Hananiah and the Emperor's Daughter

Once upon a time the daughter of the Emperor asked Rabbi Joshua, son of Hananiah, "Is it not very strange that there is so much Torah (learning) in you and you are so terribly ugly? So much wisdom in such a contemptible vessel?"

Rabbi Joshua replied, "Prithee, where do you keep your wine? In what kind of vessels?"

And she replied, "We keep our wine in simple earthenware vessels, because for many years past, wine has always been kept in earthen vessels."

Rabbi Joshua replied, "You are very rich people, you ought to keep your wine in vessels of silver only, the ordinary people keep it in earthen jars."

So she went and told the Emperor, who poured all the wine into silver jars. Within a short time the wine turned sour, and they reported to the Emperor that all his wine had turned into vinegar.

Then the Emperor asked his daughter, "Who advised you to pour the wine into silver jars?"

The princess replied, "Rabbi Joshua, son of Hananiah."

So the Emperor sent for Rabbi Joshua and asked him, "Why did you give such advice to my daughter so that all my wine has turned to vinegar?"

Rabbi Joshua replied, "As she spoke to me so I spoke to her. She said to me, 'What a pity such great learning is in such a contemptible vessel.' So I said to her, 'Why do you keep wine in a cheap vessel?' I also said that as the Torah does not stay with a man of handsome appearance, so wine does not keep in a silver vessel."

The Emperor said, "But there are many good-looking men who possess learning."

Then Rabbi Joshua replied, "If they were not so handsome they would be more learned still, for a man of handsome appearance is not a man of modesty, and therefore he forgets the Torah which he has learned."

CHAIM HURWITZ

The Only Kid

When Solomon was king, there lived in Israel a rich farmer by the name of Elkana who was very charitable. His wife, Shifra, was just as kind as he. In the course of years, their wealth dwindled but their good deeds continued.

"We have very little," Elkana said one day to Shifra. "Perhaps we have been too generous."

"Can you bear to hear of anyone in need without coming to his aid?" Shifra asked.

"And you," Elkana turned to his wife with a smile, "how you fuss over every orphan child; how you feed him and sew for him; and the feasts you prepare for the wanderers whom I invite!"

Even after their money was all gone, the couple did not desist from opening their hands to the needy. They then gave of their flock. The time came when they had nothing left but one kid. Shifra had to sell her household goods for food. Each morning Elkana brought his kid to pasture. One day, Elkana was sitting under a tree watching his only kid, thinking sadly of the good old days, when he saw someone dressed in worn and dusty clothes of a wanderer coming toward him. Elkana greeted the poor man and invited him to his house. The stranger gladly accepted the invitation.

On his way home, Elkana realized that there was no meat at home—there hadn't been any for days. Not wishing to make the wanderer feel as if he were unwelcome, Elkana was silent. However, the minute he came indoors, he took his wife aside and told her of their dilemma. Shifra's eyes filled with tears. She had nothing in the house but barley flour, some herbs and dried vegetables—nothing with which to honor a guest or satisfy the appetite of a hungry wanderer.

"All we have is the one kid," said Elkana.

"God must have given it to us for this purpose," said Shifra, "so that we can be hospitable even as our forefather Abraham was."

Elkana slaughtered the kid and Shifra prepared a fine feast. After the meal, the stranger turned to Elkana and asked, "Why do you kind people look so sad?"

Elkana told him how he had been left a large inheritance by his father; how in the course of time, because of their habit of doing acts of charity, his flocks and goods had diminished; and how the kid that he slaughtered that day was all that had been left.

"Why didn't you tell me this before?"

"How could I, when I saw you coming along the dusty road?"

The stranger took a piece of paper from his pocket and wrote something on it. Then, handing it to Elkana, he said, "If you need help, come to me with this. Show it to the guards, and they will let you in."

Elkana and his wife read what the stranger had written. It bore the signature of King Solomon! King Solomon, in his desire to know his people and gain more wisdom, would often don the clothing of a poor man and wander alone through farms and villages.

Elkana, who now had nothing left of all his flock, had no more reason for going to the pasture.

He was very dejected and Shifra did not know how to console him. One day she said, "Go to the king; he promised to help us."

Elkana took his wife's advice and set out for Jerusalem. When he came to the palace gates and showed the guards the king's personal note, they were most courteous. They told him to go in the direction of the Temple, for that was where the king had gone to pray. Elkana hurried along the path that the guards had pointed out to him and entered the Temple. There he saw the great King Solomon praying. Not wishing to intrude, he hid behind a large pillar.

A king has everything, Elkana thought, so what does he have to pray for? And he listened to what Solomon was saying.

"Hear my voice, my Lord, my God. Have mercy upon me and accept my humble prayer."

I see that a king also depends upon God's mercy, thought Elkana. I believed that a king was like God, and I came to him to beg for help. Now I, too, shall pray to Him who is Ruler of heaven and earth.

Elkana slipped out of the Temple unseen by the king, and came home full of hope and cheer.

When Shifra saw his smiling face, and noticed his light tread, she asked, "What good thing has the king done for you?"

"He has taught me to pray," Elkana answered, and told her all that had happened.

"We shall both pray," said Shifra, "to Him who is King of the universe. He will not forget us."

After their prayers, the couple felt a new strength and confidence.

"When I was a boy," Elkana said, "I would love to go into the forest with my father's servants and help them chop wood. I'll go and chop wood now and sell it. '

Elkana was not a young man. He became tired quickly and earned very little at first. But, as he became accustomed to the work, he felt stronger and was able to work and earn more. Shifra felt happier and more energetic than she had been in a long time. She was sorry that her husband was working so hard and decided to help him, so she hired herself out as a cook.

One day, the master of the house in which Shifra worked learned her name and that she was the wife of Elkana.

"I am looking for a man with that name," the master of the house said. "When I was a little boy my father died and that man saved my mother and me from a life of beggary."

Shifra told the story to her husband and found out that he was, indeed, that same Elkana who had helped the widow in her time of need. In a short time, Shifra's employer visited Elkana, bringing a gift of money.

"I am only repaying a small part of a debt. What you had given my mother was as precious as life itself."

As the visitor sat and talked of his mother's good turn of fortune after Elkana had helped her, he recalled a certain shoemaker whom Elkana had helped many years ago. At that time, the shoemaker had met with an accident and was unable to walk. Elkana sent a doctor to him, and provided the family with the necessities of life during their father's illness.

"The shoemaker has a very rich son. I will tell him about you," said the visitor.

The old shoemaker came to Elkana with some money. Others whom Elkana and Shifra had helped came to visit the poor couple. Those who had no money brought sheep and goats and wheat. Soon Elkana had money enough with which to buy a farm, and livestock with which to start it. Elkana was industrious, Shifra was thrifty, and they became wealthy once more.

One day, King Solomon and his retinue passed by the farm of rich Elkana. The farmer invited the king into his home and had Shifra prepare a sumptuous feast as befits a king. After the meal, Solomon told his host that he was looking for a very kind but poor couple. The man's name was Elkana—and the king countinued to tell the story of the only kid.

Elkana bowed before the king and said, "Your highness, I am the man you seek."

"What happened to you? How did you acquire this wealth?" Solomon asked in surprise.

Elkana told how he came to Jerusalem to ask a favor of the king, and how he heard the king pray. King Solomon embraced Elkana; and addressing Elkana and his good wife, Shifra, he said, "God, indeed, heaps his blessings on those who help the poor."

[TRANSLATED AND ADAPTED FROM THE HEBREW]

YITZHAK LEIB PERETZ

The Judgment of the Wind

In the days of King Solomon, there lived a poor widow by the name of Shunamith. Her home was a tumble-down shack in a fishing village at the shore of the Mediterranean Sea. She earned a meagre living by weaving nets for the fishermen.

This story took place during a period of storms and tempests, when no boats went to sea and no nets were cast. The widow's livelihood was entirely cut off. Poor Shunamith! Where was she to turn for help? To the fisherfolk? They too, had nothing, for those were hard times.

Some distance away, on a large estate, lived a rich man. He had been blessed with all worldly goods—gardens and fields and vineyards and orange groves, flocks of sheep and goats, and a countless number of donkeys and camels.

One morning, when Shunamith awoke and saw that the sky was leaden and the wind's fury had not abated, she threw her old wrap about her shoulders and turned her steps towards the rich man's dwelling. The master of the house was standing in his doorway. Shunamith bowed low.

"Woman, why do you prostrate yourself before me? Rise up and tell me what you want."

"Shunamith is my name. I am a widow and live in the fishing village by the sea. I am starving and I come to ask you for bread, so that I may eat and be refreshed."

The man pointed to the wealth around him and said, "Look yonder at the camels and donkeys. They are being unharnessed, for I have just come from Jerusalem and King

Solomon's beautiful palace. It is open to visitors. The king sat on his gold throne and wore a gold crown. He was surrounded by many people—attendants, elders and the general populace. When he spoke, the people hung on his words.

" 'He who despises gifts will live,' was one of his sayings. What Solomon meant was that he who wants to live should not take charity. Now, if you accept alms, you will shorten your life. I do not want to be responsible for that.

"Solomon gave further explanation of his words. 'He who borrows from his neighbor becomes a slave to his benefactor, while the man who gives the loan acquires a slave.'

"You are a widow and of my own people. It is inconceivable that I make you my slave. Therefore, I will give you nothing."

"Is it more kind or more just to allow a widow to die of hunger?"

"You won't die, Shunamith," the man answered calmly. "As God is my witness, I will not turn my back on you. How, then, will I help? With this piece of advice. Take what is free for everyone."

"*What* is free from here to the desert? And what will I find in the wilderness but withered grass? Are you mocking me? Don't you fear God, the Protector of widows and orphans?"

"Listen carefully," the man answered. "My granaries are now empty, but not long ago, they contained one hundred sacks of fine flour. I brought them all to King Solomon in Jerusalem. The boards in my granary on which the sacks rested are covered with a thick white film of flour dust. This dust is free to anybody who takes it. Go to the granary, collect the flour dust and take it home. Be sure to gather some firewood on the way. Bake your bread and God will bless the flour dust that you have gathered and you will give thanks to Him that you did not have to accept alms."

The woman had no alternative but to follow this unusual bit of advice. She went to the granary and scraped the flour dust. On the way home, she gathered some twigs that had been tossed about the ground by the storm.

When Shunamith got home, she built a fire, added water to her flour and baked three small loaves. She said grace, thanking God for His mercy, when suddenly the door of her hut flew open and a man burst in crying, "Save me! Save me! I am starving!" Between sobs, he told her how lightning had struck the village in which he lived, several fires had broken out at once, and the entire village including its men, women and children had gone up in flames. He was the sole survivor. For three days he had been running—he knew not whereto—and hadn't had a morsel to eat in all that time.

Shunamith gave him a loaf of bread. "Please," she told him, "leave me now, as I am a widow and live alone."

The man took the bread and vanished into the night. The widow thanked the Lord that He had given her bread to stay her own hunger and also something with which to save the life of a starving man.

She took the second loaf in her hand and was about to eat, when the door was flung open and another man, dazed and hungry, staggered in.

"Bread!" he cried, "Give me bread!" He told her the tragic tale of how he had been a rich sheepman and had employed many young shepherds to watch his flock. He lived with his wife and children in luxurious tents. One night, Arabian horsemen swooped down upon them with bows and arrows, killing the people and stealing the sheep; he was the only one to escape.

"Please," he concluded, "have mercy and give me food or I will collapse at your feet."

Shunamith gave him the second loaf, thanking God once more for giving her the wherewithal to help someone in need. She asked the man to please eat out-of-doors, as she was a widow and lived alone. He, too, left the hut and vanished into the night.

The widow took the last loaf and was about to eat, when a violent wind tore through the shack, threw down its walls, dragged away its roof of palm leaves, snatched the bread out of her hands and hurled it into the sea. Then the wind died down.

The sea became calm. Soon bright rays of the sun glistened on its surface. The fishermen wasted no time, got into their boats and started casting their nets. The children ran into the streets, shouting, "No more hunger, thank the Lord. We'll have bread, lots of bread!"

The poor widow could not share the joy of the villagers. She was sad and perplexed. "Why has God done this to me," she wondered. "He took one loaf away, may His name be blessed, to give to a man who had escaped from a fire. He took the second loaf from me, may His name be blessed, to give to a man who had escaped from bandits. But the third loaf! Why did He snatch it from a widow's mouth only to sink it into the sea?" Then the thought occurred to her that it was not God's doing, but that the wind had done this evil thing contrary to the wishes of Him Who feeds widows and orphans. She would not forgive the wind! She would bring it to judgment! Before whom? Before Solomon! She would go to Jerusalem and ask the king himself to judge the wind.

As soon as Shunamith had made her decision, she did not tarry, but put on her old wrap and started the long journey. Though she was weak from hunger, confidence that justice was on her side gave her the strength to reach her destination.

In Jerusalem, she asked for directions to the royal palace. When she arrived, she was admitted to the king's presence. Shunamith bowed down before him and said, "Pray, your royal highness, I beseech you, judge between me and him who has wronged me."

"Who has wronged you? I see that you are alone. In a dispute it is usual for both parties to come before me."

"The wind! I accuse the wind!" and she proceeded to make her charges against it.

"Your grievances are just," said Solomon, "but I see that you are very weak and your eyes are feverish with hunger. Rest here awhile and eat. Later I will pass judgment on the wind."

The king ordered her to be escorted to a private room and to have food and drink set before her.

Meanwhile, Solomon continued to receive his people. As he was dispensing justice, three foreigners entered with heavy sacks on their backs and asked for permission to speak to the king.

"Why have you come and what is the reason for those loads?" asked Solomon.

"We are Ishmaelite merchants, dealers in gems and precious metals, and this is our entire fortune. The three of us were sailing on the sea when a storm arose. It was a mighty tempest, but we were not afraid, for we have been sailors since our youth. We know how to steer a boat and how to rise and glide on the waves. But we noticed that water was seeping in through the bottom. There was a hole in our boat! We had nothing with which to stop up the hole and keep the water out, so we called for help. Although we were not far from shore, the wind scattered our voices in every direction and the waves caught our cries and dragged them down into the black deep. Water slowly flooded the boat and we began to sink. We prayed to our god with no response; we called upon the god of Moab, the god of the Philistines, and many others, but not one of them heard us. Then we remembered that there was One upon whom we hadn't called, the God of Israel. We vowed that if He would save us from this peril, we would give Him all the wealth that we had with us. At that very moment, the wind became most violent and something came flying into our boat, landing in the hole and sealing it. With that, the wind subsided and we glided safely to shore.

"Our first thought was to redeem our pledge. We asked for directions to the house of the God of Israel and were told to go to Jerusalem. In the big city, we asked a passerby, 'Where is your God? We must see Him.'

"We were told, 'Man cannot look upon His face.' "

" 'We have a gift for Him,' " we told them.

"Some people looked at us in surprise while others laughed. We met a group of old men and asked them the same question. They shrugged their shoulders and turned away from us. But one old man came forward and advised us to go to you, mighty ruler; you will know what we must do."

"Do you know what the wind threw into your boat?"

"Indeed we do! We found this embedded in the hole." One of the merchants took a small loaf of bread from his pocket and placed it before Solomon. Immediately, the king sent for Shunamith.

"Do you recognize this bread," he asked.

"It is mine!" she exclaimed.

Solomon handed down his verdict: the widow was to receive the three bags of gold and silver.

And so it was. The Ishmaelites handed over their treasures, blessed the king and departed.

Solomon turned to Shunamith and said, "Take the gold and silver. It is all yours. God has paid you in full. But, remember, the wind was but the messenger of Him Who is King of the universe. Nothing happens contrary to God's will."

[TRANSLATED FROM THE HEBREW]

SH. ANSKY

Laughter

(Note: The following is one of the many stories and legends about the Founder of Hassidism, Israel Baal Shem-Tov, or the "Besht," as he is known in Jewish history.)

One winter day, the Besht met his group of students, as was his custom, to sing and converse with them. In the middle of a song, the Besht started to smile. Everyone stopped singing, waiting to hear what their teacher had to say.

"Come, let us travel to another region," he said.

His pupils were delighted, for they knew that whenever their teacher traveled, wondrous things occurred.

Alexis, his faithful peasant, who acted as his servant, hitched up the wagon. The Besht gave the driver no instructions other than that they were to go wherever the horses would take them.

Toward evening, the horses suddenly stopped; they were in a dense forest. The travelers decided to say their evening prayers. Just as they finished, an emaciated nag, pulling a small wagon, stopped beside them. Propped up on the seat were a young man and a maiden, both semi-conscious.

After the Besht's pupils rubbed the young couple with snow and succeeded in rousing them from their stupor, they asked them who they were and what was their destination.

The youth told them that they were both orphans who had been working as servants at a designated inn. They had fallen in love with each other and had planned to marry. One day, their mistress, displeased by the maiden's work, started to beat her. The youth came to the rescue of his betrothed, which angered the innkeeper, who forthwith drove them both out.

With their meagre savings, they purchased a horse and wagon and journeyed aimlessly for several days, seeking a place to live. They had spent all their money and hadn't eaten for two days. Now hunger and cold had overcome them.

After the pupils of the Besht had fed the starving couple, their teacher proposed that they go to the nearest inn, so that the youth and maiden could be married. Everyone readily agreed. But, what was the dismay of the young couple, when the inn to which they came turned out to be the very one in which they had worked!

When the innkeeper and his wife came out to greet his guests and saw their dismissed servants, they started to berate them, demanding that they leave the inn at once. The Besht declared that the young couple must be permitted to enter, for they were his guests. Furthermore, the young couple planned to be married and their reason for coming was to arrange the wedding celebration.

The innkeeper and his wife laughed long and loud. Let this couple be married here? And who would pay for it? The Besht showed them a handful of gold pieces and the innkeepers stopped laughing at once; they welcomed them into the inn effusively and then hastened into the kitchen to prepare an elaborate repast.

The Besht himself performed the marriage ceremony. After the company had feasted and was in a very merry mood, the Besht arose and said, "We are obliged to give gifts to this bride and groom. I do hereby give them this inn with all its furniture, and all the buildings round about it, as well as the sheep and cattle."

When the innkeepers heard this, they laughed till the tears rolled down their cheeks. Then they sent a servant to summon the villagers so that they too might join in the fun.

At the conclusion of the Besht's speech, one of his pupils announced, "And I give them a gift of the forest round about the inn for an area of one square mile."

Another said, "I give them the water-mill."

A third declared, "I give them one thousand bushels of grain from the granary of the duke."

And so, each of the scholars offered his gift. Meanwhile the innkeepers and villagers were howling with laughter. Finally, the innkeeper himself ran to the table and announced with a snicker, "And I give this fine couple ten thousand silver pieces which the duke has received this day for his crops."

The wife of the innkeeper shouted with still greater sarcasm, "And I give to this lovely bride the gold necklace about the neck of the duchess and the earrings which she wears."

The Besht then said to them, "Perhaps you want to give them something of your own, for they were once servants in your house?"

At this the innkeeper and his wife roared with laughter and said, "Let them have the palace that stands at the edge of the village."

This was the biggest joke of all for the villagers. The palace that stood at the end of the village was a ruin without roof or doors.

"And what more will you give them?" asked the Besht.

"Nothing!" they replied.

Whereupon the Besht sighed, arose and paid the bill for the wedding feast. He also paid for the tablecloth and told the groom and his bride to gather the remnants of the food and wine into it, carry it to the wagon and continue on their journey.

"Where to?" asked the groom.

"To the right," was the Besht's only reply.

The couple did as they were told. They mounted their wagon with their bundle of food and went on their way, the mocking laughter of the villagers ringing in their ears.

They wandered all night. The next day they found themselves in a forest. Suddenly their horse stopped before a human form lying in the snow. On alighting from their wagon and coming closer, they saw it was a young man of noble appearance. He was apparently frozen.

The groom and his bride rubbed the man's body with snow until he regained consciousness. The young wife remembered the contents of the tablecloth and brought out the wine for the nobleman to drink. As he grew stronger, she fed him from the leftovers of their wedding feast. He told them that he was the son of the grand duke, that he went hunting the day before, was thrown from his horse and separated from his companions. He wandered in a daze until he came to an inn. But he looked so bedraggled that the innkeeper drove him away and so he continued wandering in the forest until hunger and cold overcame him.

As the nobleman and the young couple were talking, the sound of trumpets was heard in the forest. Soon the duke's retinue appeared and the nobleman was united with his company. They galloped forth in high spirits, leaving the young couple behind.

The duke and duchess were overjoyed at their son's return. They wanted to know exactly what had happened to him. He told them about his fall, his experience at the inn, and about the young couple who had revived him.

The duke ordered a search party to find the couple. When the bride and groom were brought before him and were asked who they were and whence they came, they told all that had befallen them at the inn. On hearing how they had lost their jobs, the duke became doubly incensed at the innkeepers.

"He drove you and my son away! Indeed! I now give you permanent possession of the inn, its furniture, the buildings round about and all the sheep and cattle."

"And I," said the duchess, "give you the forest for one square mile about the inn."

The duke's son then spoke up, "And I give you the water-mill, one thousand bushels of wheat from our granary, and one hundred casks of wine from our cellar."

The duke asked, "How will you run the inn if you have no money? I give you ten thousand pieces of silver which I received yesterday from the produce of my land."

The duchess added, "This young woman was married a day ago and she has no jewelry for her dowry. Therefore, I give her the gold necklace and gold earrings that I wear."

The astonished couple stood speechless, as if in a dream. Suddenly their hearts were filled with pity for the innkeeper and his wife, and they asked, "Now that you have driven our former employers out of the inn, where will they go?"

The duke replied, "The ruins of the old palace at the end of the village shall belong to them."

All who were standing there laughed and laughed. But the bride and groom who had seen the fulfillment of all that the Besht had foretold, wept tears of joy.

[TRANSLATED FROM THE HEBREW]

ISAAC BASHEVIS SINGER

A Piece of Advice

Talk about a holy man! Our powers are not theirs, their ideas are not for us to understand. But let me tell you a story. It happened to my own father-in-law. I was still a young man, a mere boy, and a follower of the Rabbi of Kuzmir. Was there anyone else worthy of following but the Rabbi of Kuzmir?

My father-in-law lived in Rachev and I boarded with him. He was a wealthy man and he ran his house in a grand manner. I'll give you an example: At meal times, I of course always washed my hands and said the blessing before eating. Only then were the rolls removed from the oven so that they could be eaten hot and fresh. My mother-in-law, peace be with her, timed it to the very second. She would put hard-boiled eggs into my soup. I wasn't accustomed to such luxuries. In my own home the loaves of bread were baked two weeks in advance. I used to rub garlic on a slice of bread and wash it down with cold water drawn from the well.

But here everything was fancy: brass door latches, copper pans. Before crossing the threshold you had to wipe your boots on the straw mat. And the fuss that was made about brewing coffee with chicory! My mother-in-law was descended from a family of Misnagids—the enemies of the Hasids—for whom the pleasures of this world mean something.

My father-in-law was an honest Jew, a Talmudic scholar, a dealer in timber, a mathematician of sorts. He used to have his own hut in the forest, a gun and two dogs besides, because there were many robbers in the neighborhood. He knew logarithms and who knows what else. When he tapped at the bark of a tree with his hammer, he could tell if the tree were as sound inside as outside. He also knew how to play a game of chess with a Gentile squire. But whenever he had a free moment he immediately took to the Holy Books. The "Duties of the Heart" was always in his pocket. He liked to smoke a long pipe that had an amber mouthpiece and a silver cover. He kept his prayer shawl in a hide bag, and the cases for his phylacteries were of silver.

He had two faults. First of all, he was a fervent Misnagid. What a Misnagid—he burned like fire! He called the Hasids "the Heretics" and he was not ashamed to speak evil of the saintly Baal Shem himself. When I heard him talk like that for the first time, I shuddered. I wanted to pack up and run away. But the Rabbi of Kuzmir was against divorce. You married your woman, not your father-in-law. Jethro, Moses' father-in-law, wasn't a Hasid either, he would say. When he told me that it amazed me. Jethro later became a holy man. But that's putting the cart before the horse. . .

My father-in-law's second fault was his uncontrollable anger. He was able to conquer all his moral weaknesses, but he could not overcome his bad temper. If a merchant did not repay his debt on time and to the penny, he called him a swindler and refused any further dealings with him. When the town shoemaker made a pair of boots for him, and they were either too tight or too loose, he railed at him without pity.

Everything had to be just so. He had gotten it into his head that Jewish homes had to be as clean as the homes of the Christian squires and he insisted that his wife let him inspect the pots and pans, to make sure there wasn't a spot on them. A joke was told about him, that he had discovered a hole in a potato grater. His family loved him, the town respected him. But how much of a bad temper can people take? Everybody became his enemy. His business partners left him. Even my mother-in-law couldn't stand it any more.

Once I borrowed a pen from him and forgot to return it immediately. He wanted to write a letter to Lublin, and searched for his pen. I remembered that I had borrowed it and hurried to give it back, but he had fallen into such a rage that he struck me in the face. Well, if one's own father does a thing like that, that's his privilege, but it's unheard of for a father-in-law to strike his son-in-law. My mother-in-law became sick from the incident. My wife wept bitterly. I myself wasn't that upset about it. What was the tragedy? But I saw that my father-in-law was eating his heart out with regret. So I approached him and I said, "Father-in-law, don't take it to heart. I forgive you completely."

As a rule he spoke to me very little, because just as he was particular about every little thing, so was I lax. I would take off my garbardine and not remember where I put it. I was given some coins and I misplaced them. Rachev was a tiny village but when I went beyond the market place, I could no longer find my way back. All the houses in Rachev looked alike. I wouldn't look at the women inside. When I got lost, I would open a cottage door and ask, "Doesn't my father-in-law live here?" There would be laughter and tittering within. I took a vow never to go anywhere but from my home to the study house and back again. Only later did it occur to me that near my father-in-law's house stood a landmark—a thick tree rooted who knows how deep. It must have been two hundred years old.

For one reason or another we always quarrelled and my father-in-law avoided me. After the incident of the pen, however, he began to talk to me. "Baruch," he said to me, "what shall I do? I'm a bad-tempered man. I know that the sin of anger is as evil as that of idolatry. For many years

I have tried to get rid of my bad temper but things are getting worse. I'm sinking into hell. It brings me to grief in worldly matters, too. My enemies want to destroy me. I'm afraid that I'll end up without bread in the house."

"Father-in-law," I answered, "come with me to Rabbi Chazkele of Kuzmir."

My father-in-law turned pale. "Have you gone mad?" he shouted. "You know I don't believe in Wonder-Rabbis!"

I immediately held my tongue. First of all, because I didn't want him to scold me, as he always regretted it later. Secondly, I didn't want him to go on slandering a holy man.

After the evening prayer he came over to me and said, "Baruch, we're going to Kuzmir." I was stupefied. But why go into that—we immediately prepared to leave for Kuzmir. It was winter and we had to hire a sleigh. A deep snow had fallen and the road was far from safe. In those days the forests were still full of wolves. There was also no lack of highwaymen about. But such was my father-in-law's nature. Once he decided on leaving we had to go. My mother-in-law thought that he had, heaven forbid, lost his mind. He put on his fur coat and a pair of straw overshoes, and said the special prayer for a journey. For me the whole thing was an adventure. I was going to Kuzmir and was taking my father-in-law with me—who could be happier than I? But I trembled with fear; who knew what would happen there?

All along the way, my father-in-law didn't utter a word. It snowed during the whole trip. Snow is a subject in itself. Snow comes from heaven and while it lasts one can experience the peace of the other world. According to the Cabala, red signifies the law and white is the color of mercy.

As we passed, the fields were full of swirling images. The philosophers say that each snowflake has its own unique shape. Nowadays snow is a trifle—it snows for a day or two. But in my times snow would fall for a month without stopping. Huge snowdrifts piled up. Houses were snowed under and one had to dig one's way out. Heaven and earth merged and became one. And why does the beard of an old man turn white? These things are all related. At night, the howling of the beasts could be heard. Or perhaps it was only the sound of the wind.

We arrived in Kuzmir on a Friday afternoon. Few of the Rabbi's disciples came to him in the middle of winter. My father-in-law went to the Rabbi's study to greet him. He was immediately permitted to go in. I waited in the study house, my skin tingling. My father-in-law might very likely talk back to Rabbi Chazkele. He was by nature a bullheaded man. He remained there about three-quarters of an hour, then came out white as chalk, his eyes burning like coals. He had a long beard and bushy eyebrows. "If it weren't almost the eve of the Sabbath," he said to me, "I would go home immediately."

"What happened, father-in-law?" I asked him.

"Your Wonder-Rabbi is a fool and an ignoramus to boot. If he weren't an old man, I would tear off his sidelocks." The taste of gall was strong in my mouth at these words. I regretted the whole affair. To talk this way about Rabbi Chazkele of Kuzmir!

"Father-in-law," I asked, "what did the Rabbi say to you?" "He told me become a flatterer," my father-in-law answered. "For eight days I must flatter whomever I meet, even the worst scoundrel. If your Rabbi had an ounce of sense he would know that I hate flattery like the plague. It makes me sick even to come in contact with it. For me, a flatterer is worse than a murderer."

"Well, father-in-law," said I, "do you think the Rabbi doesn't know that flattery is bad? Believe me, he knows what he's doing."

"What does he know? One sin cannot wipe out another. He knows nothing about the law."

I went away completely crushed. I had not yet been to the ritual bath, so I went there. I have forgotten to mention that my father-in-law never went to the ritual bath. I don't know why. I guess it's the way of the Misnagids. He was also a bit snobbish. It was beneath his dignity to undress among other men. When I came out of the ritual bath the Sabbath candles were already lit. Rabbi Chazkele used to bless the Sabbath candles long before dark. He himself, not his wife. His wife lit her own candles. But that's another matter . . .

I entered the study house. The Rabbi was standing in his white gabardine and his white hat. His face shone like the sun. One could see clearly that he was in a higher world. When he sang out, "Give thanks unto the Lord for He is good for His mercy endureth forever," the walls shook. While praying the Rabbi used to clap his hands and stamp his feet with all his might.

Only a few disciples had come, but they were the elite, every one of them a personal friend of the Rabbi, men of holy deeds. As they chanted, I could feel their prayers reaching the heavens. I had never experienced such a beginning of the holy Sabbath, not even at Kuzmir. The rejoicing was so real that you could touch it. All their eyes were shining. My mind became so light that I could barely keep my feet on the ground. I happened to be praying near the window. The snow had covered everything. No road, no path, no cottages. Candles seemed to burn in the snow, heaven and earth were one. The moon and the stars touched the roofs. Those who were not in Kuzmir that Friday evening will never know what this world can be—I'm not now speaking of the world to come.

I glanced at my father-in-law. He stood in a corner, his head bent. As a rule, his sternness was visible in his face but now he looked humble, quite a different person. After the prayers we went to eat at the Rabbi's table. Before the

Sabbath meal the Rabbi used to sit alone in his library, reciting chapters of the Mishnah and of the Zohar. After prayers he put on a white robe of silk, embroidered with flowers and with silver fasteners. The older disciples sat down on the benches. The younger men, I among them, stood around.

The Rabbi came out of his study and intoned the verses, "Peace be with you," and "A woman of worth who can find?" He blessed the wine and said a prayer over the white bread of the Sabbath, but he ate a morsel no bigger than an olive. Immediately after that he began the Sabbath table chants. But this wasn't mere chanting. His body swayed, he cooed like a dove and it sounded like the singing of angels. His communion with God was so complete that his soul almost left his body. Everybody could see that the holy man was not here but high up in heaven.

Who knows what heights he reached? How can one describe it? As the Talmud says, "He who has not seen joy like this has never seen joy at all." It seemed that we were at the Rabbi's court in Kuzmir and, at the same time, high above in God's temples, in the Nest of the Bird, at the Throne of Glory. It was rapture impossible to imagine. I had forgotten about my father-in-law and even about myself. I was no longer Baruch from Rachev but bodiless, sheer nothing. When we left the Rabbi's table, it was one o'clock in the morning. Such a Sabbath service never took place before and will never happen again, except maybe when the Messiah comes.

Oh yes, I forgot the main thing. The Rabbi had commented on the law and what he said was connected with what he had told my father-in-law at their meeting. What should a Jew do if he is not a pious man? the Rabbi asked, and he answered, "Let him play the pious man. The Almighty does not require good intentions. The deed is what counts. It is what you do that matters. Are you angry perhaps? Go ahead and be angry, but speak gentle words and be friendly at the same time. Are you afraid of being a dissembler? So what if you pretend to be something you aren't? For whose sake are you lying? For your Father in Heaven. The Holy Name, blessed be He, knows the intention and the intention behind the intention, and it is this that is the main thing."

How can one convey the Rabbi's lesson? Pearls fell from his mouth and each word burned like fire and penetrated to the depths of the heart. It wasn't so much the words themselves, but his gestures and his tone. The evil spirit, the Rabbi said, cannot be conquered by sheer will. It is known that the evil one has no body and works mainly through the power of speech. Do not lend him a mouth—that is the way to conquer him. Take, for example, Balaam, the son of Beor. He wanted to curse the children of Israel but forced himself to bless them instead and because of this, his name is mentioned in the Bible. When one doesn't lend the evil one a tongue, he must remain mute.

Why should I ramble on? My father-in-law attended all three Sabbath meals. On the Sabbath night he went to the Rabbi to take leave of him and he stayed in his study for a whole hour. On the way home I said, "Well, father-in-law?" and he answered, "Your Rabbi is a great man."

The road home was full of dangers. The ice had cracked on the Vistula in midwinter. Blocks of ice ran downstream, like at Passover time. In the midst of all the cold, there was thunder and lightning. No doubt about it, only Satan could be responsible for this. We had to put up at an inn until Tuesday. There were many Misnagids staying there. No one could travel further. A real blizzard was raging outside. The howling in the chimney made you shiver.

Misnagids are always the same. They heaped ridicule upon Hasids but my father-in-law maintained silence. They tried to provoke him but he did not speak one unkind word.

They took him to task: "What about this one? What about that one? What change has come over you?" But he put them off with many tricks, in a good-natured manner. If they had known that he was coming from Rabbi Chazkele, they would have devoured him.

What more can I tell you? My father-in-law did what the Rabbi had prescribed. He stopped snapping at people. His eyes glowed with anger but his speech was soft. Sometimes he would lift his pipe as if to strike, but he let it down again and spoke with humility. It wasn't long before the people of Rachev realized that my father-in-law was a changed man. He made peace with his enemies. He would stop any little brat in the street and give him a pinch on the cheek. The water carrier would splash water about when he entered our house. I know this just about drove my father-in-law into a frenzy, but he wouldn't show it. "How are you, Reb Yontle?" he would say, "Are you cold, eh?" And one felt that he did this only with great effort. That's what made it noble.

In time his anger disappeared completely. He began to visit Rabbi Chazkele three times a year. He became a kindly man, a jewel, so good-natured it was unbelievable. But this is the nature of a habit—if you break it, it becomes the opposite. One can turn the worst sin into a good deed. The main thing is to act, not to ponder. He even began to visit the ritual bath. When he grew old, he acquired disciples of his own. This was after the death of Rabbi Chazkele. My father-in-law always used to say, "If you can't be a good Jew, act the good Jew because if you act something, you *are* it. Otherwise why does any man try to act at all? Take, for example, the drunk in the tavern. Why doesn't he try to act differently?"

The Rabbi once said, "Why is 'Thou Shalt Not Covet' the very last of the Ten Commandments? Because one must first avoid doing the wrong things and later on one will not desire to do them. If one stopped and waited until all the passions ceased, one could never attain holiness."

And so it is with all things. If you are not happy, act the happy man. Happiness will come later. One must not even begin with faith. Faith comes afterwards.

[TRANSLATED BY MARTHA GLUCKLICH AND JOEL BLOCKER]

MORDECAI SPECTOR

The Feast of the Paupers

Reb Yitzhak Izik was a rich farmer with a family of many daughters. When his daughters married, Reb Yitzhak arranged fine weddings for them, always including special feasts for the poor of the nearby village. Now that the marriage of the youngest drew near, he invited the paupers, as he had done before, to join in the festivities.

Reb Yitzhak hired three wagoners and sent them and his servant, at the crack of dawn of the wedding day, to fetch the beggars. The distance was negligible—barely five miles. When the noon hour passed and there was no sign of the paupers, Reb Yitzhak became alarmed. What could have happened? All the relatives and guests were assembled; everything was ready; but the ceremony was held up because the poor, a most important segment of the wedding party, had not arrived. Suddenly, the servant came galloping on horseback into town accompanied neither by wagons nor paupers.

"Why are you alone?" Reb Yitzhak asked in surprise.

"They refused to come!"

"What? They refused? Why?" the guests and the host shouted in unison.

"They said they wanted a ruble a head or they wouldn't come."

At this preposterous request the guests burst out laughing, but quickly stopped for they wanted to hear the servant's explanation.

"There was another wedding this morning that also gave a pauper's feast. The beggars ate and drank their fill, so they made an agreement among themselves not to come here unless you promised to give a ruble to each one. The ring-leaders are 'One-Legged,' 'The Agent,' 'Feitel the Stutterer' and 'Yekel the Flat-Nosed.' All the others would have come were it not for the stubborness of these four.

"I was beside myself," the servant continued. "When I saw there was no use pleading with them any longer, I took one of the horses and hurried back."

The wedding guests could not control their laughter. Reb Yitzhak, however, was very much annoyed.

"Are you convinced that they will not accept less?" he asked.

"Not a penny! I am positive!" was the servant's answer.

"If that is how independent they have become," Reb Yitzhak burst out in exasperation, "we'll manage without them. Hurry and bring back the wagons."

At this command, the servant started to go, but Reb Yitzhak held up his hand. "Wait!" Then facing the guests, he continued more to himself than to them, "Of all things! Did you ever hear the likes of it? The beggars are giving *me* orders! Because I want to feed them and give them a generous donation to boot. *They* are striking! A *ruble* they demand, or else—ha, ha, ha! Half a ruble will not please them. What arrogance! The devil take them! I'll manage without them. Musicians, play! Where is the sexton? Have him seat the bride!" However, in the same breath, he turned to his servant and said, in a more subdued tone, "Don't go! There's plenty of time! Wherein have I sinned that my happiness should be marred? Will I be forced to give my youngest child in marriage without providing a feast for the poor? It was always half a ruble. Oh, well! I did my duty. If they don't like it, it's too bad! Why take it to heart? I'll get along without them. They'll be sorry."

The sexton approached him, "Shall we seat the bride?"

"Yes, proceed! No! Wait a minute! Reb Yitzhak's expression suddenly changed from anger to pleading. He turned to three of his closest friends and asked them to do him a favor: to drive quickly to the village and persuade the mendicants to come with them.

"Please," he said, "I can't depend upon him," and pointing to the servant, "he is so unreliable."

The committee of three hired a coachman and left with dispatch. The servant drove behind them.

"A pauper's strike! What do you think of that!" and the men chuckled and talked of nothing else all the way. "We've heard of laborers striking for an increase in wages or a decrease in hours, but beggars to strike for an increase in charity gifts in return for their eating a free meal—that's something new indeed!"

In twenty minutes, the messengers arrived and stopped in the market place. They found that the three wagons were heaped with straw and were feeding-troughs for the horses. Milling around them were about a hundred paupers—lame, dumb, blind—and on the fringe of this crowd was a mob of idlers and mischievous boys. It looked like half the inhabitants of the village were gesticulating and screaming; the noise was deafening.

The ringleaders were in a wagon. One-Legged sat tapping with his cane and shouting to the crowd. The Agent, who stood beside him, a red kerchief around his neck, was the first to see Reb Yitzhak's friends.

"Aha!" he shouted. "Here *they* come begging!"

"They come to beg *us*," said one cripple, emphasizing his words by tapping with his crutch.

"Why don't you go to the wedding?" one of the messengers asked. "You'll get a good meal and worthwhile gifts."

"How much?" they rasped.

"We don't know. Whatever they'll give you, you'll get."

"Will there be a ruble for each? Otherwise, we won't go."

A few of the idlers wisecracked, "I suppose the heavens will fall, if . . ."

The beggars pounced upon them with sticks and created an uproar.

The Agent stood up as tall as he could and shouted, "Quiet, you wretched cripples! It is impossible to hear what the gentlemen are trying to say." Then, turning to the committee, he continued in honeyed tones, "My dear friends, you must understand that our decision is final. If we're not promised a ruble a head, we won't move an inch. We are sure that Reb Yitzhak will not have a wedding for his daughter without us and we know he won't get Jews like us from another town, for he would have to hire other wagons and postpone the wedding and it would be much too much trouble and expense."

"Just because we are poor," a striker with a patch over one eye interrupted and started to climb into the wagon, "you think you can push us around! Well, there isn't a person alive who can force us to go, not the captain of the police—not even the biggest general. A ruble each, or you'll do without us."

Some jolly paupers started to jig and called upon the others to join them.

There was much angry talk. The poor gave vent to their bitterness and stored-up resentment. All their lives they had to be silent while insults were hurled at them; they had to be gracious when a penny was flung at them. Now they saw their opportunity for revenge. For the first time in their lives, they were needed by their betters. For the first time, they felt that they had the upper hand—that victory was within their grasp.

Suddenly, another messenger arrived from Reb Yitzhak and stated that the strikers would get a ruble each; that they were to come at once! What an uproar! What bedlam followed this announcement! The wagons were quickly filled amidst shouts of "Oh, my foot!," "My hand hurts!," "My broken bones!"

The horses were harnessed and the party started to move along merrily. Mischievous boys shouted, "Hip-hip-hurray!" They whistled after them and threw stones. To the mendicants, it seemed as if the populace was throwing flowers and accompanying them with bands of music.

After the wedding ceremony came the elaborate feast. Special tables were set for the poor. Reb Yitzhak, himself, together with members of his household, plied them with food and drink.

"Lechayim! For life!" the paupers toasted their host. "May you live to see joy in your children and acquire great riches yourself!"

"Lechayim, brothers, *lechayim!"* Reb Yitzhak responded. "Drink hearty! May the Lord give blessings and comfort to all Israel!"

After the feast, the musicians played and Reb Yitzhak joined the poor in a jolly dance before the bride. Whose joy could be likened to that of the father of the bride? He danced round and round, the edges of his long silk coat flapping like eagle's wings. Tears of joy rolled down his cheeks. He raised his eyes to heaven and his thoughts soared upwards. He laughed and cried like a baby, fell upon the necks of the poor, hugged and kissed them affectionately.

"Brothers," he called, "let's be merry! Jews, let's dance together! Faster . . . faster . . ."

The paupers clapped hands in rhythm and the wedding guests joined them in beating time to the music.

[TRANSLATED FROM THE HEBREW]

SYLVIA BERGER

Mrs. Perlberg's Partner in Heaven

(The incidents in this story are authentic. Mrs. Perlberg was a real woman, who, until the day she died, in 1961, at the age of 90, performed acts of charity and talked of her Partner in Heaven.)

Only a moment ago, Kornstein was down on earth, standing in front of his candy store, when the potato peddler's horse became wild, jumped the curb, and kicked him in the head. In that fraction of an instant before Kornstein found himself in heaven, he was able to see that the potato peddler, whom he knew very well as a kind and gentle soul, had cried out and fainted. Kornstein wanted to shout to him not to worry, that he knew it wasn't his fault, but there was no time . . . the Angel of Death wouldn't wait.

Kornstein blinked, opened his eyes and looked about him. He was rather frightened but also quite curious. In the hazy light, he was able to determine a large object that seemed to be shaped like a throne—the Throne of Judgment, no doubt—and at its right was a pair of scales, perfectly balanced, suspended in mid-air.

Suddenly, Kornstein was aware of music that sounded like a gentle breeze. Then the music became louder and nearer. Kornstein's face lit up in a smile of recognition. That melody . . . it was chasidic . . . of course, and the voice—he would know that "tam-ta-ra-ram-bam" anywhere. Sure enough! His old friend Yisrael was there beside him.

"Oh, Yisrael! Am I happy to see a familiar face!"

"You don't look so happy . . . I know . . . It's that potato peddler . . . crying and fainting . . . such a good man . . ."

"Yisrael, you know how things are here. So maybe you can tell me how I can get word to him. I must! I positively must! Would it be possible to send a message down to earth . . . nothing lengthy, you know, just something like 'Don't be aggravated. Not your fault. Signed, Kornstein?' "

"You'll need a messenger, and I have just the one—my wife Itkele."

Kornstein puckered his brow. He had heard that his friend Yisrael had a charming wife, but to bring a message from heaven, you had to have a person with the proper qualifications and lots of experience.

Yisrael led his friend to a nearby cloud and after they were comfortably seated, said, "Don't worry! You couldn't find a better messenger. Itkele has been that all her life.

"One afternoon, she went to buy a pair of shoes. Her old ones were so torn—you could almost see her toes. She left with the five-dollar bill pinned to her pocketbook, so as not to lose it. Well, the children were home from school, and I had already come from work, but no mama. Then she burst in with apologies for being late and with such a happy glow on her face! But she had no package in her hands.

" 'What luck I had today,' she started, as she hurried to peel potatoes, beat eggs and tell the children how to set the table. 'I nearly missed the trolley. That is, I really did, but Mr. McGuire, the conductor, saw me running and stopped for me to get on. You know who was on that trolley? The grocer's youngest son, the one who goes to night school, the one who is going to be a doctor. Oh, my! He looked so sad! You know why! He lost his job. So how can he buy books now and study to become a doctor?'

"And the shoes? What about the shoes?" I asked.

" 'I really don't need shoes. I feel so comfortable in my old ones. Am I lucky I didn't miss that trolley!' "

"That's a nice story," Kornstein conceded, "but to be a messenger from heaven . . . Do you think charity is enough?"

"Not enough? I am surprised at you, Kornstein. It is so important that even the poor who live on charity must practice it."

"What I mean," said Kornstein, "is something better than charity . . . charity done in secret."

"Is that what's bothering you? Listen! I must tell you the story of the overcoat. You remember that cold winter we had when the ink froze in the ink bottles? Nobody moved away from the kitchen stove, that is, nobody but my Itke. She was out with Birdele—the child was only nine. They had been to Mrs. Rosen, Mrs. McSweeney, Mrs. Antini, Mrs. Epstein—not for any other reason but to collect clothing. Itke had quite a pack. The child helped carry as much as she could.

" 'Mama, Papa will be mad. You know what the doctor said. You mustn't lug such heavy bundles.'

" 'What makes you think it's heavy?'

" 'I know what's in it.'

" 'Baby dresses—that's what's in it. How heavy are baby dresses?'

" 'But there's a man's coat,' said Birdele.

" 'With empty pockets! How heavy is an empty pocket?'

"Just then a man passed by, shivering. His jacket collar was turned up; he wore no coat.

"Itke stopped him. 'Pardon me, haven't we met before?'

" 'I'm afraid not,' the man answered gruffly.

" 'That's funny! I could have sworn that we met at cousin Essie's sweet sixteen party.'

" 'I don't have a cousin Essie,' said the man.

" 'That's strange. You even look like cousin Essie. Please don't be angry. I want to ask you for a favor.'

" 'I'm not angry . . . a favor?' the man asked in surprise.

"Itke opened her bundle and pulled out the coat. 'Please, take this off my hands. My husband! That's the way he is! If he doesn't want something, I must get it out of the house! You'll do me such a favor . . . Here, try it on . . . My! It fits like a glove . . . thank you . . . thank you . . .'

" 'Thank *you,*' said the stranger, as he walked off with a puzzled expression on his face, but with what a happy spring in his step!

"Oh! I forgot to tell you," Yisrael said to his friend Kornstein. We don't have a cousin Essie either . . . then there was Mrs. Zilberstone . . ."

"The rich Mrs. Zilberstone? You mean to tell me that your wife helped her?"

"Ah! Then you didn't know that her husband had lost all his money and that they had become poor, very poor. My Itkele undertook to turn Mrs. Zilberstone's 'valuables' into cash. To whom do you think she sold Mrs. Zilberstone's beaded dress? To me! For fifty dollars! Thirty-seven lamp shades we had from those beads . . . My wife found other customers for the threadbare linen cloth and the moth-eaten squirrel muff, and . . ."

"Your wife might do as a messenger, but I have one more question to ask. Will she be able to talk well enough to convince the potato peddler that I forgive him, that I know he wasn't even near his horse, that it wasn't his fault? Why a man could go out of his mind with worry . . . That's a very important matter, that 'message.' "

"Kornstein, can my wife talk! She can talk teeth right into a man's mouth. She did that to Mr. Proshansky. Proshansky needed a dental plate, but he couldn't afford to pay, so Itkele went to visit her dentist.

" 'Dr. Miller,' she said, 'why should a man take his lack of business to a stranger?'

" 'What do you mean, Mrs. Perlberg?'

" 'That you are such a wonderful dentist! I always tell my children, "When you sew a button on a coat, sew it the way Dr. Miller puts in a filling. So even when the whole coat goes, the button is still there . . ." '

" 'Thank you, Mrs. Perlberg! What did you say about business?'

" 'I wanted to tell you that you can make a plate for money any time, but how many times can you make it for nothing? I told Mr. Proshansky, "Please, go only to Dr. Miller. Don't rob him of his partnership!" '

" 'My partnership? I don't understand!'

" 'When you make a plate for money, that's business. When you make it for nothing, the Lord is your partner . . . Mr. Proshansky is waiting outside, Doctor . . .' "

"I like that story, Yisrael. I am almost convinced that your wife is the one to deliver the message, so now . . ."

"Wait," Yisrael interrupted, "I never told you about those people. There were always people staying with us, sharing our beds . . ."

"But you were a big family. Weren't you crowded?"

"Of course we were crowded! But they had no place to live; either they were poor, or they just came out of the hospital with no one to care for them . . .

" 'They are very important people,' " Itke would say.

"There was the time that Miss Thorgenson lived with us. She was studying to become an American citizen.

" 'Mrs. Perlberg, one of the things I have to know is who was the first president,' Miss Thorgenson said.

" 'The first president was Christopher Columbus,' was Mama's quick reply.

" 'Oh, Ma!' Moshele who was sitting doing his homework, blurted out. 'George Washington was the first president of the United States.'

" 'Excuse me, Miss Thorgenson,' Ma apologized, 'I made a mistake.' Then, turning to the children, she continued,

'You see how the Lord is with us at every step! If Miss Thorgenson hadn't needed a place to live, I wouldn't have learned the name of the first president.'

" 'My teacher says the world is round,' Moshele continued when he saw his mother's interest in his knowledge.

" 'Round as a ball," Itke repeated. 'You see how the work of the Lord is perfect? What is more perfect than round?'

" 'My teacher says it is all cut up with lines running all around it. Longitudes and latitudes, they're called.'

" 'Better and better!' Itke answered with excitement. 'You see how it is, children? How much can a man see of the perfection that is the world? Less than the eyes of a fly can see of an apple. So what has He done to give us a better view of it? He has cut it up into little sections·for us, and each section is held inside a latitude and longitude . . . and between the latitudes are the waters winking and the green earth greening and . . . Whose hands hold the latitudes and the longitudes, like a beautiful net spread around us for our safety? A Hand . . . too wonderful to pass my lips . . .' "

"The stories are getting better and better," Kornstein said, but his friend Yisrael was now wistfully looking off into eternal space.

Down on earth, however, Itke still had much to do.

"Ma, there are two people in my room," Moshele said.

"Yes, very important people . . . a potato peddler and his wife. I must go and have a talk with them right now."

Kornstein started to smile and hum a happy tune.

"You sound as if a weight were just removed from your heart," Yisrael remarked. "Have you decided on a messenger?"

"The Message has already been delivered, Yisraelchik! Tam-ta-ra-tam-bam!"

[ADAPTED]

ABBY ALDRICH ROCKEFELLER

Letter to My Children

Dear John, Nelson, and Laurance:

For a long time I have had very much on my mind and heart a certain subject. I meant to bring it up at prayers and then later have it for a question to be discussed at a family council; but the right time, because of your father's illness, has never seemed to come.

Out of my experience and observation has grown the earnest conviction that one of the greatest causes of evil in the world is race hatred or race prejudice; in other words, the feeling of dislike that a person or a nation has against another person or nation without just cause, an unreasoning aversion is another way to express it. The two peoples or races who suffer most from this treatment are the Jews and the Negroes; but some people "hate" the Italians, who in turn hate the Yugoslavs, who hate the Austrians, who hate the Czecho-Slovaks, and so it goes endlessly.

You boys are still young. No group of people has ever done you a personal injury; you have no inherited dislikes. I want to make an appeal to your sense of fair play and to beseech you to begin your lives as young men by giving the other fellow, be he Jew or Negro or of whatever race, a fair chance and a square deal.

It is to the disgrace of America that horrible lynchings and race riots frequently occur in our midst. The social ostracism of the Jew is less brutal, and yet it often causes cruel injustice and must engender in the Jews a smouldering fire of resentment.

Put yourselves in the place of an honest, poor man who happens to belong to one of the so-called "despised" races. Think of having no friendly hand held out to you, no kindly look, no pleasant, encouraging word spoken to you. What I would like you always to do is what I try humbly to do myself: that is, never to say or to do anything which would wound the feelings or the self-respect of any human being, and to give special consideration to all who are in any way repressed. This is what your father does naturally from the fineness of his nature and the kindness of his heart.

I long to have our family stand firmly for what is best and highest in life. It isn't always easy, but it is worth while.

Your Mother

6

The Jewish Way of Life

It hath been told thee, O man,
What is good
And what the Lord doth require of thee:
Only to do justly, and to love mercy and to walk humbly with thy God.

Micah VI, 8.

STEFAN ZWEIG

The Torah and the Menorah

In the year 455 the vandals led by Genseric swooped down upon Rome to rob and plunder, even as the Huns had done before.

The Roman army was far away, and the city was defenseless. In an hour the Teutons and the North African Berbers and Numideans, allies of Genseric, had conquered it. They went through the city methodically and ruthlessly, seizing anything of value, and piling it up to transport to Carthage.

Among the booty seized by the invaders were treasures from the Temple of Jerusalem—the Silver Trumpets, the Altar of Incense, Aaron's Rod, the Table of Shewbread and above all, the Seven Branched Gold Candelabrum or Menorah. All of these had once stood in the Holy of Holies. They had been brought to Rome by Titus after he had despoiled the Temple in Jerusalem in the year 70.

When the Jewish leaders of Rome learned that the Temple treasures were being seized by the invaders, they tried to redeem the Lampstead with gold, but their efforts were in vain; and so, they decided to go along with it into exile. In order to transmit the meaning and the sanctity of the Candelabrum to the future generations, the elders decided to take a child along with them.

Between Grandfather Abtalion and Rabbi Eliezer, trotted the boy, panting, in his eagerness not to be a drag on his elders. He was silent because the others said not a word, but his little heart fluttered against his ribs. He was afraid, now that the excitement of novelty was passing; mortally afraid because he could not guess why they had dragged him out of bed at such an hour, afraid because he did not know where the old men were taking him; most afraid of all because never before had he been in the open country after dark, and beneath the open sky. He was familiar with night in the alleys of the Jewish quarter; but there the blackness of the sky was but a narrow strip in which two or three stars twinkled. No reason to dread that ribbon of sky, which familiarity had robbed of its terrors. He knew it best as he glimpsed at it between the slats, which broke it up into tiny fragments, too small to be alarming; while he listened, before he fell asleep, to the prayers of the men, the coughing of the sick, the shuffling feet of those who went by in the alley, the caterwauling on the roof, the crackling of the logs as they burned on the hearth. On the right was Mother, on the left Rachel; he was safe, warm, cosy; never alone.

But here the night was threatening, huge, and void. How tiny felt the little boy beneath the vast expanse of heaven. Had not the old men been with him to protect him, he would have burst into tears, would have tried to crawl into some hiding-place where he could escape from the huge dome which marched with him as he marched, always the same, always oppressive.

Happily there was room in his breast for pride as well as fear; pride because the elders in whose presence Mother dared not raise her voice, and before whom the children quaked—because these great and wise men had chosen him, little Benjamin, to accompany them upon their quest. What did it mean? What could it mean? Child though he was, he felt sure that something tremendous must account for this procession through the night. Most eager, therefore, was he to show himself worthy of their choice, trying to take manly strides with his little legs, and refusing to admit even to himself that he was afraid. But the test of his courage and endurance lasted too long. He grew more and more tired, frightened of the very shadows of himself and his companions; alarmed by the sound of their footsteps upon the paved road. Now, when a bat, blundering through the night, almost touched his forehead, he shuddered and screamed at the black, unknown horror. Gripping Abtalion's hand, he cried:

"Grandfather, Grandfather, where are we going?"

Without even turning to look at the lad, his grandfather growled:

"Hold your tongue, and don't drag back. Little boys must be seen and not heard."

The youngster shrank, as if from a blow, ashamed at having given vent to his terror. In thought he scolded himself: "Of course, I ought not to have asked." Still, he could not restrain his sobs.

But Rabbi Eliezer, the pure and clear, looked reproachfully at Abtalion over the little one's head, saying:

"Nay, friend, it is you who are to blame. How natural that the child should ask that question! What could he do but wonder at our taking him from his bed and bringing him forth with us into the night? Moreover, why should he not learn the object of our pilgrimage? We bring him with us because he is of our blood, and therefore partaker in our destinies. Surely he will continue to sustain our sorrows long after we have been laid to rest? He is to live on, bearing witness to those of a coming time as the last member of our Roman community to see the Lampstand from the Table of the Lord. Why should you wish him to remain in ignorance? We have brought him with us to watch and to know, and to give tidings of this night in days to come."

Abtalion made no answer, feeling justly reproved. Rabbi Eliezer tenderly stroked Benjamin's hair, and said encouragingly:

"Ask, child, ask freely, and I shall answer with the same freedom. Better to ask than to be ignorant. Only through asking can we gain knowledge, only through knowledge can we win our way to righteousness."

The boy was elated that the sage whom all the community revered should talk to him as an equal. He would gladly have kissed the Rabbi's hand, yet was too timid. His lips trembled, but he uttered no sound. Rabbi Eliezer—whose wisdom was not only the wisdom of books, since he had also the wisdom of those who know the human heart—understood, despite the darkness, all that Benjamin thought and felt. He sympathized with their little companion's impatience to know the whither and the why of this strange expedition, so he fondled the hand which lay as light and tremulous as a butterfly in his own withered palm.

"I will tell you where we are going, and will hide nothing. There is naught wrongful in our purpose, though it must be hidden from those whom ere long we shall join. God, who looks down on us from heaven, knows and approves. He knows the beginning as clearly as we know it ourselves; and He knows what we cannot know, the end."

While speaking thus to the child, Rabbi Eliezer did not slacken his pace. The others quickened their steps for a moment, to draw nearer, and hearken to his words of wisdom.

"We walk along an ancient road, my child, on which our fathers and forefathers walked in days of yore. In ages past we were a nation of wanderers, as we have become once more, and as we are perhaps destined to remain until the end of time. Not like the other peoples have we lands of our own, where we can grow and harvest our crops. We move continually from place to place; and when we die, our graves are dug in foreign soil. Yet scattered though we are, flung like weeds into the furrows from north to south and from east to west, we have remained one people, united as is no other, held together by our God and our faith in Him. Invisible is the tie which binds us, the invisible God. I know, child, that this passeth your understanding, for at your tender age you can grasp only the life of the senses, which perceive nothing but the corporeal, that which can be seen, touched, or tasted, like earth and wood and stone and brass. For that very reason the Gentiles, being children in mind, have made unto themselves gods of wood and stone and metal. We alone, we of the Chosen People, have no such tangible and visible gods (which we call idols), but an invisible God whom we know with an understanding that is above the senses. All our afflictions have come from this urge which drives us into the suprasensual, which makes us perpetual seekers for the invisible. But stronger is he who relies upon the invisible rather than on the visible and the palpable, since the latter perisheth, whereas the former endureth for ever. Spirit is in the end stronger than force. Therefore, and therefore alone, little Benjamin, have we lived on through the ages, outlasting time because we are pledged to the timeless, and only because we have been loyal to the invisible God has the invisible God kept faith with us.

"Child, these words of mine will be too deep for you. Often and often we elders are troubled because the God and the Justice in whom we believe are not visible in this our world. Still, even though you cannot now understand me, be not therefore troubled, but go on listening."

"I listen, Rabbi," murmured the boy, bashful but ecstatic.

"Filled with this faith in the invisible, our fathers and forefathers moved on through the world. To convince themselves of their own belief in this invisible God who never disclosed himself to their eyes and of whom no image may be graven, our ancestors made them a sign. For narrow is our understanding; the infinite is beyond our comprehension. Only from time to time does a shadow of the divine cast itself into our life here below. Fitfully and feebly a light from God's invisible countenance illumines our darkness. Hence, that we may be ever reminded of our duty to serve the invisible, which is justice and eternity and grace, we made the furniture of the Tabernacle, where God was unceasingly worshipped—made a Lampstand, called the Menorah, whose seven lamps burned unceasingly; and an altar whereon the shewbread was perpetually renewed. Misunderstand me not. These were not representations of the divine essence, such as the heathen impiously fashion. The holy emblems testified to our eternally watchful faith; and whithersoever we wandered through the world, the furnishings of the Holy Place wandered with us. Enclosed in the Ark of the Covenant, they were safeguarded in a Tabernacle which our forefathers homeless as we are this night, bore with them on their shoulders; when the Tabernacle with its furniture rested, we likewise rested; when it was moved onward, we followed. Resting or journeying, by day or by night, for thousands of years we Jews thronged round this Holy of Holies; and as long as we preserve our sense of its sanctity, so long, even though dispersed among the heathen, shall we remain a united people.

"Now listen. Among the furnishings of the Holy Place were the Altar of the Shewbread, which also bore the fruits of the earth in due season; the Vessels from which clouds of incense rose to heaven; and the Tables of Stone whereon God had written His Commandments. But the most conspicuous on all the furniture was a Lampstand whose lamps burned unceasingly to throw light on the Altar in the Holy of Holies. For God loves the light which He kindled; and we made this Lampstand in gratitude for the light which He bestowed on us to gladden our eyes. Of pure gold, of beaten work, was the Lampstand cunningly fashioned. Seven-branched was it, having a central stem and three branches on each side, every one with a bowl made like unto an almond with a knop and a flower, all beaten work of pure gold. When the seven lamps were lighted, each light rose above its golden flower, and our hearts rejoiced to see. When it burned before us on the Sabbath, our souls became temples of devotion. No other symbol on earth, therefore, is so dear to us as this Seven-Branched Lampstand, and wherever you find a Jew who continues to cherish his faith in the Holy One of Israel, no matter under which of the winds of heaven his house stands, you will find in that house a model of the Menorah lifting its seven branches in prayer."

"Why seven?" the boy ventured to ask.

"Ask, and you shall be answered, child. To ask reverently is the beginning of wisdom. Seven is the most holy of numbers, for there were Seven Days of Creation, the crowning wonder being the creation of man in God's own image. What miracle can be greater than that we should find ourselves in this world, be aware of it and love it, and know something of its Creator? By making light in the firmament of heaven, God enabled our eyes to see and our spirit to know. That is why, with its seven branches, the Lampstand praises both lights, the outer and the inner. For God has given us also an inner light in Holy Writ; and just as we see outwardly with our eyes, so does Scripture enable us to see inwardly by the light of the understanding. What flame is to the senses, that is Scripture to the soul; for in Scripture all is recounted, explained, and enjoined: God's doings, and the deeds of our fathers; what is allowed to us and what forbidden; the creative spirit and the regulative law. In a twofold way God, through his light, enables us to contemplate the world: from without by the senses, and from within by the spirit; and thanks to the divine illumination we can even achieve self-knowledge. Do you understand me, child?"

"No," gasped the little boy, too proud to feign.

"Of course not," said Rabbi Eliezer gently. "These things are too deep for a mind so young. Understanding will come with the years. For the present, bear in mind what you can understand of all I have told you. The most sacred things of those we had as emblems on our wanderings, the only things remaining to us from our early days, were the Five Books of Moses and the Seven-Branched Lampstand, the Torah and the Menorah. Bear those words in mind."

"The Torah and the Menorah," repeated Benjamin solemnly, clenching his fists as if to aid his memory.

"Now listen further. There came a time, long, long ago, when we grew weary of wandering. Man craves for the earth, even as the earth craves for man. After forty years in the wilderness, we entered the Promised Land, as Moses had foretold, and we took possession of it. We ploughed and sowed and harvested, planted vineyards and tamed beasts, tilled fruitful fields which we surrounded with hedges and hurdles, being glad at heart that we no longer sojourned among strangers to be unto them a scorn and a hissing. We believed that our wanderings were finished forever and a day, being foolhardy enough to declare that the land was our very own—whereas to no man is land given, but only lent for a season. Always are mortals prone to forget that having is not holding, and finding is not keeping. He who feels the ground firm beneath his feet builds him a house, fancying that thus he roots himself as firmly as do the trees. Therefore we builded houses and cities; and since each of us had a home of his own, it was meet that we should wish our Lord and Protector likewise to have an abiding-place among us, a House of God which should be greater and more splendid than any human habitation. Thus it came to pass during the years when we were settled at peace in the

Land of Promise that there ruled over us a king who was wealthy and wise, known as Solomon—"

"Praised be his name," interposed Abtalion gently.

"Praised be his name," eachoed the others, without slackening in their stride.

"—who builded a house upon Mount Moriah, where aforetime Jacob, dreaming, saw a ladder set up on the earth, and the top of it reached to heaven; and behold the angels of God ascending and descending on it. Wherefore on awaking Jacob said: 'Holy is this place, and holy shall it be to all the peoples of the earth.' And here Solomon builded the Temple of the Lord, of stone and cedar wood and finely wrought brass. When our forefathers looked upon its walls they felt assured that God would dwell perpetually in our midst, and give us peace to the end of time. Even as we rested in our homes, so did the Tabernacle rest in the House of God, and within the Tabernacle the Ark of the Covenant, which we had borne with us for so long. By day and by night burned unceasingly before the Altar the seven flames of the Menorah, for this and all that was sacred to us were enshrined in the Holy of Holies; and God himself, though invisible as He shall be while time endures, rested peaceably in the land of our forefathers, in the Temple of Jerusalem."

"May my eyes behold it once again," came the voices in a litany.

"But listen further, my child. Whatever man possessess is entrusted to him only as a loan, and his happiness is unstable as a shadow. Not for ever, as we fancied, was our peace established, for a fierce people came from the east and forced a way into our town, even as the robbers whom you have seen forced a way into the city of the Gentiles among whom we have sojourned. What they could seize, they seized; what was portable, they carried away; what they could destroy, they destroyed. But our invisible goods they could not take from us—God's word and God's eternal presence. The Menorah, however, the holy Lampstand, they took from the Table of the Lord and carried it away; not because it was holy (since these sons of Belial knew naught of holiness), but because it was made of gold, and robbers love gold. Likewise they took the Altar and the Vessels, and drove our whole people into captivity in Babylon—"

"Babylon? What is Babylon? Where is Babylon?"

"Ask freely, child, and with God's will you shall be answered. Babylon was a great city, big as Rome, lying nearly as far to the east of Jerusalem as Rome lies to the west. Look you, we have walked for three hours since leaving the gate of Rome, and already we ache with weariness, but that march was a hundred times as long. Think, then, how far to the east the Menorah was taken by the robbers, and we driven with it into captivity. Mark this, also, that to God distance is nothing. To man it is otherwise; but perhaps the meaning of our unending pilgrimage is that what is sacred to us grows more sacred with distance, and our hearts are humbled by affliction. However, that may be, when God saw that his Word was still holy to us in exile, that we stood the test, he softened the heart of one of the kings of that alien people. Aware that we had been wronged, he let our forefathers return to the Promised Land, giving back to them the Lampstand and the furniture of the Tabernacle. Then did our forefathers leave Chaldea and make their way home to Jerusalem across deserts, mountains, and thickets. From the ends of the earth they returned to the place which they had never ceased to cherish in their memories. We rebuilt the Temple on Mount Moriah; again the seven lamps of the Seven-Branched Lampstand flamed before God's altar, and our hearts flamed with exultation. Now mark this, Benjamin, that you may grasp the meaning of our pilgrimage which begins tonight. No other thing made by the hands of man is so holy, so ancient, and so travelled hither and thither, as this Seven-Branched Menorah, which is the most precious pledge of the unity and purity of the Chosen People. Always when our lot is saddened the lamps of the Menorah are extinguished."

Rabbi Eliezer paused. At this the boy looked up, his eyes flaming like the lamps of the sacred emblem, eager with expectation that the story should be continued. The Rabbi smiled as he noticed this impatience, and stroked the lad's hair, saying:

"Have no fear, little one. The tale is not ended. Our destiny marches on. I could talk to you for years and fail to recount a thousandth part of all that has happened to us and all that awaits us. Listen then, since you are a good listener, to what befell after our return to Jerusalem from Babylon. Once more we thought that the Temple had been established forever. But once more enemies came, across the sea this time, from the land where we now sojourn as strangers. A famous general led them, son of an Emperor, and himself in due time to be Emperor; Titus was he called—"

"Accursed be his name," intoned the elders.

"—who breached our walls and destroyed the Temple. Impiously he entered the Holy of Holies and snatched the Lampstand from the Altar. He plundered the Lord's House, and had the sacred furnishings carried before him when he celebrated his triumph upon his return to Rome. The foolish populace rejoiced, thinking that Titus had conquered our God, and that this was one of the captives who marched before him in fetters. So proud of his victory was the miscreant, that he had an arch built to commemorate it, with graven images that showed forth how he had ravaged the House of God."

"Rabbi," asked the boy, "tell me, is that the arch decorated with so many stone images? The arch in the great square, the arch which Father said I must never, never go through?'

"That's the one, child. Never go through it, but pass by without looking, for this memorial of Titus's triumph is likewise the memorial of one of the most sorrowful days in our history. No Jew may walk beneath the Arch of Titus, on which are graven images to show how the Romans mocked what was and always will be holy to us. Remember unfailingly—"

The old man broke off, for Hyrcanus ben Hillel had sprung forward from the rear to lay a hand upon his lips. The others were terrified by this irreverent freedom, but Hyrcanus silently pointed forward. Yes, there was something partially disclosed by the fog-bedimmed moon—a dark shape that seemed to wriggle along the white road like a huge caterpillar. Now, when the elders halted and listened, they could hear the creaking of heavily laden carts. Above these or beside them there flashed spears which looked like blades of grass that shine in the dew of morning—the lances of the Numidian rearguard escorting the spoil.

They kept good watch, the lancers, for a number of them wheeled their horses, to gallop back with levelled weapons and uttering shrill cries. Their burnouses streamed in the breeze, so that it seemed as if their chargers were winged. Involuntarily the eleven old men drew together in a bunch, the child in their midst. The lancers did not tarry until the steel points were close to the suspect pursuers; then they drew rein so suddenly that their mounts reared. Even in the faint light, the cavalrymen could see that these were no warriors, designing to recapture the booty, but peaceful whitebeards, infirm and old, each with staff and scrip. Thus in Numidia, too, did pious elders make pilgrimage from shrine to shrine. The fierce lancers, suspicions allayed, laughed encouragingly, showing white teeth. The leader whistled, once more the troop wheeled, and thundered down the road after the carts they were convoying, while the old men stood and trembled, hardly able to believe they were to be left unharmed.

Rabbi Eliezer, the pure and clear, was the first to regain composure. Gently he tapped the little boy's cheek.

"You're a brave lad, Benjamin," he said, leaning forward over the youngster. "I was holding your hand, and it did not shake. Shall I go on with my story? You have not yet heard whither we are going, or why we did not seek our beds as usual."

"Please go on, Rabbi," answered the boy, eagerly.

"I told you, you will remember, how Titus (accursed be his name), having laid impious hands on our holy treasures, carried them off to Rome and, in the vanity of his triumph, made a display of them all over the city. Thereafter, however, the Emperors of Rome put the Menorah and the other sacred objects from Solomon's Temple for safe-keeping in what they called the Temple of Peace—a foolish name, for when has peace ever lasted in our contentious world? Nor would Jehovah permit the furniture of the Tabernacle which had adorned his own Holy House in Zion to remain in a heathen temple, so one night he sent a fire to consume that building with all its contents, save only our Lampstand and other treasures which were rescued from the devouring flames, to show once again that neither fire nor distance nor the hand of a robber has power over the Menorah. This was a sign, a warning from God, that the Romans should restore the sacred emblems to their own sacred place, where they would be honoured, not because they were made of gold, but because they were holy. But when did such fools understand a sign, or when did men's stubborn hearts bow before the light of reason?"

Having paused to sigh, Rabbi Eliezer resumed:

"Thus the Gentiles took the Lampstand and put it away in one of the Emperor's other houses; and because it remained there in safe-keeping for years and for decades, they believed it to be theirs for all eternity. Nevertheless it is untrue to say that there is honour among thieves. What one robber has stolen will be taken from him forcibly by another. Just as Rome sacked Jerusalem, so has Carthage sacked Rome. Even as the Romans plundered us, they themselves have been plundered, and as they defiled our sacred places, so have their sacred places been defiled. But the robbers have also taken away what was ours, the Menorah, the emblem which used to stand on God's Altar in King Solomon's House. Those wains which drive westward through the darkness are carrying to the coast that which is dearest to us in the world. Tomorrow the barbarians will put the Lampstand on one of their ships, to sail away with it into foreign parts, where it will be beyond the reach of our longing eyes. Never again will the Lampstand shed its beams upon us who are old and near to death. Nevertheless as those who have loved anyone when alive escort the body upon its last journey to the tomb, thus testifying their affection, so today do we escort the Menorah upon the first stage of its journey into foreign parts. What we are losing is the holiest of our treasures. Do you understand, now, little one, the meaning of our mournful pilgrimage?"

The child walked on with hanging head, and made no answer. He seemed to be thinking things over.

"Never forget this, Benjamin. We have brought you with us as witness, that in days to come, when we are beneath the sod, you may bear testimony to the way in which we were loyal to the sacred emblem, and may teach others to remain faithful. You will fortify them in the faith which sustains us, the faith that the Menorah will one day return from its wanderings in the darkness, and, as of old, will with its seven flames shed a glorious light upon the Table of the Lord. We awoke you from your slumbers that your heart might also awaken, and that you will be able to tell those of a later generation what befell this night. Store up everything in your mind that you may console others by telling them how your own eyes have seen the Menorah which has moved onward for thousands of years among strangers, even as our people have wandered. Firmly do I believe that it will never perish so long as we remain alive as God's Chosen People faithful to the Law."

[TRANSLATED BY EDEN AND CEDAR PAUL]

The Angels Jealous of Moses

Rabbi Joshua, son of Levi, says that the time when Moses went up to heaven to receive the Law, which the Lord, blessed be He, was giving him, the angels said, "Lord of the universe, what is a mortal man doing here in the heavens amongst us?"

And the Lord replied, "He has come to receive the Torah."

Then the angels said, "Wilt Thou hand over to man that hidden jewel which Thou hast treasured up with Thee during 974 generations, before Thou hadst created the world? What is man whom Thou hast created? 'Give Thy beauty to the heavens' (Ps. 8.2). Leave the Torah here and do not give it to man."

Then God said, "Moses, answer the angels concerning that which they have spoken to Me."

And Moses replied, "Lord of the universe, I would fain answer them, but I fear lest they burn me up with the breath of their mouths."

Then God said, "Moses take hold of the throne of glory and answer their speech."

And when our master Moses heard this, he began to speak, and said, "Lord of the universe, what is written in that Torah which Thou intendest to give to me? 'I am the Lord thy God who brought thee out of the land of Egypt' (Ex. 20.2). O angels, have you gone down into Egypt, Have you served Pharaoh? Then why should the Lord, blessed be He, give you the Torah? Again, what else is written in this

Torah? Is it not written, 'Thou shalt have no other gods before Me' (ibid. v.3) ? Are you living among heathens that you should serve other gods? It is further written therein, 'Remember the Sabbath day, to keep it holy' (ibid. v.8), which means, rest on that day. Are you working that you should have to be commanded to rest? Furthermore, it is written therein, 'Thou shalt not take a false oath' (cf. ibid. v.7). Are you engaged in business that you should be commanded not to take a false oath? Furthermore, 'Honour thy father and thy mother' (ibid. v.12). Have you a father and a mother that you should be commanded to honour them? 'Thou shalt not murder, thou shalt not commit adultery, thou shalt not steal' (ibid. v.13) Is there envy and hatred among you that you should be commanded not to do these things? Of what good, therefore, is the Torah to you?"

When the angels heard this, they became friendly to Moses and everyone of the angels taught him something, even the Angel of Death.

Moses Receiving the Law

Rabbi Joshua son of Levi said: After God, blessed be He, had given the Law to Moses, and Moses had come down from heaven, Satan said: "Lord of the universe, where has Thou put the Torah? To whom hast Thou given it?"

The Lord replied, "I have given it to the Earth."

So Satan went to the Earth and said, "Where hast thou put the Torah which the Lord, blessed be He, has given thee?"

The Earth replied: " 'God understandeth the way thereof' (Job 28.23). This means that the Lord, blessed be He, knows everything. But I have not the Torah."

Then Satan went to the Sea and said, "Oh, Sea, where hast thou put the Torah which the Lord, blessed be He, has given thee?"

The Sea replied, " 'The Torah is not with me' " (ibid. v.14).

Then Satan went to the uttermost depth of the earth and said, "Where hast thou put the Torah which the Lord, blessed be He, has given thee?"

The abyss of the earth replied, " 'It is not in me' " (ibid.). So Satan went all over the earth searching for the Torah, for the Lord had told him that he had given it to the earth. Then Satan went to the dead and the lost and asked them: "Where have you put the Torah which the Lord has given you?"

And they replied, "Verily we have heard of it with our ears, but we know nothing more." (cf. Ps. 54.2).

Then Satan came again before the Lord, blessed be He, and said "Lord of the universe, I have searched the whole earth, but I have not found the Torah."

Then the Lord said unto him, "Go to Moses, the son of Amram, to whom I have given it."

Then Satan went to our master Moses and said, "Moses, where hast thou put the Torah which the Lord has given thee?"

And Moses replied, "How dost thou come to ask me about the Torah? Who am I and what am I that the Lord should give me the Torah?"

When the Lord, blessed be He, heard that Moses would not admit that he had received the Torah, He said, "Thou art a liar. Why dost thou deny that I have given thee the Torah?"

And Moses replied, "Lord of the universe, the Torah is a desirable object, it filleth with joy him who is engaged in studying it. Thou rejoicest over it and studiest it Thyself every day. How then can I boast and say that I have received the Torah? It is not seemly for a man to boast of anything, even though he has reason to do so. On the contrary, it is better that he should be humble."

And the Lord said, "Since thou humblest thyself, and dost not wish to claim the honor of having received the Torah, it shall, as a reward, be called by thy name."

This is why it is written, "Remember the Law of Moses, My servant, and keep the Law of Moses." (Mal. 3.22) .

EMMA LAZARUS

Gifts

"O World-God, give me Wealth!" the Egyptian cried.
His prayer was granted. High as heaven, behold
Palace and pyramid; the brimming tide
Of lavish Nile washed all his land with gold.
Armies of slaves toiled ant-wise at his feet,
World-circling traffic roared through mart and street,
His priests were gods, his spice-balmed kings enshrined,
Set death at nought in rock-ribbed charnels deep.
Seek Pharaoh's race today and ye shall find
Rust and the moth, silence and dusty sleep.

"O World-God, give me beauty!" cried the Greek.
His prayer was granted. All the earth became
Plastic and vocal to his sense; each peak,
Each grove, each stream, quick with Promethean flame,
Peopled the world with imaged grace and light.
The lyre was his, and his the breathing might
Of the immortal marble, his the play
Of diamond-pointed thought and golden tongue.
Go seek the sunshine race. Ye find today
A broken column and a lute unstrung.

"O World-God, give me Power" The Roman cried.
His prayer was granted. The vast world was chained
A captive to the chariot of his pride.
The blood of myriad province was drained
To feed that fierce, insatiable red heart.

Invulnerably bulwarked every part
With serried legions and with close-meshed Code.
Within, the burrowing worm had gnawed its home,
A roofless ruin stands where once abode
The imperial race of everlasting Rome.

"O Godhead, give me Truth!" the Hebrew cried.
His prayer was granted; he became the slave
Of the Idea, a pilgrim far and wide,
Cursed, hated, spurned, and scourged with none to save.
The Pharaohs knew him, and when Greece beheld,
His wisdom wore the hoary crown of Eld.
Beauty he hath forsworn, and wealth and power.
Seek him today, and find in every land.
No fire consumes him, neither floods devour;
Immortal through the lamp within his hand.

MOSHE PRAGER

A Stray Leaf from a Prayer Book

It happened at a social gathering in Jerusalem with conversation on politics and current happenings. Someone touched upon the days of the Hitler holocaust, and there was sudden silence. Everyone became absorbed in his own emotions as he remembered his own experiences. Soon the quiet became oppressive, and the "Siberian" was unable to keep his thoughts to himself any longer. He began to speak—softly at first—as if he were talking to himself; his companions paid no attention to him. But soon he became agitated, his voice rose and his words became heated. The rest of the company perked up its ears.

"The age-old question, 'what is the greatest necessity in the world for man's survival,' has never been answered. Each person has a different view. I know what's in the minds of most of you—gold, or bread, or some such material thing. But I, the Siberian, after the many strange experiences into which fate has thrown me, have my own opinion on the subject. I am convinced that although bread and gold are very important, there is something more valuable than both of them put together.

"This gold, after which all men strive, is nothing but a mirage. If chance were to bring you to a gold mine, as it did me, you would be ready to barter one whole pound of it for a crust of bread; and yet, though you may live by bread and depend upon it for sustenance, it is still not of the greatest importance. During a time of hunger, it is possible to forget one's craving for food and become aware of spiritual hunger. When this need is satisfied, one experiences real physical pleasure."

The speaker's words were so compelling, as to make everyone move closer and listen to his story.

"I am a child of fate," he continued. "Why am I called the 'Siberian?' Do you think it is because I was born there? Not at all! The word 'Siberia,' rouses in me memories of freezing cold and everlasting snow. My cruel Jewish fate had tossed me about and hurled me beyond the mountains of darkness to the Arctic zone. Satan was given a free hand to vent his fury upon the Jews and to burn them with fire. The same fate permitted him to exchange the fires of the crematoria for the frosts of Siberia.

"When the sled, drawn by a dozen Siberian dogs, first brought me to the ends of the earth, the shores of the Arctic Ocean, I was truly glad. It felt good to be far, far away from the Nazi crematoria. My joy, however, was short-lived, for the very next day my stomach began to demand food and 'What is there to eat?' became the constant gnawing question.

"There are many kinds and degrees of hard labor in Siberia. The land itself is the very symbol of slavery. It is a prison, a land where nature vents its cruelty upon humans, and people turn with brutality upon each other.

"The officers, the overseers of the slave laborers, were 'committed' to the 'principle' of showing no mercy. We received nothing but animosity and hatred from them. We were the slaves of slaves; no degradation is lower than that.

"But chance brought me right into a gold mine and I became completely surrounded by the precious metal—real, shining gold, untouched by human hands. I was in a gold world. There was so much gold that it might have spouted from a volcano; the dust beneath my feet was gold; the cliffs of the savage mountains that cast melancholy and fear upon those who gazed on them, were streaked with veins of gold. And all this, I learned, was mine!

"When I was brought to Siberia, I was a prisoner in fetters. Suddenly, my chains were broken so that I might work unhampered in the gold mines. I became a miner. That's no work to be ashamed of. It wasn't easy, but the work was clean. All day long, I stood up to my knees in a stream that trickled down from the mountains. My job was to sift the sand that was being swept down with the water and to remove the gold dust. At times, the dust was very fine, but I also found nuggets and sometimes, big lumps of this precious ore. Would you believe it? I became drunk with gold! I contracted gold fever! All my senses were afire! The distant world was submerged in refuse and blood, but I was mining gold!

"One thing puzzled me: my overseer was very lax in his duty. In the center of our barracks was a big iron stove for refining the gold. The moment the sun would set, I would drag my weary, frozen bones to the stove to dry and warm up. But first, I had to hand over the bag of gold that I had gathered during the day. The taskmaster took it away without asking any questions. Nobody searched me. How fortunate was I! It meant that the gold was nature's treasure and was there for the taking. Wonderful! How wonderful!

"I was stricken with gold fever and it got the best of me. I accumulated a whole bottle of gold and hid it. My hoard grew each day. The gold was everybody's. Whoever wanted it, took it. The overseers paid no attention to me. It was apparently no crime to put aside a little gold for oneself. The gold had robbed me of my reason. It nourished my imagination by day and fed my dreams by night . . . gold . . . gold. . . .

"The glitter of gold proved to be an idle dream. Bitter disillusionment came very quickly. One day, I was hungry and went out to seek bread. I thought, 'Now I can get whatever I want; I won't be in need any longer.' You see, I already had piles and piles of gold hidden away. But when I approached the miserable slaves who had worked in the gold mines for years and offered them gold for bread, they laughed in my face. Their abusive scorn was as bitter as death.

"What value did gold have compared to bread? Bread is life; bread is heat; bread is a beloved friend. Gold is a madness, a snare, a void and a wasteland.

"Only then did I understand why the overseers did not search me; why all the gold in the mines was free for me. I threw all my gold on the ash heap. It was worthless, though it looked like a treasure. Yes, I threw away the gold that I had hoarded, and in so doing overthrew the kingdom of gold.

"From the moment that the greed for gold had taken hold of me, I had kept completely to myself; I had mistrusted everyone, suspected everyone of having designs on my gold. . . .

"Now I began to understand the reasons for the disunity among the Jewish inmates. We had been very close on that long-suffering trek to Siberia. We were captive Jews, brothers in misery, with a single destiny, but the curse of gold had divided us. Each of us had shut himself away with his own yellow bubble.

"After I freed myself from the spell of gold, I became the slave of bread. There really was no bread; I pursued only its shadow. Gold lay in the streets, but as for bread, there wasn't a crumb to be found. No scheming, no searching could help obtain it. With luck, one might find a wild mushroom, a treasure, a substitute for bread. All we had was the ice and snow in vast stretches before us and the dense snow-blanketed woods as far as the eye could see.

"Paper was a most important item. Sometimes it had greater value than bread. A cigarette could be rolled from it, and when a cigarette was lit and smoke rose, it could dull the appetite, dim the ugly realities, and give rise to a far-fetched hazy dream. One could scrounge in the ash heap and with luck, come up with a piece of paper.

"You must wonder what was the use of a cigarette, when it was nothing but a torn, dirty piece of paper and all one could get from it was a filthy, choking smoke. A cigarette was priceless, because it was a special nostrum for us; it fired our imagination and gave us a means of forgetting.

"Siberia had very little paper. Man lives primitively there, and doesn't depend upon civilization. The arctic dogs and the polar bears supply him with meat and fur—food and clothing. The mail comes twice a year—once in mid-winter by dog sled and once during the short summer after the snow melts, by kayaks that navigate the numerous rivers.

"It was during the coldest period of winter when the bells rang announcing the arrival of the mail. Although there never was anything for us, I would get a violent craving for a piece of paper during mail delivery. This time Lady Luck smiled upon me.

"The battalions stationed in Siberia consisted of men who were native to the north country and well able to withstand the Siberian climate. These men were the recipients of the mail. One of the soldiers, a farmer in civilian life, had a son fighting on a faraway front. In the army, the boy was taught to write, and he sent his father a letter stating that he was alive and well. The farmer-soldier received the letter, but was unable to fathom the secret of those strange marks on paper, so he called upon me for help.

"My reward was far beyond any expectations. The letter was in an envelope and the soldier, in his excitement on hearing the glad tidings, threw the envelope carelessly away, and walked off. The treasure was mine! It was a good piece of paper and would make a wonderful smoke.

"I went straight to my barracks. I wanted to hide so that I shouldn't have to share my booty with any of my brothers. I did not do this out of selfishness, Heaven is my witness! I had no choice, for if I were to give each one a puff, I would become the cause of bickering and quarrels; there would not be enough to go around.

"I was delirious with excitement. I hid in a corner, started to roll a cigarette, when suddenly I noticed that the paper in my hand had familiar letters on it, Hebrew words, and not just common words, but holy ones, words of a prayer book. A page out of a prayer book, a wonderful visitor had come to me! Only then did I realize that the Hebrew prayer books are in exile as are the Jews themselves. The prayer books are tossed about the streets, battered and torn, and a Russian soldier, even one born in Siberia, fighting on a far front, can use their pages for anything he wished. Since chance had brought one of these leaves to me, I would see to it that it would be profaned no longer. That stray page created a turmoil within me and had a similar effect upon every Jew in camp. It was a message from a world of long ago, a world antedating the flood, a world that had disappeared without leaving a trace. Now the bond was renewed, the sign was given, memory was awakened. . . .

"I held the torn page in my hand and felt unworthy of keeping this holy treasure. I decided to give it to someone for safe-keeping, to the one we called the "Little Rabbi." We named him thus, partly out of respect and partly to tease him. We never understood how the "Little Rabbi" figured things out, but he always knew when the holidays occurred.

"Now came the Little Rabbi's shining hour. When I showed him my holy treasure, tears of joy came to his eyes. He kissed the torn page lovingly. From the moment that I gave it to him, his importance in camp was established.

He wrapped it up, tied it carefully, and wore it next to his heart. Like a beacon light that attracts the lost wanderer, the Jews of our camp and of the others around us were drawn to this prize. How did the news spread? No one really knew. But when Jews that had been driven, forgotten, lost, started to come to the Little Rabbi, we were confident that we were outcasts no longer. No longer were we without aim or purpose, uprooted from our Jewish origin. We discovered in ourselves a holy affirmation of faith in our being. And this indestructible purpose breathed new life into us and awakened in us the ancient hope, the old, old faith that we had a right to live, and the confidence that someday we would leave this hell-hole, Siberia.

"This stray page from a prayer book held many magic cures for us. If anyone had to take an oath because of some quarrel or misunderstanding, he did so with his hand on this page. The dejected and melancholy kissed the page and were helped. Whoever had a frozen limb and was in danger of losing his life, was cured by having the page placed at his head.

"With the help of this torn page, the Little Rabbi, who never skipped a Sabbath or holiday, called all the Jews together for prayer. We all came. The prayer was short, consisting of only a few words. Every day another inmate was given an opportunity to read the few phrases. I remember one of them. 'Oh, God in Heaven, have pity upon us in your great compassion.' This short prayer was the most wonderful thing for us. We prayed with devotion, with fervor, and after the service, we all felt good. It was a feeling of real satisfaction.

"This tyrannical, frozen land with nothing but death in its grip, could not withstand the radiance kindled in the Jewish heart during prayer. A driven leaf from a Jewish prayer book protected us until our redemption from Siberia."

[TRANSLATED FROM THE HEBREW]

AIME PALLIERE

The Unknown Sanctuary

When I was seventeen years of age, a strange incident occurred which came to exercise an influence over my whole life. I call the attention of my readers to what I am about to relate to them. On a certain Thursday in the autumn when I was still on my vacation at Lyons, I was walking with a comrade on the Quai Tilsitt where the synagogue stands. We noticed that a number of shops had remained closed that day. My companion had heard that it was the great festival of the Jews and suggested to me that we enter the temple. I consented not without hesitation. Alone I would never have done it, for the pious Catholic does not permit himself to enter any building belonging to another religion, and for imperative reasons he must abstain from taking part in any ceremony. The synagogue was quite filled. All the votaries were standing and silent. I understood later that I had arrived at the moment of the prayer of Neila[1] on Yom Kippur.[2]

I will seek to analyse the impression that I felt in contemplating that which met my gaze. It was such that from that unique moment my life was to be shaped. This may seem inexplicable, and for me it is an unfathomable enigma, but all my plans for the future were to be upset and finally ended. I was to find myself unconsciously led in a direction which would have roused my indignant protestations, if at

---

[1] Neila—the prayer at the close of the Atonement Day known as "the closing of the gate."

[2] Yom Kippur—Day of Atonement.

that moment it had been revealed to me. There was not within me reflection or reasoning of any kind, and for a long time nothing was to manifest the change which was to come into my life, and nevertheless everything dates from then. Thus the traveler who through inadvertence decides at a crossway on a route apparently parallel to the one he wishes to take, finds, after a long journey, that he is at a great distance from the point at which he thought to arrive.

* * * * *

That which revealed itself to me at that moment was not at all the Jewish religion. It was the Jewish people. The spectacle of that large number of men assembled, their shoulders covered by Taliths, suddenly disclosed to my eyes a far-off past. The Hebrews of the Doré Bible were there on their feet before me. But two details struck me particularly while I noticed all about me the faithful bent over their rituals. At first on seeing the prayer-shawls uniformly worn by all the participants in the service, I thought that in a way they were all officiating. Sevcral of them robed in white shrouds were scattered about here and there in the crowd, just like the priests who remained in the centre of the sanctuary. In the second place it seemed to me that this silent assembly was in expectancy of something about to happen. What are they waiting for, I asked my companion. This double aspect which Judaism disclosed to me held nothing that could trouble the faith of a young Christian such as I then was. But here was revealed to me at least very clearly, so that I could understand what followed, two characteristic traits; the form of collective priesthood of which the Judaism of the dispersion consisted, and the spirit of expectancy and of faith in the future which stamps its entire cult with a special seal.

In fact, in the synagogue service all Jews are equal, all are priests, all may participate in the holy functions, even officiate in the name of the entire community, when they have the required training. The dignity which distinguished the Hakham, the doctor, the sage, is not a clerical degree but rather one of learning and of piety quickened through knowledge. The Talith would not have given me the understanding of that peculiarity of Judaism which would have escaped me, had my attention not been captured from the first by this spectacle so new to me, of a multitude of men in white shawls at prayer. It is thus that rites and symbols often constitute a more expressive language than the best of discourses. The practices which have had the consecration of centuries come to us charged with accumulated thoughts of believing generations. They preserve the poetry, the incomparable power of evocation. They may be suppressed, but not replaced.

A precious legacy of antiquity, and yet Judaism's trend is not toward the past, but toward the future. An unconquerable faith in the final triumph of the good and the true has preserved it during the centuries and permeates through and through. It awaits the Messiah. This attitude gives an unusual aspect to its age old beliefs. Whenever the modern conscience busies itself with ideals of social regeneration, whenever it affirms its will to build the city of the future upon the ruins of wrongs and injustices, it is in communion with the soul of Judaism as it has not ceased to vibrate in the course of its long history. Later I was to understand how the aspirations of national resurrection complete and define in Israel this attitude of expectancy, so different from the conceptions of other religions, but from my first contact this spirit revealed itself to me in the silent "amida" of the closing of Yom Kippur.

And this it was that made another impression upon me, which was less confused, and was to be more decisive. Fancy a young Christian, brought up in the naive conception that the Old Testament had no mission other than preparation for the New which was definitely to replace it, and that since the advent of Christianity the role of Israel had come to an end. The Jew lives on today only as a blind and powerless witness of the truth of prophecies fulfilled to his hurt. Every Christian brought up within the pale of the church thinks of him as the Wandering Jew of the legend—"March, march, Ahasuerus; wandering and alone, thou bearest the stigma of hopeless condemnation."

And now suddenly Israel appeared to me, still living its own life, with nothing to indicate the foretold decrepitude. This Judaism of the diaspora appeared to me a strongly organized collectively, which since nineteen hundred years, in despite of the will to destroy conjured up against it, continued to exist for ends that I still did not grasp, but in which I felt that my Christianity was no longer directly interested. All my philosophy of history was confounded. The three years of public life of Jesus no longer formed its central point. It became a simple episode in the whole. Thus in the teaching that I had received until that day, I discovered a lacuna, and the premise being false, the conclusions must be equally false. The legitimacy of the age-old protestation of Judaism against the Christian pretentions stood out at this first contact in a vague way but nevertheless in such a way that the impression could never be effaced. Israel has still the right to live. Israel lives.

This is what I realized on that day. In saying that it was not the Jewish religion, but the Jewish people which revealed itself to me at that moment, I set down a fact that was only clear to me personally. In truth, for the most part concerning the men who surrounded me and who to my eyes were so visibly of different descent from my own, the idea of their "raison d'etre," of their historic role, of their powers of resistance and persistence was doubtless very vague, almost non-existent. Nonetheless it emanated from the collective spirit of these Jews regathered. The breath of the race filled the precincts of the synagogue and my own soul was penetrated by it.

Beloved and ancient race which holds so much of grandeur and of moral wealth side by side with so many defects, some day I shall know some of thy beautiful spirits, true Jews of biblical times, still vibrant with ever renewed youth. I shall understand thee and love thee to the point of being able to say to thee with Ruth, "May the Lord do so to me and more also, if aught but death part thee and me." But it was on this Day of Atonement that my eyes first beheld thee and that I knew that thou wast ever a people blessed by the Eternal!

When I was a child I was occasionally taken to visit a very old lady who had been an intrepid traveler. Thirty-three times in succession she had pilgrimaged to Jerusalem, and on her mantelpiece she kept small frames brought from Palestine, in which were enclosed fragments of olive wood and dried flowers. These precious frames were shown to me and I piously pressed them to my childish lips. I was not conscious then of the significance of a kiss upon the flowers of the Holy Land, but began to understand from my first visit to the synagogue. It was the homage unconsciously rendered to the biblical treasures which come to us from this sacred soil, to the revelation of the holy "Torah," to the piety of the Psalms, to the faith of the ancient prophets, to all that the Hebrew scriptures contain that is vital to humanity.

And it was also the homage rendered to the people of the Bible toward whom the nations have shown themselves so ungrateful and whom they have overwhelmed with contempt and injustice without remembering that from them they have received the treasure of revelation; the people who despite all things resisted, survived, while other great peoples, Assyrians, Egyptians, Carthaginians, Greeks, Romans have disappeared from the face of the earth. Ground to dust among the nations, this people has nevertheless survived as a living entity—preserved for providential ends, and on that day my eyes beheld them.

Would the result have been the same for me, if instead of entering a Synagogue, I had been present at some great manifestation of Jewish life such as a Zionist Congress—for example? It may possibly be so, nevertheless in the mood that I then was, if one take into account my education and my inclinations, one must admit that no other aspect of Judaism could have impressed me to a greater degree than its religious vitality, and there is certainly no other which implanted by the Neila, this revelation was to affirm itself and the role of Israel.

This was the revelation that came to me on that Thursday in October, in the synagogue of Lyons. And surely words are too inadequate to express anything so confused, so mysterious to me at that moment; and for some time I could not formulate that impression in my thoughts, still less interpret it to the outside world. But with me, like a germ implanted by the Neila, this revelation was to affirm itself and grow stronger and stronger.

Near me, within reach of my hand, I noticed a book of prayer, left on a stall. I opened it. The unfamiliar characters had the effect upon me of notes of strange music, that I looked upon with curiosity. The next day I bought a Hebrew grammar on the Quai, and quite alone I set myself to study Hebrew.

[TRANSLATED BY LOUISE WATERMAN WISE]

SHOLOM ALEICHEM

The Inheritors

The Maiers and the Schnaiers . . .

Actually there was only one Maier and one Schnaier. They were twins and they looked so much alike that there were times when it was impossible to tell which of the two was Maier and which was Schnaier. As babies, the story goes, a queer thing happened to them. They were almost exchanged—and it is possible that they really were exchanged. This is how it happened.

Their mother, you may know, was a tiny woman and quite frail, but very fruitful. Every year without fail she gave birth to a child, but the sickly infant barely lingered through its first twelve months and then died. This went on until she finally stopped having children and thought she would never have another. But in the end a miracle happened. In her old age the Lord blessed her again, and this time with twins. And since it was too hard for her to suckle two babies, she had to hire a wet nurse. What else was there to do? A Kasrilevkite—no matter how poor he may be—will never throw a child of his into the streets or give it to a stranger to raise, unless, God forbid, the child be an orphan.

Having hired the nurse, the mother took Maier for herself (he was older than Schnaier by half an hour) and she gave Schnaier to the nurse. But since the nurse was herself not such a healthy woman, neither Maier nor Schnaier got too much milk. Both babies were equally starved; they screamed all night long; tore the house apart with their noise. It happened one day that the women were bathing the babies, naturally in one basin. They undressed them and put them into the hot water. Then, adding fresh water to the basin, they watched the children, red and bloated, splashing their little hands and feet, rolling about like beetles, enjoying themselves hugely. When they were through bathing them they took the babies out, wrapped them in a sheet (naturally one sheet) and put them to bed (naturally one bed) to dry. But when they started to dress them again, they couldn't tell which was Maier and which was Schnaier. And an argument took place between the two women.

"Look here, I could swear that this is Maier and this is Schnaier."

"How could you say that? This one is Maier and that one is Schnaier. Can't you see?"

"Do you think I'm dreaming? Either you're crazy, or just out of your head!"

"Good Lord! Can't you tell by their eyes that this is Maier and that is Schnaier? Look at those two eyes of his!"

"A fine argument! What do you want him to have—three eyes?"

Well, one of them kept insisting that Maier was Schnaier and Schnaier was Maier, and the other that Schnaier was Maier and Maier was Schnaier. Until at last the men came in and offered a solution. After all, they were men, with superior brains.

"Do you know what?" they suggested. "Try nursing the babies and we shall see. The one who takes his mother's breast must be Maier and the one who takes the nurse's must be Schnaier. That's simple enough."

And so it happened. As soon as the babies snuggled up to the breast, they each began to suck hungrily, smacked their lips, kicked their legs and made sounds like hungry puppies.

"A miracle of God!" said the men, with tears in their eyes. "See how the Almighty has created His world!"

And as a final test they decided to change the babies and see what would happen. The poor infants were torn away from their breasts and changed about, Schnaier taking Maier's place and Maier Schnaier's. And what do you suppose happened? Do you think they stopped sucking? They sucked as hard as ever!

From that time on they gave up trying to tell them apart. Let them be Maier-Schnaier and Schnaier-Maier. And they were given the name of the Maiers and Schnaiers, as though each one was both a Maier and a Schnaier. More than once it happened in *cheder* that Maier was whipped when Schnaier should have got the whipping, or the other way around, Schnaier was punished for Maier's misdeeds. And in order to avoid hard feelings, the rabbi hit on this scheme (do they not say where there is learning there is wisdom?) :

"You know what, children? Both of you stretch out. Then there will be no argument that I beat this one or that one. It will all remain in the family . . ."

But much, much later—after their *Bar Mitzvah,* when the Maiers and Schnaiers had reached manhood—something happened that made it possible to tell them apart a mile away even at night. What wonders God can devise! The brothers began to sprout beards (they must both have begun to smoke cigars too early) and on Maier's cheeks and upper lip there appeared black hairs (black as ink) and on Schnaier's face red hairs (red as fire). These beards grew as if the devil possessed them (they must both have continued to smoke cigars), so that by the time there were married they both had full beards. Did I say beards? Feather dusters was more like it. A black duster and a red one, that looked as if someone had glued them on.

Great are the works of the Lord, and His wonders are without end. For who knows what would have come to pass after their weddings if the beards, too, had been alike? In the confusion, even the wives might not have known which one of the brothers they had married . . . I do not know how it is with you in the big cities, but here in Kasrilevka it has never yet happened that husbands and wives should start exchanging each other. It is possible that there are husbands among us who would not object to this, but they know their wives and they know what they would get from them. However, all this is beside the point. The real story begins now.

Up till now we have concerned ourselves only with the Maiers and Schnaiers, that is with Maier and Schnaier, and we have become slightly acquainted with their mother and nurse, but we have not said a word about their father, as though they had never had a father. God forbid! Such a thing may have happened to others, but never to our kind of people. We have, thank God, no homes for foundlings where children are raised by strangers. It has never happened among us that a child should grow up and not know who his real father was. And if such a thing has happened, it has happened somewhere in Odessa or in Paris or in faraway America . . . As for Kasrilevka, I can swear that such a thing has never happened, and if it did, it happened to some servant girl or some other unfortunate maiden who was led astray by accident, through no fault of her own—an unhappy victim of another's lust . . .

In short, the Maiers and Schnaiers had a father, and a very fine father, too. He was a virtuous and an honest man named Reb Shimshen, and he had a magnificent beard, long and rich and luxurious. In fact, it could be said without exaggeration that Reb Shimshen had more beard than face. And for that reason he was known in Kasrilevka as Reb Shimshen Beard.

And this Reb Shimshen was—I don't even know what he was. But you can be sure that all his life he struggled and sweated for a meager living, waged constant warfare against poverty. Sometimes he overcame poverty; sometimes poverty overcame him, as is usual with Kasrilevkites, who are not afraid of want, but thumb their noses at it . . .

And Reb Shimshen lived out his life and finally he died. And when he died he was given a handsome burial. Almost the whole town followed his remains to the cemetery.

"Who is it that died?"

"Haven't you heard? Reb Shimshen."

"Which Reb Shimshen?"

"Reb Shimshen Beard."

"A great pity. So Reb Shimshen Beard is gone from us too."

That is what they said in Kasrilevka and mourned not so much for Reb Shimshen himself as for the fact that with his death there was one person less in Kasrilevka. Strange people, these Kasrilevkites! In spite of the fact that they are so poor that they almost never have enough for themselves, they would be pleased if no one among them ever died. Their only comfort is that people die everywhere, even in Paris, and that no one can buy his way out. Even Rothschild himself, who is greater than royalty, has to get up and go when the Angel of Death beckons.

Now let us turn back again to the Maiers and Schnaiers.

As long as Reb Shimshen was alive the Maiers and Schnaiers lived as one, brothers in body and soul. But when their father died they became enemies at once, ready to tear each other's beards out. Perhaps you wonder why? Well, why do sons ever fight after a father's death? Naturally, over the inheritance. It is true that Reb Shimshen did not leave behind any farms or woodlands, houses or rental property, and certainly no cash. Nor did he leave any jewelry, silver or furniture to his children—not because he was mean or avaricious, but simply because he had nothing to leave. And yet don't think that Reb Shimshen left his children absolutely nothing. He left them a treasure that could be turned to money at any time, a treasure that could be pawned, rented or sold outright. This treasure we speak of was the seat he had had in the old Kasrilevka Synagogue, a seat along the east wall right next to Reb Yozifel, the Rabbi, who was next to the Holy Ark. It is true that Kasrilevka wits have a saying that it is better to have an acre outside than a seat inside, but that is only a saying, and when the Lord is kind and a person does have his own seat, and along the east wall at that, it's not so very bad—and certainly better than nothing . . .

In short, Reb Shimshen left behind a seat in the old Kasrilevka Synagogue. But he forgot one small detail. He didn't indicate who was to inherit the seat—Maier or Schnaier.

Obviously Reb Shimshen—may he forgive me—did not expect to die. He had forgotten that the Angel of Death lurks always behind our backs and watches every step we take, else he would surely have made a will or otherwise indicated in the presence of witnesses to which of his two sons he wanted to leave his fortune.

Well, what do you suppose? The very first Saturday after they arose from mourning, the quarrel began. Maier argued that according to law the seat belonged to him, since he was the older (by a good half-hour). And Schnaier had two arguments in his favor: first, they were not sure which of the two was older because according to their mother's story they had been exchanged as infants and he was really Maier and Maier was really Schnaier. In the second place, Maier had a rich father-in-law who also owned a seat along the east wall of the synagogue, and since the father-in-law had no sons the seat would eventually be Maier's. And when that happened Maier would have two seats by the east wall and Schnaier would have none whatever. And if that was the case, where was justice? Where was humanity?

When he heard of these goings-on, Maier's father-in-law, a man of means, but one who had made his money only recently, entered the battle. "You've got a lot of nerve!" he exclaimed. "I am not forty yet and I have every intention of living a long time, and here you are, dividing up my inheritance already. And besides, how do you know that I won't have a son yet? I may have more than one, see!" he stormed. "There is impudence for you!"

So their neighbors tried to make peace between them, suggested that they determine how much the seat was worth and then have one brother buy his share from the other. That sounds reasonable enough, doesn't it? The only trouble was that neither brother wanted to sell his share. They didn't care a thing about the money. What was money—compared to stubbornness and pride?

"How can one's own brother be so pigheaded as to keep a person away from his rightful seat?" "Why should you have our father's place, and not I?" It became a matter not so much of having things his own way as it was of preventing the other from having his. As the saying is: If I don't, you don't either. And the rivalry between the Maiers and the Schnaiers increased in fury. Stubbornness gave way to cunning as each tried to outwit the other!

The first Sabbath Maier came early and sat down in his father's seat; and Schnaier remained standing throughout the services. The second Sabbath Schnaier came first and occupied his father's place, while Maier remained standing. The third Sabbath Maier got there still earlier, spread himself out in the seat, pulled his *tallis* over his head, and there he was . . .

The next time it was Schnaier who hurried to get there first, sat down in the coveted seat, pulled his *tallis* over his face—and just try to budge him! The following week Maier was the first to get there . . . This went on week after week till one fine Sabbath both of them arrived at the same time —it was still dark outside—took their posts at the door of the synagogue (it was still shut) and glared at each other like roosters ready to tear each other's eyes out. It was like this that long ago the first two brothers stood face to face in an empty field, under God's blue sky, full of anger, ready to annihilate one another, devour each other, spill innocent blood . . .

But let us not forget that the Maiers and Schnaiers were young men of good family, respectable and well behaved—not rowdies who were in the habit of assaulting each other in public. They waited for Ezriel, the *shammes,* to come and open the door of the synagogue. Then they would show the whole world who would get to their father's seat first—Maier or Schnaier . . .

The minutes passed like years till Ezriel arrived with the keys. And when Ezriel, with his tangled beard, arrived he was not able to reach the door because the brothers stood against it—one with the left foot, the other with the right foot, and would not budge an inch.

"Well, what's going to happen?" said Ezriel casually, taking a pinch of snuff. "If the two of you insist on standing there like mean scarecrows I won't be able to open the door and the synagogue will have to remain closed all day. Go ahead and tell me: does that make sense?"

Apparently these words had some effect, because the Maiers and Schnaiers both moved back, one to the right, the other to the left, and made way for Ezriel and his key. And when the key turned in the lock and the door swung open, the Maiers and Schnaiers tumbled in headlong.

"Be careful, you're killing me!" yelled Ezriel the *shammes,* and before he could finish the words the poor man lay trampled under their feet, screaming in horror: "Watch out! You're trampling all over me—the father of a family!"

But the Maiers and Schnaiers cared nothing for Ezriel and his family. Their only thought was for the seat, their father's seat, and jumping over benches and praying stands they made for the east wall. There they planted themselves firmly against the wall with their shoulders and the floor with their feet and tried to shove each other aside. In the scuffle they caught each other's beards, grimaced horribly, gritted their teeth and growled: "May the plague take you before you get this seat!"

In the meantime Ezriel got up from the floor, felt to see if any of his bones were broken, and approached the brothers. He found them both on the floor clutching each other's beards. At first he tried to reason with them.

"Shame on you! Two brothers—children of the same father and mother—tearing each other's beards out! And in a Holy Place at that! Be ashamed of yourselves!"

But Ezriel gathered that at the moment his lecture was in vain. Actually, his words added fuel to the flame so that the two children of one father became so enraged that one of them clutched in his fist a tuft of black hair (from Maier's beard) and the other a tuft of red (Schnaier's beard); blue marks showed on both faces and from the nose of one streamed blood.

As long as it was merely a matter of pulling beards, slapping and pummeling each other, the *shammes* could content himself with reading a lecture. But when he saw blood streaming, Ezriel could stand it no longer, for blood, even though only from a punched nose, was an ugly thing fit for rowdies and not God-fearing men.

He wasted no time, but ran to the tap, grabbed a dipper of water, and poured it over the two brothers. Cold water has always—since the world was created—been the best means of reviving a person. A man may be in the greatest rage, but as soon as he gets a cold bath he is strangely refreshed and cool; he comes to his senses. This happened to the Maiers and the Schnaiers. At the unexpected shower of cold water to which Ezriel had treated them, they woke up, looked each other in the eyes, and grew ashamed—like Adam and Eve when they had tasted of the forbidden fruit of the Tree of Knowledge and saw their nakedness . . .

And that very Saturday night the Maiers and Schnaiers went together with their friends and neighbors to the home of Reb Yozifel, the Rabbi, to have the dispute settled.

If Kasrilevka had not been such a tiny place, stuck away in a forgotten corner, far from the great world, and if newspapers and periodicals had been printed there, the world would surely have come to know the works of our Rabbi, Reb Yozifel. The papers would have been full of tales about him and his wisdom. The great, the wise and the famous of the world would have traveled far to see him in person and to hear from his own lips the words of wisdom. Photographers and painters would have made portraits of him and spread them to the four corners of the earth. Interviewers would have plagued him, given him no rest. They would have asked him all his views—what his favorite dishes were, how many hours a day he slept, what he thought about this and that, about cigarette smoking and bicycle riding . . . But since Kasrilevka is a tiny place stuck away in a forgotten corner, far from the world, and papers and periodicals are not printed there, the world knows nothing of the existence of Reb Yozifel. The papers never mention his name. The great, the wise and the famous do not come to him, photographers and painters do not make pictures of him. Interviewers leave him alone. And Reb Yozifel lives his life quietly, modestly, without noise or fanfare. No one knows anything about him except the town of Kasrilevka, which marvels at him, glories in his wisdom, and pays him great honor (of riches there is little in Kasrilevka, but honor they will give one as much as he deserves). They say that he is a man who modestly conceals his wisdom and it is only when you come to him for judgment that you find out how deep he is, how profound, how sharp. Another Solomon!

With the Sabbath over and the benedictions completed, the Maiers and Schnaiers came to Reb Yozifel to have their dispute settled, and there they found the house already full of people. The whole town was anxious to hear how he would settle it, how he would divide one seat between two brothers.

First he gave both sides a chance to unburden themselves. Reb Yozifel works according to this theory: that before the verdict is handed down the litigants should have the right to say anything they want to—because after the verdict all the talking in the world won't help. After that he let Ezriel, the *shammes,* talk. After all, he was the chief witness. And then other townspeople had their turn—everyone who had the public welfare at heart. And they talked as long as they wanted. Reb Yozifel is the kind of person who lets everyone talk. He is something of a philosopher. He feels this way about it: that no matter how long a person talks, he will have to stop some time.

And that is just what happened. They talked and talked and talked, and finally stopped talking. And when the last person was through, Reb Yozifel turned to the Maiers and Schnaiers and spoke to them quietly, calmly, as his custom was.

"Hear ye, my friends—this is my opinion. According to what I have heard from you and from all the other citizens it is apparent that both of you are right. You both had one father, and a very noble father, too— may he enjoy the blessings of Paradise. The only trouble is that he left you only one seat in the synagogue. Naturally, this seat is very dear to both of you. After all—it is something to own one's seat along the east wall of the old, old Kasrilevka Synagogue. You can't dismiss that with a wave of the hand. What then? Just as it is impossible for one person to use two seats, so it is impossible for two people to use a single one. On the contrary, it is much easier for one person to use two seats than for two to use one."

And so with example and precept he went on to explain the difficulty of the situation.

"But there is one way," he continued, "in which each of you can sit along the eastern wall in adjoining seats. I have come upon this solution after much reflection. And this is what I have to say. My seat in the synagogue is right next to the one your father left. One of you can have my seat and then both of you brothers can sit next to each other in peace and amity, and you will have no need to quarrel any more. And if you will ask what will I do without a seat? then I will answer you with another question: "Where is it written that a Rabbi or any other man, for that matter, must have his own seat and especially at the east wall, and at the old Kasrilevka Synagogue at that? Let us stop to consider. What is a synagogue? A house of prayer. And why do we go to the synagogue? To pray. To whom? To the Almighty. And where is He found? Everywhere. All the world is filled with His glory. If that is the case, then what difference does it make whether it is east or north or south, whether it is near the Ark or by the door? The important thing is to come to the synagogue and to pray.

"Let me give you an example. Once there was a king . . ."

And there followed another of Reb Yozifel's parables of the two servants who began to tear each other's beards in the presence of the king. And they were sent away with this admonition: "If you want to tear each other's beards, go outside and do it as much as your heart desires, but do not defile my palace . . ."

Thus Reb Yozifel chided them gently, and then he said, "Go home now, my children, in peace and let your father be an advocate in heaven for you, for us, and for all Israel."

Thus the Rabbi handed down his verdict and all the people went home.

The following Sabbath, the Maiers and Schnaiers came to the synagogue and stationed themselves near the door. No matter how much they were entreated by the *shammes* on one side and the Rabbi on the other, they refused to occupy the seats by the east wall.

If there is anyone who would like to have his own seat by the east wall in the old, old Kasrilevka Synagogue, the seat next to Reb Yozifel, the Rabbi, at a reasonable price, let him go to Kasrilevka and see the children of Reb Shimshen Beard, either Maier or Schnaier, it does not matter which. They will sell it to you at any price you say, because neither of them uses that seat any more. It stands there—unoccupied.

What a waste!

[FROM *The Old Country*]

MIRIAM SHOMER ZUNSER

Havdalah

It is Saturday, at twilight. The Sabbath is about to end, but the peace of the day is still in full possession of grandfather's house. The men folk are in *shul.* The young people are walking by the river's edge. Because no work is permitted on the Sabbath, by man, woman, or beast, the peace is complete. The servants are either sleeping, sitting idly on the garden steps, or visiting their kin. Only old Sosche, the aged servant who has been in the house for fifty years, lingers in the kitchen. She watches the family with tender regard. Someone may want a glass of tea. Since no fire may be kindled on the holy day and the samovar could therefore not be set up, she had an earthenware jug full of hot water ready in the depths of the still warm oven.

For some reason there is no one but grandmother Yentel in the large livingroom on the other side of the house. The snow-white Sabbath cloths still cover the tables in the *salle* and in the smaller dining-room. Grandmother Yentel sits alone by the smaller table. The back of her chair is placed against the wall so that she faces the clock in the living-room. She is dressed in her Sabbath clothes: a black satin jacket buttoned down front with many little buttons, over a black satin skirt. A collar of white ruffled lace sets off her face, which is soft, pink and round. Her eyes are a lustrous brown, her eyebrows arched and fine. The hair of her handsome brown wig is parted in the middle, drawn down over her ears. The back of her head is covered by a black lace headgear which falls in graceful folds down to her shoulders. She wears long earrings made up of many little diamonds. They are so long and heavy that they have stretched the lobes of her ears to an unusual length. Her cherished possession is her necklace of true pearls which she wears wound three times about her throat. Because one must not carry anything on the Sabbath, her large white handkerchief is fastened under the belt of her jacket.

Grandmother Yentel sits in her chair, a short round figure, her plump white hand resting on the table. The twilight deepens. It is dusk now. She turns her head slowly and glances out of the window to see if the first star of the evening has yet appeared. With it will come the end of the Sabbath. She waits. Presently a little light twinkles in the sky. Swaying softly, Yentel chants in a low, sweet voice:

> God of Abraham, Isaac and Jacob
> Guard your beloved nation Israel from all evil.
> The beloved holy Sabbath is passing
> And the beloved week is approaching
> With fortune and prosperity
> With health and blessing. Amen.

She chants on and on, telling a tale of a cock dressed in gold and silver standing on top of something or other; but the import of the tale escapes me, for the room is dark now, and Dvayre has told me of goblins and evil ones, and lost stray souls who linger in the shadows of the Sabbath and will not return to their torments until the lights are lit. Then, suddenly, there is joyous commotion on the steps and in the entrance hall. Grandfather and a number of men with him have come from *shul.* They come in with a cheerful greeting: "A good week! A good week!"—stressing the "good." Immediately someone brings a light from the kitchen, the *Havdalah* candle is produced together with the spice-box containing herbs from the Orient, and a large silver beaker for the blessing of the wine. The candle, prettily colored, is made of six strands, one for each day of the week. Burning together they represent the holy light, the radiance of the Sabbath. The beaker is large, luminous and engraved. The spice-box, made of beautiful filigree silver, boasts a steeple and silver flag. Grandmother sets wine and eggcakes and a bottle of brandy on the table.

With everybody standing around him, grandfather lights the candle. He fills the beaker with brandy, allowing the liquid to overflow its rim. This is for a "full week" to come. Holding the cup on the palm of his hand, he blesses the Creator of the fruit of the vine. Grandmother hands him the spice-box. He opens its little door. A curious fragrance fills the air. Something strange, remote, envelops us—spices from the Land of Israel, we are told. The strangeness is dear to us, the remoteness near, for always, whenever there is rejoicing, we are told of our home, of Land of Israel from which we had been exiled and where some day we shall return. Grandfather makes a blessing for the Creator of all manner of spices. Other ceremonies follow, indicating the hope of honest toil, and the everlasting faith in God.

Finally the moment we children have been waiting for arrives. Grandfather dips the lighted candle into the saucer holding the overflow of the *havdalah* cup. The liquid leaps into a blue flame, through which everybody passes his fingers for good luck. The men do it quickly, catching the flames in their hands and dipping these into their pockets. This is for riches and prosperity in the coming week. Then, still rubbing their hands together, all cry, "A good week! A good week!" The Sabbath is over. The tablecloths are removed. The Sabbath clothes are taken off. Voices, manners, conversations change. Quiet, orderly speech is over. The noisy, prosaic ways of everyday life have returned.

ALICE BARR

The Singing Name

I remember I was seven years old when a momentous event took place in my life. I lived in a tiny village in Pennsylvania where nothing seemed to happen that was very exciting. But this was different. Everyone talked about it.

Someone was building a store right in the middle of our town. What a store that was going to be! Mom was pretty excited about it and said she could buy a new wash boiler now and maybe get wallpaper for my room. The other women were all excited too, for now here was a store that carried fresh meat and bread wrapped in wax paper and yards and yards of materials with lovely little flowers on it.

I wanted to go every day to watch the men hammer and saw at the wood, but Mom did not let me out of the yard very often. She did promise me, though, that I could buy licorice at the store the first day it opened. And I knew that day was soon, for the last time I had been downtown I had watched the men put into place the biggest window I had ever seen. It was a beautiful window and I could look through it to clean new shelves in the store. I wanted to know which shelf would hold the licorice but no one paid any attention to me.

And then one day Mom told me that the store was finished. It would be opened on Monday morning. Mom seemed worried about something. I heard her tell Dad that it was a good thing the minister was coming this Sunday, because they would talk to him about those people.

"What people, Mom?" I asked her.

"The people who own the store," she answered, and her voice was angry.

On Sunday, when the minister came to the little white church to preach, the men and women gathered about to tell him the news. He came to our church only once a month, for he had to preach at other villages around us. I noticed that he seemed a little sad today and I wondered what the people had said to him.

I knew that they had told him of the new store, but would that make him look so unhappy? It gave me no unhappiness. I could hardly wait until tomorrow when I could go there to buy my licorice. And maybe there would even be shoes in the store. I had never seen shoes in a store, for Mom had always bought mine from the catalogue, so I had no idea how they were sold. Would they be out on the counter like the candy or would they be hidden away? Would the storekeeper let me see them?

The minister's face was still sad when he stood at his pulpit. Did he think us bad that we were excited on Sunday about something that wasn't God? He started to talk about a Jew and a Gentile, but I did not understand the words, so I stared at my shoes and dreamed they were red with black buttons on the side instead of brown with laces up the front. The laces were broken and tied in ugly knots to hold them together. Maybe the storekeeper would have red shoes I could see; that is, if he was a nice man. And he must be nice, because he had such a lovely name, Samuel Wechsler. It was a very different name from the ones I knew—Brown, Smith, Williams, Johnson. His name was a singing name.

We always had our Sunday dinner right after church and I had to help by setting the table, so that day I gathered the dishes in my arms and placed them on the table to a sing-song rhythm, Samuel Wechsler, Sam-uel Wech-sler. Mom's voice stopped me.

"What are you trying to do, break what's left of my dishes, acting like that?"

I smiled up at her. "I'm being careful, Mom. It's just that it's such a lovely name. Don't you wish you had such a lovely name. Don't you wish you had such a lovely name?" Mom looked very angry, the same kind of look as the time she caught me stealing grapes from Mr. Johnson's backyard vines.

"You must be crazy, child. That's a Jew name." Never before today had I heard the word Jew and now my mother knew it as well as the minister. I felt proud. My mother must be very smart to use words the preacher used. I followed her to the sink, where she started to pare the potatoes. I loved to watch her, for she would make the knife cut only the thin brown skin off. And, too, she always gave me a thick slice of the potato to eat.

"What's a Jew, Mom?" I asked her. The knife dug sharply into the potato and scraped out a rotten spot.

"You'll find out soon enough. They're just like this potato, rotten on the inside."

"All of 'em, Mom?" I persisted.

"Yes, all of them. And soon they'll overrun the place, hordes and hordes of them."

"You mean like the rats did last winter in the cellar?" The knife stopped completely now, and when she answered me I did not know her voice.

"Yes, that's what I mean. Just like rats." I was frightened, for I was deathly afraid of rats and they had taken over the cellar last winter so completely that even Mom wouldn't go down there. And now Jews were coming just like rats.

That night when I went to bed I prayed to God not to let the Jews hurt me and I thrust the name of Samuel Wechsler from my mind.

Monday was a lovely, sunny day, but I was too worried to enjoy the sunshine. I had my money to buy my licorice, but how could I go see the new store if Jews were all over the place? They could do awful things to me and might, Mom said, even take my money and not give me my candy. But worse than all this, I did not know what a Jew looked like. Would he pounce on me before I had found out who he was? And how many were there in the store?

Mom came out on the porch where I was sitting and gave me a little push. "Stop this worrying and go get your candy." She laughed at me. "I guess I scared you too much, but you can't be too careful with things like this."

"But won't all those Jews hurt me?" I asked her. She shook her head. "There's only one Jew in the store and he won't hurt you. He'll be afraid of a girl as strong as you." Her smile reassured me and I started down to the center of the village. But once at the store I was frightened again. What if this Jew was a big Jew? Would he be afraid of me then? I stared through the big glass window, but I could see nothing move. I couldn't even see Samuel Wechsler. I glanced around warily. Maybe I could find the shelf with the licorice. The many shelves only confused me, however, and I was about to turn around and go home when I saw them. Big, black, shiny boots! Over there in the right hand corner. If there were boots over there, wouldn't shoes be kept there, too? I opened the door cautiously and tip-toed over to the boots. Only a little bell somewhere in the back of the store broke the stillness. If I was very quiet, maybe the Jew would never know I was in the store.

"Hello, little girl. Could I help you with the boots?" a voice said in back of me. I was so startled I fell over the boots. The voice laughed and a hand helped me up. "I didn't mean to scare you." I looked up and a man stood there, a smiling man with a tiny, round cap on his head. I stared at him intently.

"Why are you staring at me?" he asked, and the smile faded a bit.

"I never saw anyone with black eyes before and they're very pretty," I told him. He laughed at me and the black eyes sparkled. "Did you want to buy something, some boots, for instance?"

"Oh, no, no boots, only licorice. See? I have my penny here." I held it out to him. "I just wanted to see if the storekeeper had any little girl's shoes. Maybe red shoes—do you think he does?" For answer, the man reached scross me to the shelf and took down a box. He pointed to a small chair. "Sit down there and I'll let you have the box so that you can open it yourself." When I sat on the chair, my legs were too short to bend and stuck out straight before me. He saw my brown shoes with the broken laces, but he said nothing, only handed me the box. I was afraid to touch it.

"Now what's wrong?" he asked. "Are you afraid of the box?" I curled my finger at him and he leaned down to me until his black eyes were only a few inches from my face.

"The Jew might not want me to touch them," I whispered. His eyes seemed to get bigger as they stared into mine and then his eyelids blinked slowly. He took the box off my lap and opened it. "I'll touch them, then," he said and his voice sounded hoarse, "I'll show you what's in the box. See? There is this nice black paper and then these shoes, red shoes, as you can see." I stared at the shoe in his hand. It was red and it had black buttons on the side. It was a truly beautiful shoe.

"Would you like to hold it?" he asked. I shook my head. I was afraid to hold it, not just because of the Jew but because I knew I would be holding only a dream.

He very quietly returned the shoe to the box and the box to the shelf. I could feel the tears stinging my eyes, but I knew I wasn't allowed to cry in front of people, so I blinked them rapidly away. My voice wasn't steady when I spoke, but he did not seem to notice. "I suppose they cost pretty near a million dollars?" His voice sounded like the preacher's when he answered me, "Yes my dear, I am afraid they do."

We were both silent then. I had forgotten all about the licorice. What did licorice matter compared to red shoes? Suddenly the man in front of me clapped his hands noisily. I looked up, startled. He was smiling and walking at me and I had to smile back.

"Now then," he laughed, and his black eyes snapped, "since this is your first day here in the store, I'm going to give you a present." He rummaged in a drawer and triumphantly held up two red shoe strings. "How would you like these for your present?" and he laughed again. I was delighted. No one else had red shoe laces. And then I thought of Samuel Wechsler. He would be very angry at this nice man. I drew back from his outstretched hands. "You better ask him, so he won't be mad at you," I whispered across to him. His smile was puzzled now. "Ask who?" "Why, Samuel Wechsler, of course." I was still whispering. His smile faded and his eyes lost their brightness.

"What do you know about him?" he asked me quietly. He was such a quiet man.

"I don't know about him at all," I answered. "Only his name. It's such a beautiful name and I sang it all the time till Mom told me it was a Jew name." The red laces were pulled tightly in his fingers now.

"And what is a Jew name?" The voice sounded queer and I looked up at him but he was watching his fingers play with the laces, so I could not see his eyes.

"Well, I don't know exactly," I admitted, squirming on the little chair. "I suppose it must be a bad name." The red lace broke with a snap before I could voice my dismay, he was looking for another one, his back turned toward me.

"What do you mean, a bad name?" I could hardly hear him. I was getting tired of sitting and wanted to see the laces in my shoes. Why couldn't he hurry? "Answer me!" he sounded like Mom gets some times, so I answered quickly.

"Mom told me that Jews are all rotten inside and are bad people who come in hordes and take your money and don't give you candy and Samuel Wechsler is a Jew name and must be a bad name, too." I finished out of breath. He stood very still and then suddenly pushed some bolts of material off the counter to the floor. He picked me up in strong hands and set me down where the materials had been. Now I was sitting high enough to look into his eyes. I put my hand on his face so that my fingertips could touch his eyelashes. He blinked them over my fingers and smiled slightly.

"You like me, don't you?" he asked.

"Oh, yes," I answered, "you're the nicest man I know and the prettiest." I added as an afterthought. He took my hands from his face and held them tigthly in his.

"And how old are you?"

"Seven, going on eight in October."

"Seven," and his laugh sounded sad again. That's a young age to begin growing up. Now then. Do you know what my name is?" I shook my head. "My name is Samuel Wechsler." He said the name slowly and carefully. "And not only do I have a Jew's name but I am a Jew."

I sat there frozen with terror. This was a Jew and he had a strong grip on my hands, holding me, pulling me, crushing me. He was bad and rotten inside and hurt me terribly. I pushed at him with all my strength, but his hands just tightened on my arms so I kicked at him savagely. I was too frightened to hear his grunt of pain. I knew only that he was lifting me from the counter to the floor. When I felt solid wood under my feet, I raced in blind fear for the door. I ran until my knees hurt and my breath caught in my throat. But I knew I had run far enough to be safe, for I was within shouting distance of my home and Mom.

Mom was sitting on the steps on the porch when I saw her. Her apron was full of pea pods which she opened expertly. I loved to hear the little plunking noise the peas made as they fell into the pan beside Mom's lap. She waited until I was almost beside her on the steps before she spoke.

"Find any Jews down at the store?" and her voice laughed at me.

"Could I sit here beside you, Mom, and help with the peas?" I asked. She moved over to make room for me on the steps. "That Jew must have taken a bite out of you down there," and her voice still laughed. Somehow the laughter made me silent, and I could not tell her of the terror I had gone through in the store.

Just before supper that night I went out to the pump to get a bucket of fresh water for the table and as I reached for the pump handle, I heard a voice say "Good evening, little girl." I turned around swiftly, for few passed this way and all knew my name—all except one person. And there he was, smiling at me across the closed gate. He held out his hand.

"You forgot these, you know," he said. He was holding the red shoe laces. I stared from the laces to his face. His eyes seemed completely black now in the soft twilight. "I'll leave them here on the gate and you may pick them up when I'm gone," and the sadness came into his voice again. I wanted to run over to him, touch his eyes and say goodnight to him. I dropped my hand from the pump and started toward him.

"I'll get them now, Samuel Wechsler," I began, then stopped. That name! That Jew name! We stared at each other silently and then he turned and with a quiet "Goodnight, my dear," he walked up the road. I waited until he reached the corn field before I raced to the gate for my treasure. They were really such beautiful laces. Wait till Mom saw them!

Mom was waiting at the door for me. Her voice was terrible when she spoke. "What did that Jew want with you?" I stared at her. "You knew from here that he was a Jew?" I asked in bewilderment.

"Of course, child, I knew he was a Jew," she was impatient. "I can tell one a mile off." I clutched at her apron, the red shoe strings forgotten.

"But, Mom," and I was pleading with her now, "how could you tell? He looks just like Dad looks." She pushed me away roughly.

"Of course he does. He's just a man like your Dad or Mr. Johnson or Mr. Smith." She stopped suddenly, a peculiar expression on her face. "Only very different," she continued quickly. "As I told you this morning, all rotten inside."

"And Samuel Wechsler is the same kind of Jew, you mean?" I persisted. "There is only one kind of Jew," Mom snapped at me. "A bad one." She looked down at me and I stared at her unblinkingly. She had told me all Jews were rotten, were bad, would sometimes take my pennies and not give me any candy. I had told this to Samuel Wechsler and had run from him in terror. Yet I still had my penny and besides that, a pair of beautiful red shoe strings. I remembered how he blinked his eyelashes over my fingers and how his black eyes laughed and sparkled. I held up the shoe strings to Mom. They fell in a bright line down my hand.

"See? Samuel Wechsler gave these to me," I told her. "And he didn't take any money either." She stared at the shoe laces and then she straightened her body slowly like she does when she gets very angry with me. Her voice was angry, too, when she spoke. "I want you to take those strings and throw them into the garbage heap," she said. "That's the only place fit for them. And furthermore, if you ever take another thing from that Jew again, I'll beat you with a piece of kindling wood." I never talked back to Mom when she talked to me in that kind of voice, so I turned away from her, and the shoe strings swung softly against my fingers.

The next day I went back to the store. And again the little bell rang when I opened the door. I walked past the boots, past a counter of bread and cookies, past the counter of candy and then he stood in front of me. His face didn't smile and his eyes were very still, just staring at me. I had to do it very quickly, I knew, for my knees felt funny, as though I had run all the way from home. I held up my penny.

"I would like my licorice now, please," I said, and my voice wasn't more than a whisper, but he heard me. Still without speaking, he stepped behind the candy counter and reached for the licorice. He held two ropes of it for me to see. And then he spoke. "Do you want to hold it this way or should I put it into a paper bag for you?" His voice sounded tireder than any voice I had ever heard.

"Put it into the bag, please," and then I took a deep breath and blew it out on the next words, "Samuel Wechsler." His hands tightened on the paper bag and his black eyes began to widen. My next words came in a rush. "I really didn't want to buy licorice today. I just wanted to show you something. Would you lift me up on the counter, Samuel Wechsler?" He reached me in two long strides and his eyes and his mouth and his face smiled at me. He swung me lightly to the counter and I beckoned him closer with my finger.

"Cross your heart to keep a secret," I whispered. He smiled at me, "Jews don't cross their hearts. Would it be all right if I just promised God to keep a secret?"

"Oh, yes, I answered, "That would do fine. Now I'll show you what I have. I lifted my dress and thrust my hand into my bloomer pocket. "These are my special bloomers," I explained to him. "See? They have a secret pocket where I keep all my secrets." He nodded wordlessly. "And this is my biggest secret." I pulled my hand out and thrust it in front of him. "Look here, Samuel Wechsler," I directed him, and he looked and his eyes sparkled and laughed. The red shoe laces lay crumpled in my hand.

LEAH AIN GLOBE

The Tears of the Generations

Way up, in the highest regions of the heavens, at the gates of compassion, is the Temple of Tears. The doors of this temple are open day and night, year in, year out; they are never shut. The angel of all good and mercy ministers there. In it are two cups that hold the tears of the world—the cup of sorrow and the cup of joy. Whenever the angel of the Temple sees even one teardrop in the eye of any human, he descends to earth, picks the tear up in one swoop, and places it in the appropriate cup.

The cup of sorrow has been emptied many times. Its tears have swelled into mighty rivers, from which rises a dense fog that turns into black, evil clouds. The sun hides, the fields lie desolate, the trees are bare, and wailing, piercing winds accompany the rain that drips down from the clouds. From morning till night, from night till morning, the rain falls. Man feels miserable and foresaken and sighs, "Even the heavens weep."

The angel who supervises the Temple of Tears grieves because of the rivers of sorrowful tears that flow endlessly. He comes before God each day and implores, "Oh, God! Woe is me! When will you erase the tears from the face of man?"

———

Once a very long time ago, in the days of antiquity, when the angel went to empty the cup of sorrow into the rivers, he counted, and learned that there are more rivers of

Jewish tears than those of any other people. This grieved him sorely and he appeared before God and complained.

"Oh, God of compassion! When will you take pity on the sons of Abraham, Isaac and Jacob? They have already wept so many rivers of tears—the rivers formed by the tears they shed when Egypt enslaved them and forced them into hard labor; the river when Pharaoh ordered each male child to be drowned; the river when he decreed the set number of bricks each Israelite was to produce; the river from the lashes of the Egyptian taskmasters on their backs; the river. . . ."

Then God interrupted him and said, "I have indeed seen the suffering of My people and have heard their cry. I will take them out of Egypt, the crucible of affliction, and will bring them to the land of Canaan. They will then send spies into the land. On the day when the spies come back and report to the Children of Israel of the land's pleasantness and goodness, of its milk and its honey, you may go down and bring up their tears of thanksgiving, so that I will know that they are worthy people who give thanks to Him Who deals kindly with them."

On hearing these words, the Angel of compassion was elated. Soon the day arrived when the spies returned from exploring Canaan, and the angel went down into the wilderness where the Children of Israel were encamped. As he approached their dwellings, he heard men weeping, each in his own tent. The angel quickly gathered up their tears, put them into his cup, and hurried up to heaven to appear before God.

God looked at the tears and became angry. Immediately, the stars were dimmed and the heavenly angels were agitated. Panic seized the Angel of compassion; he trembled with fear and cried out, "Oh, God! I have but done as you have commanded!"

And God answered him and said, "Look at the tears in that cup! Listen to the sound that emanates from them and tell me what you hear!"

The angel did as God said. He listened, and immediately stood back, horrified.

And God said, "What do you hear that disturbs you so?"

And the angel answered, "Oh, God! Woe is me! Your people has sinned grievously. These surely are not tears of sorrow; neither are they tears of joy because of their liberation from Egypt. These are tears of cowardice, tears of slaves longing for the whips of their masters. They mourn because they remember the fish that they ate in their land of affliction. Pray, God! Pity your people and do not punish them in Your anger!"

No sooner had the angel spoken when the cup of tears fell from his hand and shattered before the Seat of Glory, and the tears became a flowing river.

And God said, "Only when this shameful river, the very one that is a reminder of Israel's sin, will dry up, shall I return to them and pity them."

And the angel asked, "How can Your children dry these tears?"

"With the fire of their love for the land that I have promised them," was His answer.

———

Every evening the Angel of Compassion scans the heavens and looks down on earth upon the children of Israel—the old and the young. On one such night, on the ninth day in the month of Ab, generations ago, the angel saw the holy Temple of Jerusalem in flames. The blaze reached the river of tears, and disappeared in it.

Years passed; once again, on the ninth of Ab, the Second Temple was set afire. This flame was likewise unable to dry up the river of tears.

The Angel of Compassion was greatly grieved and again appeared before the Almighty on behalf of the people of Israel.

And God told him, "Gather for Me all the sparks of love that you can find in the hearts of My people for their deserted and desolate land, and it shall be, that when these sparks will add up into a mighty flame, they will dry up the river of tears."

———

The people of Israel became divided and scattered among the nations of the world. Each year the rivers of sorrow multiplied. The angel of mercy continued to come down to earth from time to time, to look for every spark of love that the children of Israel had for their land, the land of their fathers. He gathered them up, spark by spark, but the sum was not enough to make a flame that could swallow the flowing river of tears.

More years passed, and again the angel of kindness looked down at the earth. It was once more on the ninth of Ab. He saw tremendous fires in Spain. Jews were being put to the torch; they were being expelled from Spain and their homes were being burned. And again the river swallowed the blaze and still its bitter waters flowed on. . . .

The Angel of Compassion sighed and wept, "How much longer, Oh Lord! How much longer?"

And the Lord's voice was heard in answer, "Till the day when the fire in their hearts for their home land will dry up the river of tears. Then I will pity them."

The Angel of Compassion went down among the Children of Israel. He listened, watched, scrutinized every moment of their daily lives and picked up the sparks, one by one, gathered them together, and waited for the coming of the big day.

———

Once more, flames rose high—so high as to be seen from every part of the world. It was the burning of the Jewish books; the burning of the Jewish synagogues; the fires of the German crematoria and the six million dead. And yet the river flowed on.

And the Angel of Compassion appeared weeping before God.

"God, oh God! You see these new rivers of tears! Will they never be dried up?"

And God answered, "Watch now, and see those sparks which have been hidden, forgotten, neglected, deep down in the hearts of My people. They are at long last the sparks of love of freedom and love for Israel; they are about to burst forth now, now!"

And behold! There was the uprising of the Jews in the Warsaw Ghetto; there was the heroism of the Israeli youth; there was the return of thousands upon thousands to the land of Israel. And these sparks burst into a mighty flame that drew into it all the sparks of love for freedom for the land of Israel, from Jews all over the world. Sparks were added to sparks and flame to flame, till the whole world could see that Israel was free, Israel was a state! The fire of rejoicing and the fire of dedication in the hearts of the Jews of the world had at last dried up the river of tears.

[ADAPTED FROM A LEGEND]

7

The Good Life

After God had created Adam, He took him on a tour of the Garden of Eden. He pointed out to him the beauty and excellence of His works and said, "I have done all this for you. Live in My world and enjoy it. But do not mar it nor corrupt it. The responsibility is yours. If you desolate My world, no one will come after you to set it right."

Midrash

The Upright Man

(Psalm XV)

O Lord, within
Thy Tabernacle,
Who shall make his dwelling place?
And high upon
Thy holy mountain
Who shall see Thee face to face?

The upright man
Who, all his days,
From faith in Thee will not depart—
Whose works are works
Of righteousness,
Who speaks the truth within his heart;

Upon whose tongue
No slander lies,—
Who, mindful of man's good name,
Will never bring
His neighbor harm—
Nor bear the guilt of spreading shame—

Ilo Orleans

A FOLK TALE

The Ten Commandments

"The Ten Commandments is a map," a rabbi once told his disciples, "to show us the way."

"Once there was a powerful king of an eastern country, who was very fond of hunting. For his enjoyment, he had a vast domain, a dense forest, where wild animals roamed. He ordered a map of the forest to be drawn up, to enable him to find his way easily.

"The king took the new map and set out for the hunt. As he was chasing a fox, the animal disappeared in the clump of hedges through which the monarch was unable to pass. The king called for his map, to find a path around the hedges. It was of no help to him, for it contained neither traces of hedges nor of trees. Only the pathways and waterways of the forest were indicated.

"The king returned to the palace out of humor. He ordered a larger map, one that would contain every hedge and every tree in the forest. It took five men five weeks to complete the task. Then the king, armed with the new map, went forth to hunt.

"During the chase, the king's horse stumbled over a rock, and the fox he spied disappeared from view. He called for his map. It was unrolled with great difficulty, as the forest paths were very narrow. When the king examined it, he was furious. Every tree, hedge, pathway and stream was indicated, but the stones were unmarked. When he returned to the palace, he ordered a still larger map to be drawn up—

one to contain every stone and rock in the forest. Fifty men worked fifty weeks until they could satisfy the king. The map was made into a tremendous royal carpet and was so large, that when the king went out to hunt, fifty men had to carry it.

"The monarch was highly pleased. Now he could enjoy his sport to the utmost. No fox would ever again get away from him! So confident was he in the value of his new map, that when he went hunting with it, he led his party deep into the forest and continued the chase with no thought of turning back. However, when the hour became late, he ordered that his map be unrolled so that he might study it. Alas! It was so cumbersome and the paths were so narrow, that it could not be unrolled; not even a corner of it could be seen clearly. The king and his party were forced to spend the night in the forest, an experience for which they were completely unprepared. But they put the map to some use —they cut it up and made shelters of it.

The following day, a search party with a small map found their monarch and his retinue and brought them back safely to the palace. The king then realized his folly, and ever after, used nothing but a small map to show him the pathways of the forest.

"The Ten Commandments is a small map," the rabbi concluded. "They show us the pathways of life. If we follow them, we cannot get lost."

[ADAPTED]

G. ROSENTHAL

The Secret

In a village on the other side of the big river there once lived a young farmer who was very poor. His barn and chicken coops were empty, and all because he was too generous. His friends knew it and winked at each other while they spent every penny he earned.

One evening, returning from his field, he found a strange old man waiting in front of his house. The young farmer invited him into the house and placed food and drink before him: "You have shared your bread with me. Ask of me whatever you wish and with the help of the Lord it shall be granted."

The youth answered without hesitation:

"I should like a larger farm."

"A difficult request, indeed," answered the old man. "But wait three years. At the end of that time I shall return and if you will have kept my visit and my promise a secret your wish shall that day be fulfilled."

It was difficult for the young farmer to keep the secret. The villagers were a curious lot. Who was the mysterious visitor, they wanted to know, and what did he want? The young farmer's silence angered his friends, and they began to avoid him. This made the farmer feel sorrowful indeed. But a strange thing was happening. The lonelier he grew, the richer he grew. For the money that he would usually spend on his friends was now accumulating in his money box.

Months passed and lengthened into years. One day, some two years after the old man's visit, the young farmer met a girl and fell in love. But the girl would marry him on only one condition.

"Tell me your secret," she smiled sweetly.

The young farmer scratched his head. If he broke his promise to the old man he would lose the field he was hoping for. When she saw his hesitation, the girl cried: "How can you support a family on such a tiny farm?"

The young farmer gave in. After making her promise to reveal the secret to no one, he told the girl everything. His wife-to-be wiped away her tears and promised faithfully to keep the secret.

Soon after their marriage, the young wife began an endless stream of demands. And when her husband pleaded poverty, she would answer:

"How can you say that? Soon you will be rich. Why can't you buy me things now?"

And each time the farmer would consent, and little by little the money he had saved disappeared.

At the end of the third year the old man came back.

"Have you fulfilled your promise?" he asked the farmer. "Have you kept the secret?"

The young man blushed.

"For two years I guarded the secret. The anger and scorn of my friends meant nothing to me. But I could not hold out against the tears of my wife. I had to tell her the secret."

"I will forgive you this once," said the old man, "for you have revealed the secret out of love for your wife. You may make another request."

Without hesitation the young farmer said: "I should like to have a large field, some chickens and a cow."

The old man stroked his white beard. "That is a most difficult request. It will require a five-year wait. But if you will keep my promise and my visit a secret your wish shall be fulfilled."

Again the villagers were overcome by curiosity. Why did the old man return to the farmer's house? What did they talk about?

But the farmer revealed not a word, not even to his wife.

His wife knew that something had gone wrong when her husband's farm grew no larger. She stopped urging him to buy her dresses and kerchiefs and ornaments and began to help her husband in his work. As a result the money again began to accumulate in the money box. The young farmer began to feel happier. And then one day his joy passed all bounds. His wife bore him a son, a beautiful child.

Four years passed. The young boy was now old enough to play with the neighbors' children. But whenever his father appeared they would shout, "The little man with the big secret!" The boy begged his father to tell him what this meant. He pleaded and cried until his father could no longer resist. He told his son about the old man and the promise, making him swear that he would not reveal the secret to anyone.

Soon the child too began to make demands—just as his mother had once done—new clothes, new toys, sweets. And when the father refused, the boy cried: "Aren't you going to be a rich man? Why can't you buy me what I want now?"

Before long the money box was again empty.

When the old man reappeared the farmer had to admit that he had not kept his promise.

"You have not done well, my son," said the old man. "But again it was out of love that you told. I shall give you one more chance to make a wish."

Unhesitatingly the farmer replied: "I should like a large field, a cow, chickens, and a comfortable house for my family."

"You are asking a great deal," said the old man, "and it will take seven years to fulfill this request. My conditions are still the same. But I must tell you that I shall not return again, for in seven years I will be one hundred years old. You must come to me instead."

Again curiosity ran high in the village but the farmer was now more close-mouthed than ever. And since both his wife and son knew that his money was all gone, they threw themselves into the work of the farm and before long the money box grew heavier and heavier.

Seven years passed. The farmer took the money he had accumulated, placed it in a bag which he hung around his neck, dressed in his Sabbath best, and set out for the old man's home. His wife and son insisted that he tell them his destination but he refused.

Soon the farmer was sitting beside the old man's bed.

"Have you kept my secret, my son?" the old man whispered.

"Yes," said the farmer. "This time I have kept your secret."

"You have done well," the old man answered. "But what is it that you are wearing around your neck?"

"This is what I have saved for the past seven years. It is the fruit of my work and the work of my family."

Then the old man said: "Because you have kept the secret, you have not been forced to spend your money. Open your purse and you will see that you have enough to buy a large field, a cow for your barn, chickens for your coops and a comfortable home for your family."

The farmer counted his money and saw that the old man was right. He began to murmer his thanks but the old man interrupted and said, "Don't thank me. Everything you have you have earned. All I did was give you some good advice. I am no maker of miracles. I am a simple man and if I have helped you I ask only that you remember one thing."

The old man sighed and turned his face to the wall.

"Hard work," he said, "can accomplish more than miracles."

JUDAH STEINBERG

Hemdan

There once lived in a town of Assyria a lad so fine of form and so fine of face that he was called by all who looked on him Hemdan, The Beauteous Youth. None so comely had lived before his day, nor has there been any so handsome since.

It was his delight to go out into the fields to watch the harvesting. No sooner did he appear than the reapers dropped their sickles, and sheaves were left unbound, while the binders feasted their eyes to the full on his marvellous beauty. The men always went back to their toil with hearts that were light and merry.

Whenever the lad walked in the city streets a whisper went along with him: "Look, Hemdan is passing." Women heard it behind their lattices, and cast longing looks at him —and their gaze followed him until he was out of sight.

There was one singular quality to his beauty. It was his only so long as he did not know that he possessed it. So soon as he became aware of what men were saying when they looked after him, so soon as he heard on their lips the praise of his face and looked at it in stream and in mirror, and knew that he was comely, a cloud came over his countenance, his lips became twisted, his beauty faded. Straightway those that had been loud in his praise fell to taunting him, and loathed to look at him.

The lad had also a voice of rare sweetness. When he used it in song, the minstrels cried: "Hark to the harp!" The tired and burdened and downcast forgot trouble and care, and dried their tears. Men whose hearts were joyous and who had never had sorrow were moved to weeping.

As with his face, so with his voice. So long as Hemdan lived unaware of its power the charm was his; the moment his own ear detected the quality of his song, his voice cracked, and its notes did not hold true. Those who heard were dismayed, and cried out against him, and sought to drive him away.

Sick at heart he wept and prayed: "O God, most gracious, why didst Thou pour out Thy favor upon me to be my sorrow and hurt? Why do the gifts Thou didst bestow on me bring gladness and heart's ease to all men save to me alone? Why can I not have the joy in the talent wherewith Thou hast endowed me?"

The youth did not know that anyone heard his supplication, and he put into it his whole soul, and men forsook their tasks and women their looms, and the tired rose from their couches, and one and all drew near and added their prayers to the lad's, and wept with him. Whereupon the boy recognized that there was some peculiar power in his voice to sway men, and he grew vain, and lo, its charm left him.

At last the lad quit his own city, and wandered in many others. Always it was the same story. Men seeing him in the streets, looked and were astounded, and whispered: "It is Hemdan!" No matter how often they saw him, they marvelled at the fineness of his form and face. He paid no heed, until one day he was passing beneath a window behind which was a servant baking the daily loaf. She saw him, and forgetting the coals, put her hand on them; in her pain she dropped her pan out of the window right in the lad's way. He saw in its polished surface the restored beauty of his face, and he was glad. Then a cloud came over his countenance, his lips twisted—his beauty vanished.

Sick and broken-hearted he fled the city. Out into the forest he wandered and, tired and exhausted, lay down to sleep. The beasts of prey, the lions and tigers and their kin, smelled the blood of a man, and hastened to find him. When they came upon the sleeper, and beheld the beauty of his face, they could do him no harm. They crouched before him, and sheathed their claws, and marvelled at his wondrous beauty.

"How fine!"

"How lovely!"

"How gentle!"

"How beautiful!"

The murmurs awakened the lad, and he heard his praise before he knew his peril. He was glad. His beauty vanished.

The lions began to growl, the tigers to purr, and they struck at him with their claws, and were about to devour him, when he fell on his knees, and renewed his supplication.

"O God, most gracious, why didst Thou pour out Thy favor upon me to be my sorrow and my hurt? Why do the gifts Thou didst bestow on me bring gladness and heartease to all men save to me alone? Why can I not have joy in the talent wherewith Thou hast endowed me?"

The birds of the forest were drawn by his song. They hovered close by, and at the close of the prayer responded: "Amen!" Then they sang with him, until the beasts sheathed their claws, and withdrew to their lairs.

The youth sang and sang with no thought save to sing. The sun went down, dusk fell, night cast her black pall over the earth, midnight came, and the lad never rose from his knees. Suddenly thunder crashed, streaks of lightning like flame-colored birds flashed before his eyes. The lad looked up, and wondered to see a clear heaven dotted with dazzling stars and not even a tiny cloud on its surface.

"What meant the thunder and lightning?" he asked himself, afraid. He arose, and the thunder pealed anew, and the sky was rent end to end by the lightning. Down to earth on a black cloud flew a cherub with wings outstretched. The brightness of the cherub's eyes made the night seven times as light as any day. On the cherub's back rode a man clad in linen, who, dismounting, drew near the lad, and thus addressed him:

"Be still. Cease your outcries. The heavens are distressed. They can no longer bear it. The spheres have had to hush their music. It is not seemly that a Hebrew lad should kneel. Arise and listen to me. I set before you two ways. If you wish to gladden the world and find favor in its sight, you will not be aware of your own power. If you wish to have joy in yourself and be self-conscious, certain that you are of value, all men will despise you. Now choose, and as you choose, so shall it be."

The thunder pealed, the lightning flashed. Man and cherub vanished.

The boy stood rooted to the spot. He was wondering which choice to make. Was it better to have joy in himself and be of little worth in the eyes of the world, or was it better to let others have joy and be a burden to himself?

Weeks drifted by, and months followed, and the lad was unable to choose. He stood without food or drink, turning over and over in his mind the choice he must make. The rays of the sun dried his skin. The east wind froze his marrow, and he stood stock still and never chose, until his life passed from him, and his body became stone in the midst of the forest.

There it stands, a stone image, to this day.

Every year, on the anniversay of the day that the lad went into the forest, a kind wind blows at night over the image, and the lips become rosy again and open in song. The birds draw near and join in the singing. The beasts of prey sheathe their claws. Even the river becomes quiet. Over all is peace.

But when the transformed child hears his praises, and thinks that he is comely and that his voice is sweet, a wind blows a shadow across the face, and drives away its beauty; the birds flee in alarm, and the beasts go forth to rend and tear. The waters become rough and muddy. The child becomes again a silent statue.

[TRANSLATED FROM THE HEBREW BY EMILY SOLIS-COHEN]

CHAIM NACHMAN BIALIK

The Milk of a Lioness

In the days when Solomon reigned over Israel and Judea, the king of Moab fell gravely ill. The disease racked his body, so that he slowly wasted away. His doctors were unable to help him, except to advise that if he would drink the milk of a lioness, he would be restored to health. The milk, in order to be curative, would have to be absolutely fresh, which meant that it would have to be taken from the breasts of a lioness in her lair.

The king summoned his select guard, the lionmen of Moab, and told them what his physicians had prescribed. "Who will volunteer to go for the king to the lioness' lair and bring back her milk?"

No one answered; no one was brave enough to risk it. "It is impossible," the thought flitted through their minds, "to enter the den of a lioness, to milk her and come out alive."

"Cowards!" the king bellowed, "Dumb curs! Is this how you prove yourselves? Not one of you will endanger his life to save that of his king."

Two Moabite lionmen stepped forward, prostrated themselves before the king and said, "We are your faithful servants who would willingly forfeit our lives to save one of your little fingernails. Not one of us is worth a hair of your head. Say the word, and we will capture alive and bring to you every lion and lioness in the wilderness. But to fulfill the king's request is beyond mortal man. Maybe your advisors can tell you how this impossible feat might be accomplished."

The king consulted his wise men and physicians, but they had neither read nor heard of anyone performing such an act. The king's health continued to decline and in desperation he decided to turn to King Solomon, who was famous for his wisdom. He sent a letter to him by messenger in which he disclosed the sad state of his health and the cure that his physicians had prescribed. He concluded: "Now that I have confided in you and have told you of my miserable plight, please, I beg of you, please help me. In doing this, you will repay the kindness with which my forefathers received your ancestors when they came to Moab during a famine. My ancestors allowed yours to establish themselves and live amongst them in peace. You, no doubt, recall that during their sojourn we became related, for you are a great, great grandchild of Ruth, the Moabite. She was of my family, but chose to cling to your people.

"God has given you wisdom surpassing that of all men, so that no problem is too difficult for you, and nothing is beyond your understanding. Have pity and answer my plea."

With the same messenger, the ruler of Moab sent choice products of his land, as a gift for the king of Judea. As soon as his messengers departed, the king of Moab arose in great anger, turned to his soldiers and advisors and cried, "Miserable slaves! Today you have disgraced your king and this throne. Your silence proves that there is neither courage nor wisdom in Moab. Let the king of Judea but succeed in obtaining for me what I need and I will throw your carcasses to the dogs. Get out of my sight!"

On reading the message, Solomon felt very sorry for his neighbor. He called the captain of his host, Benaiah, the son of Jehoida, and showed him the letter.

"What do you say, Son of Jehoida, will you get the milk from a lioness?"

"That I will do," the captain answered, "for your honor and for the glory of the God of Israel."

"What will you need?"

"I'll need ten kids," Benaiah answered.

Solomon smiled, as he divined his warrior's strategy. "You have courage and wisdom. Nothing will deter you. Go, then. Keep your eyes and ears open, and may God bless you."

Benaiah did not tarry. He took with him ten kids and a young shepherd boy and set forth in search of a den of lions. Benaiah was as swift of foot as a lion. His eyes were sharp as an eagle's; they could pierce the heaviest darkness. His ears were so sensitive, they could catch the slightest rustle from the farthest distance.

It was wintertime. They walked until they came to the borders of the Senir and Hermon Mountains, where, from time immemorial, lions were known to roam. The mountains and surrounding areas were covered with ice and snow. Benaiah noticed lion tracks. He hid his flock and boy in a rock crevice and ordered the lad to remain there until he called him. Benaiah followed the lion prints, thinking that they would lead him to the den. But as he reached the mountain top, he observed that the tracks suddenly veered —a turn that was perplexing. He hesitated for a moment, when a terrible roar reached his ears, a growl similar to, but not quite that of a lion. The difference was so slight that it baffled him. Then suddenly, it all became clear to Benaiah. Those were the footprints of the Moabite lionmen and that was their war cry. They had come here for but one reason: to kill him. Solomon's warning, "Keep your eyes and ears open," came to his mind. With fearlessness and singleness of purpose, he decided what his next step would be.

Benaiah had indeed appraised the situation accurately. When the lionmen of Moab heard that the captain of the Judean army had set out for the milk of a lioness, they were frightened to death, for they recalled their king's anger.

They could save themselves only by doing away with Benaiah, and that was what the two leading lionmen conspired to do.

The lionmen were swift, strong and more ferocious than wild beasts. In stature, they were giants, frightening to behold, arrayed as they were in copper and iron. Their hair and beards were like lions' manes. Lions' pelts girded their loins, and their shoes were the shape of lions' paws. Their war cry was a lion's roar.

For many years,. they had molested the people of Israel. But now they lost confidence in their own strength, for they knew that nobody could defeat Benaiah, and so they resorted to cunning. Their plan was to follow him, and when they would meet up with him to say that they had come to assist him in his difficult task. Benaiah, however, had left secretly and had sped like an eagle through places where no foot had ever trod, so that the lionmen had to change their strategy and wait for him in the mountains where the wild beasts dwelt. They hid behind the crevice of a rock and planned to force him into the open by their trickery. They thought to entice him into going in the direction from which their roar came and thus to catch him.

Benaiah clothed himself in a white sheet which he had brought for that purpose, so that his appearance would blend into the snowy landscape. He returned to the crevice where his boy and flock were hidden and ordered the lad to come out and follow in the direction of the "lion" prints. He told him what to do and say.

The boy walked along the mountain slope, weeping as his master had instructed. Benaiah kept close on his heels. As the boy rounded a cleft in a rock, the two Moabites rushed out of their hiding place and pounced upon him shouting, "Who are you? What are you doing here?" The weeping boy answered between chattering teeth, "Please sirs, I am a shepherd watching my master's flock. One of my sheep strayed and I came to look for him on the mountain slope —but I am afraid of the lions—there are so many here."

One of the Moabites, suspecting that the boy was not telling the truth, shook him violently and roared, "Who is your master, son of a dog, and where is he?"

"Just behind you," a voice answered, and in that very instant a spear pierced the neck of the soldier who was choking the lad. Before the second lionman could realize what had happened to his friend, a flashing sword split his head open like a pumpkin. Benaiah with his spear and sword had destroyed them both. He threw their bodies into a pit.

Benaiah looked up and saw a lion, attracted by the smell of blood, leaping toward him. The warrior killed him, too, thinking, "Another hazard out of my way," and dragged his carcass into the same pit. He then followed the true lion's prints until he reached its lair. The sun was beginning to set, so Benaiah decided to spend the night in the crevice of a rock.

By the light of morning, Benaiah easily found the den of a lioness, the very one whose mate he had killed the day before. She was giving suck to her cubs. Benaiah threw a kid to her and stood off at a distance. The following day, he came a little closer and threw another kid to her. He repeated this every day until the lioness became accustomed to him, allowed him to touch her and finally to milk her. Benaiah hastened to bring the milk to Solomon who gave it to the messengers of Moab.

"Here is the milk of the lioness. Bring it quickly to your king that he may drink and be cured. Tell him that Benaiah, my courageous warrior, bravely risked his life for it. Go in peace!"

Night fell on the way back to Moab and the messengers lay down to sleep. Their chief, who was also the king's physician and had prescribed the lioness milk, dreamt a strange dream in which the members of his body argued with each other.

The feet said, "We are the most important. Had it not been for us, who would have gone to get the milk for the king?"

The hands contended, "We are more important than all of you. Were it not for us, how would the lioness have been milked?"

The eyes said, "We are the best. Without us, no one could find his way."

The heart said, "Not at all! None of you would amount to anything had I not advised you."

Then the tongue spoke up. "I am the most important. Were it not for speech, you could accomplish nothing."

The words barely popped out of the tongue's mouth, when all the others pounced upon him, ridiculed and insulted him.

"Hush, you boneless, spineless creature! You, who live in darkness, can you dare say you are better than we? How dare you stand up among your betters!"

"Say what you will," said the tongue, "but before the day is over, you will be forced to admit that I am your master."

The king's physician awoke and was able to recall every detail of the dream. That day, the messengers arrived in Moab, and their chief, whose heart was still pounding from the dream, presented the milk to the king with these words, "Your royal highness, we have just arrived with the dog's milk."

The king's face contorted in anger and he shouted, "Get him out of here and hang him!"

As the physician was being dragged out by the executioner, all the parts of his body shook with the fear of death. "That's the proof that you are all in my hands," the tongue boasted. "Do you concede that I rule over you?"

"We concede, we concede," they all shouted at once, only save us before it is too late!"

The tongue then turned to the executioner and pleaded with him, "Please take me back to my king. I have something to tell him that will mean everything to his peace and welfare." The tongue was so persuasive that the executioner was convinced that the man was telling the truth and he brought him back to the palace.

The physician fell at the king's feet and pleaded, "Oh, your royal highness, why did you order me put to death when I brought you the drink that will restore your health?"

"Didn't your own mouth testify against you that you brought me the milk of a bitch?"

"If you will but taste the milk," the man answered, "you will feel so much better, you will believe me that it it truly the milk of a lioness. In hunter's language. a lioness is sometimes called a "dog." Please, forgive the slip of the tongue. I apologize most humbly for not being more careful of my speech in the presence of the king."

The king drank the milk of the lioness and was healed. He was most grateful to Solomon and to Benaiah. He dismissed his entire company of lionmen and ordered them disbanded, so that they could trouble Israel no more, and there was a true peace between Israel and Moab till the end of king Solomon's reign.

These were the things that Solomon had in mind, when he wrote in his "Proverbs":

"The Tongue has Power over Life and Death."

[TRANSLATED FROM THE HEBREW]

The World Testifies

Once a heretic came to Rabbi Akiba and asked in a mocking tone, "Who created the world?"

"God created the heaven and the earth."

"Prove it," said the heretic.

"What are you wearing?" asked Rabbi Akiba.

"A coat."

"Who made it?"

"A tailor, of course."

"Prove it," said Rabbi Akiba.

"Everyone knows that a tailor makes coats."

"Don't you know that God made the world?" Rabbi Akiba retorted.

At this the heretic lett.

Then the disciples of the great teacher turned to him and said, "Please explain how you have proved it."

Akiba answered, "Everything testifies to its maker—the chair to the carpenter, the coat to the tailor, the house to the builder and the world to its Creator."

BACHYA IBN PAKUDAH

Beauty of Simplicity

In our tradition, that which is holy has beauty that does not depend upon embellishments, but on the contrary, rejects them. Thus it is that the Torah, so holy and dear to the Jewish people, may only be written with black ink on parchment. Gold or illuminated lettering may not be used. The law specifically prohibits the use of gold. The same law applies to phylacteries.

Among the musical instruments in the Temple, there was a thin reed pipe that had come down from the days of Moses. It had a very pleasant sound. But since it was so plain, the king decided to enhance it. He ordered a goldsmith to encrust it with gold. But this covering dulled the sound of the pipe and the king had the gold removed.

A similar thing happened when one of a pair of bronze cymbals in the Temple was damaged, and the king sent for craftsmen from Alexandria to mend it. The artisans covered the bronze cymbals with gold. This muffled their clear ring. In order to restore their original sound, the gold was removed.

LEAH AIN GLOBE

The Two Gems

Pedro the Great, king of Aragon, Spain, in the twelfth century, had a troubadour in his court named Nicholas de Valencia who sought to humiliate and persecute the Jews. One day Nicholas incited the king to summon Ephraim ben Sancho, a Talmudic scholar, for a public debate with him.

When the scholar appeared before the court, the king asked, "Which religion is better, ours or yours?"

"For us Jews, our faith is better," was Ephraim's answer. "When we were slaves in Egypt, the Lord performed miracles, delivered us from bondage, and He has been our Shield. For you, your religion is better. It has given you power."

"You are telling me the advantages that these religions have for their respective followers," said the king. "What I want to know is their real value as religions."

"Your Majesty, pray give me three days in which to think this matter over, then I will return with my answer."

The king granted his request. Three days later, Ephraim ben Sancho, looking very dejected, appeared before him.

"What makes you so sad?" the king asked.

"A very distressing thing happened to me. I was insulted for no reason at all. I have a neighbor, the father of two sons, who decided to leave for another country. He wanted his children to be happy and to live peacefully together, so he gave each one a gem of great value. No sooner did their father leave when they started to worry about whose gem was more costly. This morning they came to me and insisted that I tell them the value of the jewels and how one differs from the other. I advised them to go to their father. He is a connoisseur of precious stones; he would certainly tell them the truth. For this they insulted and berated me."

The king banged his fist on the table. "These men should be punished," he shouted. "They have abused you for no reason at all."

"Your majesty," Ephraim ben Sancho said calmly, "the brothers are Esau and Jacob. Our Father in Heaven gave each a precious jewel. Now your majesty asks me to tell which is more valuable. Let your majesty send a messenger to our Father in Heaven. He knows the relative worth of each religion. He will tell you which is better and how they differ."

At this, the king turned to his wicked advisor and said, "Do you see the wisdom of the Jew? He deserves to be honored, while you should be punished for bringing false accusations against him and his people."

[ADAPTED FROM A FOLK TALE]

A FOLK TALE

The Baby Sitter

Men, women and children, dressed in their holiday best, were leaving their homes, with solemn expressions and hurrying steps, going to the many places of worship in town. It was Yom Kippur Eve, the most holy time of the year. Soon the *Kol Nidre* would be heard from every synagogue, every house of prayer and every lesser congregation where Jews gathered to usher in the sacred day. They would pray to God, long and fervently, to open the gates of His mercy, to forgive their trespasses of the year that had just passed, and to record in His eternal book each one's name for a good year.

In a very short time, the big synagogue was overflowing with worshippers. The tall wax candles sputtered and crackled, throwing their light and casting their shadows upon the congregants. The men covered their heads with their prayer shawls. The cantor and his choir were in their places. It was time for the service to begin. But where was the rabbi? Rabbi Israel Salanter was not one to be late on Yom Kippur Eve.

An uneasiness gripped the elders and soon spread to the rest of the congregation. There was a nervous buzzing of voices, a fear of an unforeseen catastrophe. The rabbi—not in the synagogue for *Kol Nidre!* How nightmarish! Had Satan trapped him in his net? Was he called to heaven to plead for his people, or was he perhaps lying ill somewhere? The sexton was sent to the rabbi's home and came back with the report that the house was empty; all of its inhabitants had apparently left for services.

The sun was about to set and the prayer could no longer be deferred. With heavy heart and much foreboding, the cantor started the chanting of the "Kol Nidre."

Rabbi Israel Salanter had indeed left his house in ample time. His heart was filled with the solemnity of the occasion, as were the hearts of all Jews at that moment. The very street held a stillness, a holiness, as the Rabbi hastened to the synagogue.

A child's cry pierced the silence. The rabbi was so deeply absorbed in the gravity of the approaching holiday that he barely heard it. But as he continued walking, the cry became louder and turned into a hysterical wail. The child now cried and gasped as if it had lost all ability to control its weeping.

The sound drew the rabbi like a magnet, so that before he realized it, he had swerved from his course. He knocked at the door of a house. A little girl of about nine or ten, with large frightened eyes, opened it. The room was neat. Holiday candles flickered in their copper holders on the table.

The rabbi entered, picked up the crying infant from its cradle, and held it to his breast.

"What is your name, little girl?" he asked.

"Sarah."

"Where is your mother?"

"She went with my father to the synagogue and left me to watch my little brother. But I don't know what to do! He won't stop crying."

"Do you know to what synagogue your mother went?"

"Oh, yes! To the big one."

"Would you like to call her? But, wait! Maybe we won't have to frighten your mother and take her away from her prayers."

While he talked, the rabbi walked up and down the room with the infant in his arms. The hysterical weeping slowly subsided, giving way to short gasps that turned to a quiet whimper.

The rabbi looked out of the window and saw that the sun was about to set. *Kol Nidre,* he began to chant, "All vows and self-prohibitions . . . " The infant stopped crying, looked in surprise at the man who was holding him, curled its tiny fingers into the grey beard, and smiled. "And the congregation of Israel shall be forgiven . . ." the rabbi continued. The infant cooed and gurgled its "Amen." The rabbi's chant, barely a whisper, was as much a lullaby as a prayer. The baby closed its eyes and fell asleep.

"Watch your little brother, Sarah," Rabbi Salanter told the older child, as he placed the infant gently into its cradle. "You are a good girl." Then he hurried out to join his congregation.

Imagine the relief of the worshippers when they saw their beloved rabbi! Imagine the questioning thoughts to which they could not give verbal expression because of the solemnity of the hour!

The rabbi did not keep the people in suspense. He went up on the *bimah* and addressed the congregation. "The matter that delayed me tonight was one of great importance —greater than the *Kol Nidre* service . . . it was the cry of a child! We can only pray to God for mercy, we can only ask forgiveness of Him, if we ourselves have heard another's plea. It is never too late for prayer, but the cry of a child must be answered at once."

Tears filled the eyes of his congregants. They understood their rabbi well. Goodness and mercy must come from man to man, before he may ask it of God. And with great humility, the people turned to their prayer.

[ADAPTED]

Glossary

Aliyah—ascent; going up to Israel, any migration to Israel; honor extended by being called up to the reading of the Torah.

Bar Mitzvah—son of the commandment; a boy who has attained his religious majority.

Bas Mitzvah—daughter of the commandment; a girl who has attained her religious majority.

Bimah—pulpit.

Brit Milah—covenant; circumcision.

Challa—Sabbath white bread.

Cheder—beginners' class for the study of Hebrew.

Gemora—major constituent part of the Talmud (oral discussions and instructions relating to Holy Writ).

Halutzot—women pioneers of Israel.

Haskalah—enlightenment; an intellectual movement which appeared at the end of the 18th century in Eastern Europe to adopt the culture and manners of the people among whom the Jews dwelt.

Hassidim—followers of the Hassidic movement founded by Baal Shem (1700-1760).

Keporah—atonement; sacrifice.

Kiddush—sanctification; benediction for sanctification of Sabbaths and holidays over a cup of wine.

Kohanim—priests, descendants of Aaron.

Kol Nidre—all vows; a prayer chanted on the eve of the Day of Atonement.

Kvass—a soup made of fermented red beets.

Kvutzah—communal Israeli settlement.

Mazal Tov—good luck.

Mezuzah—doorpost; parchment scroll attached to a doorpost, consists of the words from Deut. 4-11 "And thou shalt write them on the doorpost of thy house;" the word *Shaddai* meaning Almighty is inscribed on the reverse of the scroll.

Mikvah—ritual bath.

Minyan—number; quorum; 10 men above the age of thirteen who are required for public worship.

Mitzvah—commandment; good deed.

Rashi—the most distinguished commentator on the Bible and Talmud.

Shalom Aleichem—hello; peace be with you.

Shavuot—Feast of Weeks; festival of the first harvest seven weeks after Passover.

Shulhan Zruch—set table; code of laws presented in simple form for everyone to understand.

Siddur—prayer book.

Tallis and Tefillin—prayer shawl and phylacteries.

Targum Onkelos—an Aramaic translation of the Bible.

Third Aliyah—immigration to Palestine from 1919-23 of youthful Jews affiliated with the *halutz* movement in Russia and Poland.

Yeshivah—academy; school of higher learning for study of Talmud.

Biographical Notes

AGNON, SAMUEL JOSEPH (1888–) ranks as the foremost novelist in modern Hebrew letters. His works have been translated into a score of languages. His writings are deeply rooted in the Jewish tradition. That which flows from his pen, reads like an old fashioned yarn. This narrative form is Agnon's individual style.

ALEICHEM, SHOLOM, the pen name of Shalom Rabinowitch (1859-1916), was the greatest Yiddish humorist of modern times. In America, he has often been called the Jewish Mark Twain. With I. L. Peretz, he was one of the "Fathers" of Yiddish literature. During World War I he settled in New York where he resided for a short time until his death.

His works have been translated into many languages, including Japanese and Esperanto. In the Russian translations alone more than 3,000,000 copies of Sholom Aleichem's books were sold in the twenty-five years between 1917 and 1942. The love and warm admiration which Sholom Aleichem has evoked may be seen in some measure, in Maurice Samuel's captivating, homage-paying book entitled *The World of Sholom Aleichem* (Knopf, 1943).

ANSKY, SH. (1863-1920), was the pen name of a poet and dramatist who wrote in Yiddish and Russian. His most notable work, *The Dybbuk,* achieved world fame and was dramatized on stage and on film in the world's leading capitals.

Asch, Sholem (1880-1957) was the most productive of Jewish writers. Although quite well versed in other languages, Sholem Asch did his best in Yiddish. He was the author of many well-known novels and plays, among them *Salvation, Kiddush Ha-Shem, Three Cities, Moses,* etc.

Sholem Asch was remarkable for his ability to create his novels in various settings such as Russia, America, Poland, Palestine—old and new, medieval Europe and other lands and climes. He depicted Jewish life with deep love and understanding. His works, which run to some 30-40 volumes, have been translated in most of the modern languages.

Ausubel, Nathan (1899—) is best known for his books *A Treasury of Jewish Folklore, A Treasury of Jewish Humor* and other fine anthologies in the fields of Jewish poetry and knowledge.

Bachya Ibn Pakudah (c. 1050-c. 1100) was a philosopher who lived in the Golden Age of Arabic-Jewish Spain. His book written in Hebrew, *The Duties of the Heart,* from which the excerpt included here is taken, is one of the classics in the field of Jewish Ethics.

Barash, Asher (1889-1952), Hebrew novelist, short story writer and poet, came as a youth to Palestine where he achieved a reputation as an author of juvenile literature, editor of magazines for youth and translator of world literature into modern Hebrew.

Ben-Eliezer, Moshe (1882-1944) was a Hebrew writer and editor particularly notable for his literary work in the juvenile field. It was he who introduced the Jewish child of Eastern Europe into the world of Anderson, Dickens and others.

Berger, Sylvia (1914-1958) was a script writer for radio and television programs. For more than ten years she was a regular staff writer for the "Eternal Light" radio programs broadcast under the sponsorship of the Jewish Theological Seminary of America.

Bialik, Chaim Nachman (1872-1934) is recognized as the greatest Hebrew poet and literary genius of modern times. Early in life his reputation as a poet spread quickly. He was very active in Zionism, in the rebuilding of the Jewish Homeland (where he settled in 1924) and as a Hebrew publisher of classic works. In this capacity he exerted great influence on the development of Hebrew literature, culture, and education. In a real sense he may be considered the greatest influence in modern Hebrew literature in our day.

Chagall, Bella (1895-1944), wife of the famous artist Marc Chagall, wrote, in *Burning Lights,* a biography of her childhood, giving us a charming picture of traditonal Jewish home life in Russia, and reminding us of a world that tragically is no more.

Epstein, Zalman (1860-1937) was a leader in the "Lovers of Zion," and "Sons of Moses," renowned pioneer organizations active in the upbuilding of Palestine (now Israel).

Fineman, Irving (1893–) was born in the United States and was graduated as an engineer from the Massachusetts Institute of Technology and Harvard. For a while he taught at various universities; but he has devoted a great deal of his time to writing. He is known for such novels as *Hear Ye Sons, Jacob*—an autobiographical novel and others. Fineman wrote a number of screen plays for the major movie studios.

Gaster, Moses (1856-1939), linguist, scholar, leading Zionist, was born in Rumania where he soon won renown as folklorist and orator.

He fled Rumania, where he incurred the wrath of the government because of his liberalism, and settled in England where he became Haham of England (Chief Rabbi of the Spanish and Portuguese congregations).

He was the author of a number of works, one of which is a collection of medieval Jewish stories called the "Maase Book" from which the selections in this book are taken.

GOLDEN, HARRY L. (1902–) meteored into fame almost overnight as the author of *Only in America,* a compilation of his writings in the *Carolina Israelite* of which he is writer, editor and publisher. He had been a reporter on the *New York Post, New York Mirror* and then settled in Charlotte, N. C. *Only in America* and *For 2¢ Plain,* its sequel, were on the best seller list in the *New York Times* Index for many months. The books deal largely with immigrant life on the East Side of New York. Golden has also written penetrating critical articles about Jewish life in the South.

GORDON, SAMUEL (1871-1927) came to London as a child from Bavaria. He served most of his life as secretary of the Great Synagogue. He was author of *Sons of the Covenant, Lesser Destinies, God's Remnants,* and other books on Russian Jewish life.

GRAZOVSKI (GUR), YEHUDAH (1862-1950) was an Israeli translator, pedagogue, and author of standard Hebrew and Hebrew-Russian-German dictionaries. He was a pioneer in using the Hebrew language as the language of instruction in the schools of Palestine.

HAMEIRI (FEURSTEIN), AVIGDOR (1890–) is a poet novelist, philologist and short story writer. He wrote a superb collection of stories of World War I from his experiences and observations as an officer in the Austro-Hungarian army. He came to Palestine in 1921 and took an active part in the rebuilding of Israel. He is a leading figure today in the Israeli literary world.

Kishon, Ephraim (1904–) was born in Hungary and settled in Israel after World War II. He achieved a reputation as an author of books, plays and articles. He is most famous for his outstanding satires of Israeli life.

Lamdan, Yitzhak (1899-1954) was a poet and literary figure of high stature in modern Israel where he worked first as a road builder, farm laborer and *halutz.* He was editor of a famous Hebrew monthly, but his best known work, *Masadah,* an epic poem of the pioneers who made modern Israel possible, has already become a classic in modern Hebrew.

Lazarus, Emma (1849-1887) began her literary career distant and estranged from the Jewish tradition. Her work was praised by William C. Bryant, Ralph W. Emerson, E. C. Stedman, John Burroughs and others. She was awakened to the plight of her people when she witnessed the waves of Jewish immigrants who were the victims of the Czarist pogroms in 1882. Stirred by this experience she became the spokesman for her people. She wrote verses and essays and translated the medieval Spanish Jewish poets, Heinrich Heine and others. She also became active in the Jewish community in alleviating the lot of her immigrant brethren. Her poem, The New Colossus, is affixed to the Statue of Liberty.

Lerner, Max (1902–) is best known as lecturer and as a widely syndicated columnist. He is professor of American Civilization at Brandeis University and has taught at Sarah Lawrence, Wellesley and other colleges. He was editor of *The Nation* and author of books which have been acclaimed far and wide for their trenchant and scholarly analysis of American life.

ORLEANS, ILO (1887-1964) was an outstanding member of the New York bar and attained national prominence as a children's poet. His poems appeared in school texts, anthologies, music books and teachers' manuals, and he was honored by membership in the Poetry Society of America.

PALLIERE, AIME (1875-1950), a Frenchman, was born into a pious family of the Catholic faith and was destined for the Seminary and the Church. Until he was seventeen he never felt the slightest doubt about the divinity of the church. Then one day he entered an "unknown sanctuary . . ." At the age of 20 he became a proselyte to Judaism without being formally converted. *The Unknown Sanctuary,* from which this excerpt is taken, is his autobiography.

PERETZ, YITZHAK LEIB (1852-1915) laid the foundation of modern Yiddish literature and became its central figure. He achieved immortality as a writer of unforgettable short stories. His modern Jewish folk and hassidic tales are literary gems which place him among the great short story writers of the world. Many clubs of Yiddish writers and a publishing house are named after him. His works have been translated into almost all European languages. He himself translated and helped translate his works into Hebrew where they will endure as long as the language lives.

PRAGER, MOSHE (1908–) is a Hebrew and Yiddish writer, editor and anthologist of note. His stories, essays and collected works center about the tragedy and heroism of European Jewry during the Nazi holocaust, and about the rebirth of Israel.

REICHENSTEIN, SOLOMON (1902-1942) was a member of a *kibbutz.* He wrote a novel as well as short stories about life on a *kibbutz.*

ROCKEFELLER, ABBY ( ) was an exemplary mother of six. She knew the Bible well and felt a kinship with Israel's ancient prophets. The verse in the Bible that summed up the teaching of the prophets "What doth the Lord require of thee, etc." was often quoted by her to her children. When the children were young, she copied Bible verses on cardboards for them to memorize.

When John (Jr.), Nelson, and Laurance were in college, she wrote them a letter which "eloquently records her hope for their own intelligent and human behavior as American citizens."

SCHWARZ, LEO W. (1906–), is an author, editor and a noted anthologist. His books, *The Jewish Caravan, Golden Treasury of Jewish Literature, Memoirs of My People,* and others have achieved fame and a wide circulation.

SINGER, ISAAC BASHEVIS (1904–), one of the leading novelists today, was born and educated in Poland where he began his literary career. He came to the United States in 1935 and became associated with the *Jewish Daily Forward,* a leading Yiddish daily paper. Most of his works have been translated into Hebrew, English and other modern languages.

SPECTOR, MORDECAI (1858-1925) was a prolific Yiddish writer, journalist and editor. He was well versed in the life of the *shtedtel,* the small Russian-Jewish hamlet, from which he drew the subjects and characters of many of his works.

STEINBERG, JUDAH (1863-1908), was a Hebrew pedagogue and author, made his mark especially as a writer of imaginative and nature stories for children.

STEINBERG, MILTON (1903-1950), the distinguished and beloved Rabbi at the Park Avenue Synagogue from 1933 until his death, was a great spiritual leader of American Jewry. His works, *The Making of the Modern Jew, Basic Judaism, A Partisan Guide to the Jewish Problem* and his novel *As A Driven Leaf,* have earned him enduring fame in American Jewish life and literature.

STERN, GERALDINE made her first trip to Israel in 1949. She lived in kibbutzim where she came to know the people intimately. She is a world traveler, painter, as well as writer and lecturer.

SYRKIN, MARIE (1900–) was born in Switzerland and came to the United States at an early age. After the Second World War, in 1945, she went to Palestine, interviewed Jewish heroes and survivors of the Jewish Underground for *Blessed is the Match,* from which the selection in this book is taken. She also wrote *Woman of Valor, Nachman Syrkin,* biographies of Goldie M. and her father respectively and numerous articles and translations of verse. She is at present on the faculty of Brandeis University and is editor of the *Jewish Frontier,* the labor Zionist monthly.

ZUNSER, MIRIAM SHOMER (1882-1951) was a daughter of the pioneer Yiddish novelist and playwright Nahum Meir Shaikewich (Shomer). In 1905 she married Charles Zunser a lawyer and social worker, the son of the Yiddish poet Eliakum Zunser.

In 1917 she took an active part in the formation of the American Jewish Congress. She organized a society dedicated to popularizing Jewish music in the United States and in Palestine. In 1939 she published a book, *Yesterday,* a family chronicle which depicts the members of her family and the milieu in which they lived. The selection herein comes from this book.

ZWEIG, STEFAN (1881-1942), a famous European literary figure, studied in German and French universities. In 1935, as a result of Nazi persecution, he emigrated from Austria to England and then to South America. He wrote a number of plays, poetic works and historical studies which won high acclaim. Much of Zweig's work has been translated into English.

The Bas Mitzvah Treasury offers the best in Jewish literature for the youth of today. A collection of folk tales, poetry, and fiction designed to create a warm glow of understanding for and identification with the Jewish people, past and present, it gives insight into their sacrifice, heroism, and martyrdom through the ages. Here is a picture of Jewish life presented with humor, with warmth, and with pathos.

Ranging from the wisdom of the great sages to the work of such modern writers as Sholom Aleichem, S. J. Agnon, Stefan Zweig, Sholem Asch, and Harry Golden, *The Bas Mitzvah Treasury* cannot be simply catalogued or measured any more than its great human themes. Heroism is portrayed in the martyrdom of Hanna Senesch and in the agony of the ghetto mother who (in *The Secret of the Pudding*) faces her starving children. The ways of love are explored in Biblical times *(The Way of a Man With a Maid)* and in modern Israel *(The Wedding on the Hill)*. There is humor in *A Piece of Advice, The Feast of the Paupers,* and *Yigal and the Inquisition*. The sections of the treasury called Home and the Woman and Love Thy Neighbor take their themes from the Torah.

This is a volume that will be cherished, read, and reread by every member of the family.